Mechanical Properties
of Metals

WILEY SERIES ON THE SCIENCE AND TECHNOLOGY OF MATERIALS

Advisory Editors: J. H. Hollomon, J. E. Burke, B. Chalmers, R. L. Sproull, A. V. Tobolsky

New York
London

Mechanical Properties
of Metals

by D. McLean, D.Sc.

NATIONAL PHYSICAL LABORATORY

John Wiley & Sons, Inc.

Preface

In the last 10 to 20 years a great deal of knowledge has been accumulated about the way in which the metallographic and defect structures of metals combine with the atomic forces to produce the observed mechanical properties. This book tries to describe the insight which this knowledge has given into the mechanical properties of metals.

Work in this field has followed a normal course. At first, following the realisation that dislocations play such a strikingly prominent role in deformation and fracture, attention was concentrated on the dislocations themselves without much regard for their environment. The basic results which have emerged give general explanations of several phenomena. This period has been summed up in a number of books. Subsequently, dislocations have been studied in relation to their environment in the midst of particular metallographic structures, in particular lattices, and taking into account some details of the atomic forces. The tremendous variety of possible behaviours and controlling factors which has been discovered gives ample scope for explaining individual peculiarities of particular metals and alloys. The decisive step has been, and still is, to understand from the new point of view the important processes during cold working, fracture, etc., and to single out the factors which are the controlling ones under any given conditions. This has been and is being accomplished partly by making appropriate experiments, and partly also by looking into the immense fund of knowledge about the mechanical properties of metals for regularities which are significant from the new point of view. Whereas 10 or 20 years ago the mechanical properties of metals could be understood (it might now be better to say *rationalised*) in terms of behaviour on the microscopic level, as a result of all this work today they can usually be understood in terms of behaviour on the level of atoms, often as yet only in principle but sometimes in detail. The great advantage of this is that the new explanations are much more precise, and are often semiquantitative, compared with the explanations on the microscopic level which are only qualitative. With the better precision there generally goes greater clarity and sometimes greater simplicity.

As a result, the relation between structure and mechanical properties is now so much better understood than previously that the power to specify the structure which will best realise given properties has grown a great deal in both precision and range of application. We must be careful here, since such a hope has so long been entertained in vain that many metallurgists will think sceptically of this statement. It is not within sight to predict the properties of an alloy from first principles. Perhaps the most accurate way of stating the present possibilities is to say that already in certain fields rather specific guiding lines can be indicated along which development should proceed, and that this ability can be confidently expected to spread to other fields.

It also must be borne in mind that metallurgy has been an active technology for 5000 years, and much has been discovered in that time. Consequently, not much improvement can usually be expected from well-tried metals in well-tried applications except perhaps by a quite new approach. In fact it is very interesting to observe that modern research sometimes shows that a thoroughly established process produces almost exactly the structure that modern ideas would prescribe for the purpose in hand—for example, the nickel-based creep-resistant alloys and hard-quenched and tempered vanadium steels. However, it is fairly certain that there are deficiencies in some well-tried metals—probably, for example, in mild steel—and here as well as in the development of new metals to meet new uses the theory should have a big part to play.

It must be admitted, however, that at present there are substantial difficulties about realising the existing potentialities. One sort of difficulty is that besides the serious gaps in knowledge that still exist, the factors that control the mechanical properties, such as the energies of defects and interfaces, are often ones which have not been seriously considered hitherto, and about which quantitative information is therefore still scarce. With time this kind of difficulty can probably be overcome. The other kind of difficulty arises from the fact that in many fields there are few connections between the knowledge of those on the practical side and of those on the scientific side. It is equally difficult to bridge the gap from either side; yet if full advantage is to be taken of the existing potentialities successful efforts will have to be made.

Teddington, England   D. McLEAN
May, 1962

Acknowledgements

I should like to express my thanks to a number of people. First and foremost I wish to thank my wife for her help in many ways, and I must not forget to mention my daughter. My colleagues have always been willing to give their advice and experience. The Director of the National Physical Laboratory has given permission to use some unpublished material. Several workers have enabled me to use material before publication or have provided illustrations, and I am very grateful to them and to the organisations who have allowed diagrams to be reproduced. All such instances are acknowledged specifically at the appropriate point in the book.

D. McL.

Abbreviations of Journals

American Society for Metals	A.S.M.
Journal of Applied Physics	J.A.P.
Journal of the Institute of Metals	J.I.M.
Journal of the Iron and Steel Institute	J.I.S.I.
Proceedings of the Physical Society	P.P.S.
Proceedings of the Royal Society	P.R.S.
Transactions of the American Institute of Mining and Metallurgical Engineers	T.A.I.M.E.
American Society for Testing Materials	A.S.T.M.

Contents

1

Elasticity

1.1 Survey

Metals belong to the large class of substances in which the elastic behaviour is determined by direct separation, compression, or shear of the atoms, unlike the class of which rubber is an example, in which the behaviour is determined by the resistance to straightening out the kinks in the chains of atoms arising from thermal vibration, and which causes this class to have low elastic moduli. Since a single atomic bond has a breaking strength of the order of 10^{-4} dyne and atomic spacings are about 3×10^{-8} cm, the moduli of the class to which metals belong are of the order of $10^{-4} \div (3 \times 10^{-8})^2 \sim 10^{11}$ dynes/cm^2.

A perfect crystal would have a unique modulus—more strictly, allowing for elastic anisotropy, a unique set of elastic constants—and would stretch elastically by several per cent. Whisker crystals do in fact stretch elastically by relatively large amounts as Fig. 1.1 illustrates, but ordinary crystals do not, nor do they have a unique modulus. Good measurements show differences of several tenths of 1% between different samples. The imperfection and impurity of ordinary crystals are believed to be responsible for both of these deviations from the ideal behaviour. The chief source of error is believed to arise from movements of dislocations when a stress is applied, which give an *anelastic* strain in addition to the elastic strain (chapter 3). With nearly pure metals, probably all such sources of error lower the measured modulus, so that the best value in a set taken

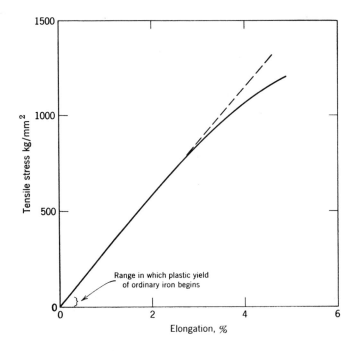

Fig. 1.1.   Elastic loading curve of iron whisker 1.6μ in diameter (Ref. 1).

after different heat treatments, etc., should be the highest.   It seems likely that the nearest approach to the modulus of the perfect crystal is obtained by incorporating a small amount of solute to lock the dislocations against small stresses.

1.2   Theory

The elasticity of crystals has been fully treated in books[2, 3] and review articles.[4, 5]   Only a brief treatment will be given here of those parts required most frequently by metallurgists.

For a generalised but small deformation, the normal stresses σ_{xx}, etc., and shear stresses τ_{xy}, etc., are linear functions of the extensions ϵ_{xx}, etc.,

[1] S. E. Brenner, *J.A.P.*, 1956, **27**, 1484.
[2] W. Voigt, *Lehrbuch der Kristallphysik*, Teubner, Berlin 1910, 2nd impression 1928.
[3] E. Schmid and W. Boas, *Plasticity of Crystals*, English ed. pub. 1950, F. A. Hughes, London.
[4] R. F. S. Hearman, *Rev. Mod. Phys.*, 1946, **18**, 409.
[5] R. F. S. Hearman, *Adv. in Phys.*, 1956, **5**, 323.

and shears ϵ_{xy}, etc. Thus,

$$\left.\begin{array}{l} \sigma_{xx} = c_{11}\epsilon_{xx} + c_{12}\epsilon_{yy} + c_{13}\epsilon_{zz} + c_{14}\epsilon_{yz} + c_{15}\epsilon_{zx} + c_{16}\epsilon_{xy} \\ \tau_{yz} = c_{14}\epsilon_{xx} + c_{24}\epsilon_{yy} + c_{34}\epsilon_{zz} + c_{44}\epsilon_{yz} + c_{45}\epsilon_{zx} + c_{46}\epsilon_{xy} \end{array}\right\} \quad (1.1)$$

where the c_{11}'s, etc., are elastic constants. There are equivalent equations which express ϵ_{xx}, ϵ_{yz}, etc., in terms of the stresses, the elastic constants then being replaced by "coefficients of elasticity" denoted by S_{11}, etc. The thirty-six elastic constants and thirty-six coefficients thus obtained reduce to twenty-one each by virtue of symmetry, and these twenty-one are often written in the form:

$$\begin{array}{cccccc} c_{11} & c_{12} & c_{13} & c_{14} & c_{15} & c_{16} \\ & c_{22} & c_{23} & c_{24} & c_{25} & c_{26} \\ & & c_{33} & c_{34} & c_{35} & c_{36} \\ & & & c_{44} & c_{45} & c_{46} \\ & & & & c_{55} & c_{56} \\ & & & & & c_{66} \end{array}$$

If this square array were completed to include all thirty-six constants, it would be symmetrical about the diagonal $c_{11} - c_{66}$. The elastic coefficients can be written similarly. In the common metal crystal lattices there is a further simplification because many of these twenty-one elastic constants and twenty-one coefficients are either equal to others or to zero. The simplification is greatest for the most symmetrical lattices. For cubic lattices there are only three different nonzero constants and for hexagonal lattices there are five, provided, in the case of anisotropic crystals, that the crystal axes coincide with the axes of the coordinate system (cubic crystals), or the crystal c axis and basal a direction coincide with the z and y axes of the coordinate system (hexagonal crystals). For cubic crystals the elastic constants then are:

$$\begin{array}{cccccc} c_{11} & c_{12} & c_{12} & 0 & 0 & 0 \\ & c_{11} & c_{12} & 0 & 0 & 0 \\ & & c_{11} & 0 & 0 & 0 \\ & & & c_{44} & 0 & 0 \\ & & & & c_{44} & 0 \\ & & & & & c_{44} \end{array}$$

and for hexagonal:

$$\begin{array}{cccccc} c_{11} & c_{12} & c_{13} & 0 & 0 & 0 \\ & c_{11} & c_{13} & 0 & 0 & 0 \\ & & c_{33} & 0 & 0 & 0 \\ & & & c_{44} & 0 & 0 \\ & & & & c_{44} & 0 \\ & & & & & \tfrac{1}{2}(c_{11} - c_{12}) \end{array}$$

with similar arrangements for the coefficients of elasticity. Values of many of these constants have been collected.[4, 5] In principle, the elastic constants can be calculated from quantum mechanics, although early successes[6, 7, 8] now seem fortuitous. It is difficult to take the various electronic factors fully into account.[9]

The relations between the elastic constants and the conventional moduli are simple in the case of an isotropic cubic crystal

$$E = \frac{1}{S_{11}}, \qquad G = c_{44} = \frac{1}{S_{44}}, \qquad \nu = -\frac{S_{12}}{S_{11}} \qquad (1.2)$$

where E is Young's modulus and G is the shear modulus. The relations between the moduli themselves are:

$$G = \frac{E}{2(1 + \nu)} \quad \text{and} \quad K = \frac{E}{3(1 - 2\nu)} \qquad (1.3)$$

where K is the modulus of volume expansion and ν is Poisson's ratio. Equations 1.3 hold for any isotropic body. For example, they apply to a random polycrystalline aggregate whose individual grains are elastically anisotropic.

When a solid is stretched adiabatically and elastically, its temperature drops slightly. The temperature rises if the solid is compressed instead of stretched. A thermodynamic argument yields the relation[10]

$$\left(\frac{\partial T}{\partial \epsilon}\right)_S = -\frac{\alpha E T}{C_v} \qquad (1.4)$$

where T is the absolute temperature, $\partial \epsilon$ is the small change in length, E is Young's modulus, the suffix S refers to constant entropy (i.e., corresponding to an adiabatic experiment), α is the coefficient of thermal expansion, and C_v is the specific heat at constant volume. Thus, an extension of about 0.1% is needed to cause a temperature drop of $0.1°C$.

The moduli are lowered by the strain energy of any defects present. Physically, this effect arises in the following way. The curve representing the energy W of an atom as a function of the distance x of shear with respect to its neighbours above or below must be something like a sine wave. Atoms normally lie in the troughs of this curve. In the troughs, the shear modulus is a maximum since it is proportional to $\partial^2 W / \partial x^2$. Any shear movement takes an atom up the side of the sine-like curve

[6] K. Fuchs, *P.R.S.*, 1935, **151**, 585.
[7] K. Fuchs, *P.R.S.*, 1936, **153**, 622.
[8] K. Fuchs, *P.R.S.*, 1936, **157**, 444.
[9] R. S. Leigh, *Phil. Mag.*, 1951, **42**, 139.
[10] J. F. Nye, "Physical Props. of Crystals," Oxford University Press, London, 1957, p. 178.

where $\partial^2 W/\partial x^2$, and hence the shear modulus, is smaller. In most strained conditions there is much more shear strain energy than dilational strain energy,[11] which of course means that the lattice is sheared rather than dilated. Consequently, the effect referred to is usually the important one and leads to a reduction in the shear modulus and therefore also (eq. 1.3) in the Young's modulus. An estimate of the effect leads to the relation[11]

$$\frac{1}{G}\frac{\partial G}{\partial W} \sim \frac{3}{2NkG}\frac{\partial G}{\partial T} \tag{1.5}$$

where G is the shear modulus, W is the shear strain energy (usually $\sim$ total strain energy) per unit volume, N is the number of atoms per unit volume, and k is Boltzman's constant. With $\partial G/\partial T = 3 \times 10^{-4}$, which is a typical value, $\delta G/G \sim 3.2 \times 10^{-11} \delta W$ with δW in ergs/cc. As an example, in a cold worked metal the stored energy δW is about 3×10^8 ergs/cc (section 2.3b), giving $\delta G/G = 0.01$. In point of fact, cold working can reduce the moduli by considerably more than 1% so that other effects such as the effect of dislocation movement and perhaps that of the preferred orientation developed by cold work are important when this is the case.

Since the Cauchy relations, which for cubic crystals reduce to $c_{12} = c_{44}$, are approximately valid for ionic crystals, it is usual to point out that they do not apply to metals. Their derivation assumes that all forces on each atom are central, that is, they lie along lines joining atoms; but in metals the interactions between the electrons prevents this from being so and accounts for the inapplicability of the Cauchy relations.

1.3 Measurements of Moduli

Elastic constants are measured in three kinds of experiment. In one, a steady stress is applied to the specimen and the steady strain is measured. Stresses of the order of 10^8 kg/mm^2 are used.* In a second, the specimen is put into resonance and the appropriate modulus calculated from the theory of resonance; kilocycle frequencies are generally involved and the peak stresses applied are usually about 0.01 kg/mm^2. In a third method, pulses of waves whose wavelength is small compared with the specimen dimensions are transmitted through the specimen and their time of transit measured; megacycle frequencies are involved and the peak stress is usually less than 0.001 kg/mm^2. An experimental complication is liable to occur in the pulse method with polycrystalline specimens whose

---

* 1.575 kg/mm^2 = 1.544×10^8 dynes/cm^2 = 1 ton/in^2 = 2240 lb/in^2.

[11] C. Zener, *Acta Cryst.*, 1949, **2**, 163.

individual grains are anisotropic.   From the point of view of the travelling wave, every time it crosses a grain boundary into the next grain of different orientation it enters material of different elastic properties, since the effective elastic constants in the direction of propagation change from grain to grain.   As with any kind of wave transmission, this causes a sharp increase in attenuation when the grain size is comparable to the wavelength.   Since grain sizes are commonly 0.1 to 0.01 mm, this occurs at frequencies of a few megacycles.

In dealing with the elastic behaviour of real metals, we have to face complications which rise from the anisotropy of most metals as well as the other difficulty already hinted at of getting reproducible material.   For cubic crystals one measure of the degree of anisotropy is the ratio $c_{44}/\frac{1}{2}(c_{11} - c_{12})$.   The constant c_{44} measures the resistance to shear on a cube plane along a cube edge, and $\frac{1}{2}(c_{11} - c_{12})$ the resistance to shear on a (110) plane along a [110] direction.   Some values of this ratio are [4, 5]

Fe	Mo	W	Al	Ge	Cu
2.5	0.79	1.00	1.22–1.68	1.68	2.8–3.2

Ni	Ag	Ag–7.3% Mg	Pb	Beta Brass
2.0–2.37	3.02	3.1	3.85	8.7

The range given for three of these metals indicates the experimental variation met with.   It will be seen that most metals exhibit considerable elastic anisotropy.   Further examples of this are that the Young's modulus of lead single crystals varies with orientation by more than 3:1, as shown in Fig. 1.2, and that of zinc single crystals varies by 4:1.   In metals the anisotropy is such that the maximum value of Young's modulus E is along the $\langle 111 \rangle$ direction, and the minimum is along the $\langle 100 \rangle$ direction. In ionic crystals the reverse is true.   The only metal that is very close to being isotropic elastically is tungsten.

However, polycrystalline samples of all metals behave isotropically provided the crystals are randomly oriented, and a problem in the theory of crystal elasticity has been to calculate the polycrystalline elastic constants given those of single crystals.   The results differ according to the assumptions made; for example whether the stresses or the strains are equal in all crystals.   Comparisons between calculated and measured values show that the calculated values are in error by about 10% for a metal with the degree of anisotropy of, say, copper.[4, 5]   Some insight into the reason for this is given by experiments [12] on iron bi-crystals in which the boundary between the two crystals was normal to the tensile stress direction.   The elastic extension over short (1 mm) gauge lengths

[12] H. Möller and F. Brasse, *Arch. Eisenhüttenw.*, 1955, **26**, 231.

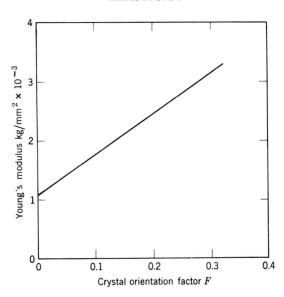

Fig. 1.2. Variation of Young's modulus of lead single crystals with orientation. The abscissa F is defined as follows: If the stress direction makes angles with the three cube axes of the lead crystal of γ_1, γ_2, and γ_3, $F = \gamma_1^2\gamma_2^2 + \gamma_2^2\gamma_3^2 + \gamma_3^2\gamma_1^2$ (Ref. 4).

was measured. Near the boundary there was a sharp change in extension —in some specimens exceeding 2:1—which accommodated the different extension in each crystal arising from their different orientations. These experiments confirm that in a polycrystal both stress and strain vary, not only from crystal to crystal but also across each crystal, and that the assumptions referred to are both somewhat approximate. One difficulty in obtaining reproducible experimental results on polycrystals is, there-fore, that of producing a sufficiently random distribution of orientations for a polycrystalline specimen to behave isotropically, although methods have been developed of computing the elastic constants of randomly oriented material from the measured constants of material having a moderate preferred orientation.[13] Conversely, the elastic anisotropy per-haps could be used as a measure of the degree of preferred orientation.

The influence on the moduli of the precise state of the metal may also be substantial. Cold work may reduce the modulus substantially, and on annealing cold worked silver, copper, and some copper alloys, increases of 2 to 30% have been found.[13] Probably cold working alone accounts

[13] G. Bradfield and H. Pursey, *Phil. Mag.*, 1953, **44**, 437.

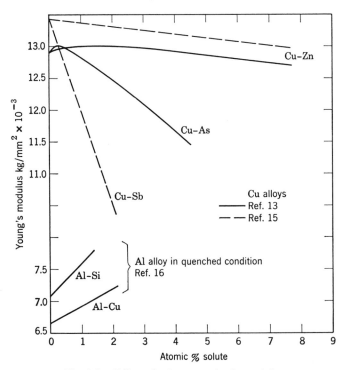

Fig. 1.3.   Effect of solutes on elastic modulus.

for about a 1% change, and preferred orientations developed on re-crystallising can account for the substantially larger changes.   The state of stress seems to affect the modulus to a measurable extent.   During a tensile test, the "tangent modulus" can be measured.*   Measurements of this kind have shown mean changes of about 0.03% and 0.3% in steel and aluminium respectively for every 1 kg/mm² change in stress, although the effect is not strictly linear.[14]   Furthermore, even in the annealed condition heat treatment affects the modulus, probably by influencing dislocation mobility; thus after the elastic properties of copper have been stabilised by annealing at 550°C, they can still be increased by annealing at 650°C.[13]   Temperature itself of course affects the moduli, because with rising temperature the atomic separation increases and binding forces weaken.   Examples of this effect are shown in Fig. 3.4.   The moduli typically drop by about 0.03% per 1°C temperature rise.

* The "tangent modulus" is given by the tangent to the stress-strain curve at the stress in question.

[14] M. F. Markham and I. D. Hewin, *J.I.M.*, 1960–61, **89**, 77.

[15] W. Köster, *Z. Metallk.*, 1948, **39**, 145.

[16] B. J. Elliott and H. J. Axon, *J.I.M.*, 1957–8, **86**, 24.

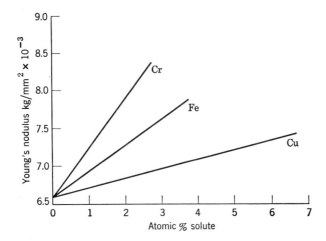

Fig. 1.4. Effect on Young's modulus of Al of elements forming hard second phases (Ref. 20).

Composition is another factor which affects the elastic properties. Solute elements may increase or decrease the moduli. Figure 1.3 shows some results which illustrate both types of behaviour. There seem to be at least three factors at work here.

1. The internal strains around the solute atoms should reduce the moduli; as already mentioned, this is a general property of internal strains.

2. Solute atoms may prevent dislocations moving and so mitigate the reduction in modulus this produces.[13, 17] What seems to be a clear example of this kind of effect is the increase in modulus produced by irradiation with neutrons; for example, a $\frac{1}{4}\%$ increase in the Young's modulus of copper.[18] There is hardly any other possible explanation of such a result other than the locking of dislocations by the point defects created by the irradiation. In Fig. 1.3, the initial rise when arsenic or zinc are added to copper is perhaps due to this effect.

3. Solvent-solute binding stronger than solvent-solvent should help to raise the moduli and vice versa.

Hard second phases, on the other hand, always raise the modulus, at least in aluminium alloys.[19, 20] Some results for these alloys are shown

[17] J. Friedel, *Phil. Mag.*, 1953, **44**, 444.
[18] D. O. Thompson, T. H. Blewitt and D. K. Holmes, *J.A.P.*, 1957, **28**, 742.
[19] N. Dudzinski, J. R. Murray, B. W. Mott, and B. Chalmers, *J.I.M.*, 1948, **74**, 29.
[20] N. Dudzinski, *J.I.M.*, 1952–3, **81**, 49.

in Fig. 1.4. Presumably, the second phases have higher moduli than the matrix and there is a mixture effect, coupled perhaps with a hampering of dislocation movement. Increases of 30% in Young's modulus have been achieved in aluminium alloys. With the Al–Si and Al–Cu alloys of Fig. 1.3, the modulus was raised whether the alloys were quenched to obtain a solid solution or aged to produce a precipitate. Some other alloying elements behaved similarly.

Two less general effects may be mentioned. The elastic constants in nickel are affected appreciably by the state of magnetisation[21, 22] (the maximum effect is a few per cent). Chromium exhibits a curious behaviour. This metal passes through a transformation near room temperature whose nature has not been explained theoretically but in which the elastic constants and electrical resistivity change while the lattice parameter is unaffected.[23, 24] The temperature and magnitude of the changes depend on purity, and samples have been produced which have a negative Poisson's ratio over a limited temperature range.[25] In this condition, chromium possesses the remarkable property that when a compressive stress is applied there is a lateral contraction.

[21] J. de Klerk and M. J. P. Musgrave, *P.P.S.*, 1955, **1**, 181.
[22] T. Watanabe, Y. Gonde, and Z. Funatogawa, *Sci. Rep. Yokohama Nat. Univ.*, 1956, **5**, 36.
[23] M. E. Fine, E. S. Greiner, and W. C. Ellis, *T.A.I.M.E.*, 1951, **191**, 56.
[24] H. Pursey, *J.I.M.*, 1957–8, **8**, 362.
[25] H. Pursey, *Nature*, 1953, **172**, 864.

2

Imperfections
in Pure Metals

Whereas the elastic properties of metals are determined primarily by the atomic forces, and the crystal imperfections only introduce small deviations from the ideal behaviour of a perfect crystal of an amount of not more than the order of a few per cent, the plastic properties are determined primarily by these imperfections. Metals with big atomic forces still tend to have high flow and fracture stresses and vice versa, but the fraction of the perfect crystal's strength that is realised depends on the number, arrangement, and properties of the imperfections present. The imperfections known or believed to be present in pure metals and which affect the mechanical properties are dislocations, grain boundaries, vacancies, and interstitial atoms. Of these, there are known to be differences in kind of properties from one metal to another only for dislocations; for the others it is only known that the energy varies. However, the differences already known seem enough to explain the variation in mechanical properties between one metal and another.

This chapter describes what is needed as a background for the rest of this book. Several full-length reviews exist.[1-7]

[1] A. H. Cottrell, *Dislocations and Plastic Flow of Crystals*, Oxford University Press, London, 1953.
[2] W. T. Read, "Dislocations in Crystals," McGraw-Hill, New York, 1953.
[3] J. Friedel, *Les Dislocations*, Gauthier-Villars, Paris, 1956.

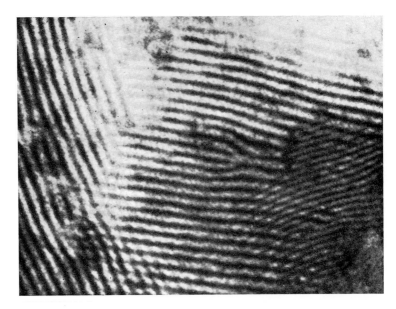

Fig. 2.1. Direct observation of a dislocation in a metal. The figure shows a Moiré pattern from palladium deposited onto gold. In the centre is a dislocation which shows up as two terminating lines, probably because of the particular diffraction conditions used. × 750,000 (Pashley, Bassett and Menter)

2.1 Dislocations

There is now abundant direct experimental evidence for the existence of dislocations. In organo-metallic crystals having a layer structure wide enough (separation between the layers about 10 A) to be resolvable in the electron microscope, edge dislocations have been seen directly.[8] In metals they have been seen directly with the field ion microscope,[9] and also with the electron microscope by making use of the extra magnification given by the Moiré fringe technique.[10]   Figure 2.1 shows an example of a dislocation seen in this way.   We can see dislocations with the electron microscope at lower power as black lines if we use the thin foil-transmission

[4] A. Seeger, *Handbuch der Physik*, Vol. 7, Part 1, *Kristallphysik* 1, Springer, Berlin, 1955.

[5] F. R. N. Nabarro, *Advances in Physics*, 1952, **1**, 319.

[6] D. McLean, *Grain Boundaries in Metals*, Oxford University Press, London, 1957.

[7] B. Chalmers, *Physical Metallurgy*, John Wiley and Sons, New York, 1959.

[8] J. W. Menter, *P. R. S.*, 1956, **A.236**, 119.

[9] E. W. Müller, *Z. Physik*, 1959, **156**, 399.

[10] D. W. Pashley, G. A. Bassett, J. W. Menter, *P.R.S.*, 1958, **A.246**, 345.

technique; they move when a stress is applied, and cross slip, pile up, polygonise, and split into partial dislocations[11] in a way similar to that theoretically predicted. Figure 2.2 shows a polygonised group of dislocations in iron seen in this way. The dislocations, or rather their strain fields, are seen as dark lines because they scatter electrons relatively strongly, and the corresponding place in the image appears dark. In a similar way, dislocations are revealed by X rays, although the useful magnification is lower.[12, 13] With the optical microscope, dislocations can be seen in transparent crystals if a suitable foreign substance is precipitated on to the dislocations; the networks and arrays of dislocations expected on theoretical grounds have been seen in these substances in this

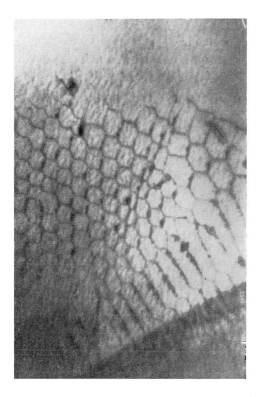

Fig. 2.2. A network of dislocations comprising a subboundary. Fe, × 28,000. (Carrington, Hale and McLean; Crown copyright reserved.)

[11] P. B. Hirsch, R. W. Horne, and M. J. Whelan, *Phil. Mag.*, 1956, **1**, 677.
[12] A. R. Lang, *J.A.P.*, 1958, **29**, 597.
[13] J. B. Newkirk, *Phys. Rev.*, 1958, **110**, 1465.

Fig. 2.3. An example of the etch-pit technique for revealing dislocations. Two twins have hit the grain boundary. The stress concentration at each point of impact has created numerous dislocations. × 1000. (National Physical Laboratory; Crown copyright reserved.)

way.[14, 15]   An adaptation of this method has been to examine silicon in infrared light, to which it is transparent; copper is opaque to infrared light, and when precipitated on to the dislocations these become visible.[16] In bulk metals, dislocations can be detected by employing etching reagents which develop etch pits only where dislocations meet the surface.   That the etch pits form at dislocations is shown for example by the etch pits produced by a suitable reagent in silicon[16] at points on the surface where a dislocation, revealed by the infrared technique just mentioned, emerges; it is also confirmed by several observations of the correct relation between the number of etch pits along a subboundary and the misorientation at the subboundary.   Figure 2.3 provides an example of the etch pit technique and shows the dislocation distribution produced in iron where a twin has collided with a grain boundary.   In other fields the expected

[14] S. Amelinckx, *Dislocations and Mechanical Properties of Metals*, John Wiley and Sons, New York, 1957.

[15] J. W. Mitchell, *Dislocations and Mechanical Properties*, John Wiley and Sons, New York, 1957.

[16] W. C. Dash, *J. Appl. Phys.*, 1956, **27**, 1153.

effects of dislocations are observed; the growth spirals in crystal growth,[17] the influence of subboundaries on diffusion and the acceleration of precipitation by dislocations, for example. Altogether, the accumulated evidence has confirmed theoretical predictions most strikingly and demonstratés the general correctness of the basic theory of dislocations.

The dislocation pattern revealed in annealed polycrystalline metals by direct observation is the following. Each grain may contain fairly regular two-dimensional dislocation networks (Fig. 2.2), and when these are present the individual meshes are probably 1000 A or more across so that the networks cause only slight misorientation. The grains are also filled with an irregular three-dimensional network (Fig. 2.4). Besides these extensive networks there are isolated clusters of dislocations around many inclusion particles (Fig. 2.5) and precipitate particles, evidently produced by differential contraction between matrix and particle during

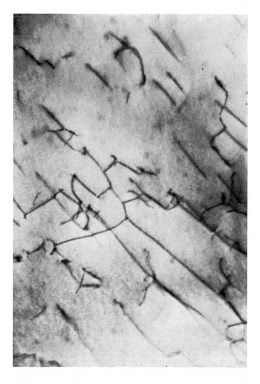

Fig. 2.4. A part of the three-dimensional network in Fe. × 28,000. (Carrington, Hale, and McLean; Crown copyright reserved.)

[17] A. R. Verma, *Crystal Growth and Dislocations*, Butterworths, London, 1953.

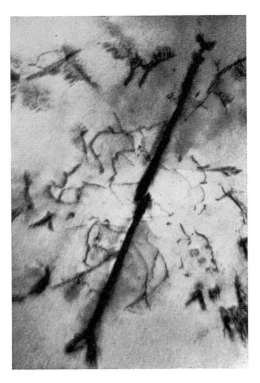

Fig. 2.5. Cluster of dislocations around an inclusion. Fe, ×28,000. (Hale; Crown copyright reserved.)

cooling.   Finally, there are isolated dislocation loops which are referred to again in section 2.1*j*.

In the rest of this section, features of dislocations which bear on the mechanical properties are described.

(*a*) *Burgers Vector.*   The Burgers vector of a dislocation denotes the amount and direction of slip associated with the dislocation; that is to say, it is the slip that occurs at any point when the dislocation passes that point. We can find the Burgers vector by comparing a path around the dislocation with the corresponding path in a perfect part of the lattice; the difference is the Burgers vector.   There is a 180° ambiguity about the Burgers vector since, for example, a dislocation which causes the top half of a crystal to slip to the right with respect to the bottom part also causes the bottom part to shift to the left with respect to the top part.   In thinking about dislocation movements we must bear this ambiguity, although trivial, sometimes rather carefully in mind.

(b) *Edge and Screw Dislocations.* The two extreme positions a dislocation can take up are the edge and the screw positions, illustrated in
Figs. 2.6 and 2.7; AA' is the line of the dislocation in both figures. The
Burgers vector of the edge dislocation is perpendicular, and that of the
screw dislocation is parallel, to the dislocation line. There is necessarily
an extra plane (half plane) of atoms immediately above an edge dislocation, or, if the bottom half in Fig. 2.6 is thought of as slipping to the left
it is equally correct to think of a plane missing below AA'. There are no
extra or missing atoms associated with a screw dislocation. It is easily
verified that a dislocation cannot end inside a crystal, and also that an
edge and screw can join up if they have the same Burgers vectors. The
experiments referred to previously have shown that dislocations generally
lie between the pure edge and pure screw positions. Such mixed dislocations may be thought of as consisting of alternate short lengths of
edge and screw dislocation. If the line of the dislocation makes an angle
θ with its Burgers vector it can be regarded as consisting of sin θ of edge
and cos θ of screw type per unit length of dislocation line.

It is geometrically possible for a screw dislocation to slip from one glide
plane on to any other plane intersecting the first which contains its Burgers
vector; in practice there is a restriction on this movement discussed later.
An edge dislocation can only move out of its glide plane by *climb*, which
occurs when the extra half plane associated with it is either added to or
partly diffuses away. A mixed dislocation is similarly restricted by its
edge component. Climb has been experimentally observed at the dislocation loops mentioned previously. As explained in section 4.6c, these
loops are believed to be initially of edge type and so shrink or grow in
diameter by climb. This shrinkage and growth has been observed in
aluminium, and is characterised by an activation energy equal within
experimental error to that for self diffusion,[18] as it should be since climb
involves mass transport.

(c) *Forces on Dislocations and Helical Dislocations.* When a dislocation of Burgers vector b passes right across a crystal which has the dimen-

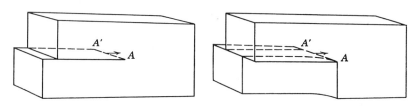

Fig. 2.6. Edge dislocation.   Fig. 2.7. Screw dislocation.

[18] J. Silcox and M. J. Whelan, *Phil. Mag.*, 1960, 5, 1.

sions of a unit cube, a shear of amount b occurs. If a shear stress τ is applied to produce this shear displacement the work done is τb. The dislocation has, however, moved unit distance, so the effective force F on the dislocation has done work equal to $F \times$ unit distance. The two amounts of work are equal, from which $F = \tau b$. This simple argument[19] has been confirmed by more sophisticated ones.[1, 20] It is easy to see from this argument that if the directions of τ and b are not parallel

$$F = \tau \cdot b \qquad (2.1)$$

that is, the shear stress component parallel to b is the effective component.

The direct stress parallel to b encourages climb of edge dislocations, since compression tends to eliminate the extra half plane and tension the reverse. A direct stress σ causing climb by unit length of dislocation through unit distance does work $\sigma \cdot b$, so that the climbing force on the dislocation is

$$F_c = \sigma \cdot b \qquad (2.2)$$

Climb occurs with the emission or absorption of vacancies or interstitial atoms. Since, if the actual concentration of, say, vacancies is c and the equilibrium concentration is c_0, the free energy change when one vacancy disappears is $-kT \ln (c/c_0)$ (k is Boltzmann's constant, T the absolute temperature), a deviation from the equilibrium concentration exerts an effective force encouraging climb. By equating work done we see this "chemical" force to be[21]

$$F_c' = \frac{kT}{b^2} \ln \frac{c}{c_0} \qquad (2.3)$$

A direct stress has no first-order effect on a screw dislocation.

The emission or absorption of vacancies or interstitials is believed to occur at steps in the extra half plane. These *jogs* as they are called, are favoured sites because they can move sideways (Fig. 2.8) without change in form, whereas emission or absorption elsewhere requires two jogs to be formed (Fig. 2.8) which needs extra energy.

An interesting situation arises if a pure screw dislocation lies in a region where the vacancy or interstitial concentration is not at the equilibrium value. Should the dislocation bend slightly into an arc of a circle, it acquires edge components of opposite signs at opposite ends of the arc.

[19] N. F. Mott and F. R. N. Nabarro, Conference on the strength of Solids, *Phys. Soc.*, 1948.
[20] M. O. Peach, *J.A.P.*, 1951, **22**, 1359.
[21] J. Bardeen and C. Herring, *Imperfections in Nearly Perfect Crystals*, John Wiley and Sons, New York, 1952, p. 277.

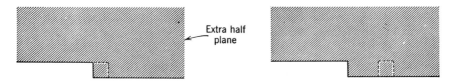

Extra half
plane

Fig. 2.8a. Capture of a vacancy at a jog moves the jog sideways but does not change its form.

Fig. 2.8b. Capture of a vacancy elsewhere than at a jog produces two new jogs.

In the nonequilibrium environment, these climb in opposite directions, wrapping the dislocation into a helix.[22, 23] Helical dislocations believed to have been formed in this way have been seen in crystals transparent to light[24, 25] as well as in metals.

(*d*) *Peierls-Nabarro Force.* The length of the Burgers vector denotes the distance between successive equilibrium positions of a dislocation. A force is required to enable the dislocation to surmount the potential hill separating the equilibrium positions. This is known as the Peierls-Nabarro force, or simply the Peierls force. Other things being equal, the wider the region over which the disturbance around the dislocation spreads, the smaller is the Peierls force. The physical reason for this is simple. Thus, at an edge dislocation n rows of atoms on one side of the slip plane face $n+1$ rows on the other side. When the dislocation moves to the next equilibrium position, each of these rows moves a distance of about an nth this distance. The force needed to accomplish this is smaller the larger n is. The width of the dislocation is of course determined by the atomic forces, and the Peierls force thus depends sensitively on these forces. The Peierls force in any case is large only if the dislocation lies in a simple crystallographic direction so that it lies along an energy valley. In other directions it lies across energy hills and valleys, and the effective Peierls force is small since at some places the dislocation is on the uphill parts of the Peierls force—distance curve, whereas at others it is on the downhill parts. It has been argued that on this account the Peierls resistance is greatly reduced, since only by chance will dislocations lie along simple crystallographic directions. How important this weakening effect is seems doubtful, for under stress the dislocation should tend to swing into a crystallographic direction of high resistance.

[22] J. Wertman, *Phys. Rev.*, 1957, **107**, 1259.

[23] F. C. Frank, *Discussions Faraday Soc.* (Mol. mechanisms of rate process in solids), 1957, **23**, 122.

[24] W. Bontinck and S. Amelinckx, *Phil. Mag.*, 1957, **2**, 94.

[25] S. Amelinckx, W. Bontinck, W. Dekeyser, and F. Seitz, *Phil. Mag.*, 1957, **2**, 355.

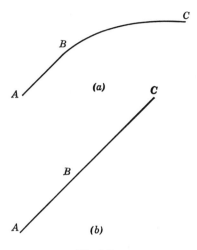

Fig. 2.9.

This will happen because any short length of a curved dislocation such as *AB* in Fig. 2.9a that lies in this direction will be held up by the Peierls force while the adjoining parts move into line, as in Fig. 2.9b. The evidence discussed in Chapter 4, where the part played by the Peierls force in different metals is considered, suggests that the weakening effect is rather limited.

(e) *Stress Field and Energy of a Dislocation.* Associated with the inevitable lattice strain around a dislocation is a stress. In an isotropic material, for an edge dislocation lying along the *z* axis, having a Burgers vector *b* along the *x* axis, the components of the stress at the position, *x, y* are, for example

$$\sigma_{xx} = -\frac{Dy(3x^2 + y^2)}{(x^2 + y^2)^2}, \qquad \sigma_{yy} = \frac{Dy(x^2 - y^2)}{(x^2 + y^2)^2}, \qquad \sigma_{zz} = 0$$

$$\tag{2.4a}$$

$$\tau_{xy} = \frac{Dx(x^2 - y^2)}{(x^2 + y^2)^2}, \qquad \tau_{xz} = \tau_{yz} = 0$$

where *G* is the shear modulus, *b* the Burgers vector and $D = \dfrac{Gb}{2\pi(1 - \nu)}$ ν being Poisson's ratio. In polar coordinates the stresses at the point *r*, θ are

$$\sigma_{rr} = \sigma_{\theta\theta} = -\frac{D \sin \theta}{r}, \qquad \tau_{r\theta} = \frac{D \cos \theta}{r} \tag{2.4b}$$

For a screw dislocation lying along the z axis with Burgers vector along this axis, the corresponding stresses are

$$\tau_{xz} = -\frac{Dy}{x^2 + y^2}, \quad \tau_{yz} = \frac{Dx}{x^2 + y^2} \qquad (2.4c)$$

$$\tau_{z\theta} = \frac{D}{r} \qquad (2.4d)$$

where D now is $Gb/2\pi$. The other stresses are zero. These stresses are computed by ordinary elastic theory and should be reasonably accurate up to a few atom spacings from the centre of the dislocation line. The region inside which the elastic approximation does not hold is usually referred to as the core of the dislocation, and is believed to have energy of about one electron volt per atom length. The strained region around the dislocation carries potential energy. The elastic approximation gives for the energy outside the core a value close to

$$W = \frac{Db}{2} \ln \frac{r}{r_0} \qquad (2.5)$$

where D has the appropriate value defined previously depending on whether the dislocation is edge or screw, r_0 is the radius of the core and r is the distance to which the strain extends. The value of r is not critical since it enters eq. 2.5 logarithmetically but, however, depends on circumstances. For example, in a cylindrical specimen which contains a single dislocation running along the axis, r is equal to the radius of the cylinder, but when other dislocations are present those of opposite sign will neutralise each other's strain fields at distances about equal to their separation and r can then be put equal to this spacing. Since the spacing varies very widely indeed according to circumstances, the energy must vary too. In an annealed polycrystalline metal, for example, the dislocations may be 10^{-4} cm apart, giving an elastic energy of about 5 ev per atom length. But in a cold worked metal the spacing may range down to perhaps only 10^{-7} cm in the dense clusters of dislocations that may be present after cold work, and for such dislocations the elastic energy is less than 1 ev. Likewise in a pronounced dislocation subboundary of about $1°$ misorientation in which the dislocation spacing will be about 10^{-6} cm, the elastic energy is approximately 1 ev per atom length of dislocation.

The energy of dislocations therefore depends on circumstances both because it varies with r, and thus on the separation between dislocations, and because the elastic part of the energy varies as the square of the Burgers vector. In all circumstances, however, the energy of dislocations is so large that a crystal containing them is thermodynamically extremely unstable. The only reason why they persist in crystals is because they are

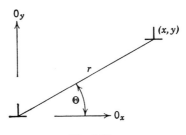

Fig. 2.10.

difficult to get rid of. The same situation characterises grain boundaries. Just as it is possible to eliminate or avoid grain boundaries by suitable means, so should it be possible to dispose of dislocations.

The stress field of one dislocation acts on other dislocations. The strength and sign of the interaction depends on the two Burgers vectors and on the mutual orientation of the dislocation lines. A simple case is that of parallel-like dislocations. If we suppose these to lie along the z axis, the components of the interaction force are, from eqs. 2.1 and 2.4, with positive signs indicating repulsion,

$$F_x = \begin{cases} Db\,\dfrac{x(x^2 - y^2)}{(x^2 + y^2)^2}, \\[2em] Db\,\dfrac{x}{x^2 + y^2} \end{cases} \qquad F_y = \begin{cases} Db\,\dfrac{y(3x^2 + y^2)}{(x^2 + y^2)^2} \quad \text{edges} \quad (2.6a) \\[2em] Db\,\dfrac{y}{x^2 + y^2} \quad \text{screws} \quad (2.6b) \end{cases}$$

in Cartesian coordinates and

$$F_r = \begin{cases} \dfrac{Db}{r}, \\[1.5em] \dfrac{Db}{r} \end{cases} \qquad F_\theta = \begin{cases} \dfrac{Db \sin 2\theta}{r} \quad \text{edges} \quad (2.6c) \\[1.5em] \text{Zero} \qquad \text{screws} \quad (2.6d) \end{cases}$$

in polar coordinates; x, y, r, and θ are defined in Fig. 2.10. Again D takes the appropriate value for edge or screw dislocation defined earlier. For unlike dislocations the forces are all reversed. More complicated cases of dislocation interaction are discussed in sections 2.1i and 4.7.

Dislocations in anisotropic materials have been investigated.[26, 27, 28] The results are rather complicated. Although most metals are elastically anisotropic to a noticeable degree, it has not often been thought worth-

[26] J. D. Eshelby, *Phil. Mag.*, 1949, **40**, 903.
[27] A. J. E. Foreman, *Acta Met.*, 1955, **3**, 322.
[28] A. N. Stroh, *Phil. Mag.*, 1958, **3**, 625.

while to use anisotropic expressions, partly, no doubt, because of the difficulty of making measurements that are accurate enough to justify doing so.

(*f*) *Line Tension of a Dislocation.* Since a dislocation has energy, it tries to reduce its length. This tendency shows up as a line tension, equivalent to surface tension, the magnitude of which can be derived by a virtual work argument from the change in energy when a bent dislocation straightens slightly. The argument is not quite the same as for, say, the surface tension of a soap film, since in that case the tension arises entirely from a free energy which is located in the film. With a dislocation, on the other hand, the tension arises mainly from the elastic strain energy around it since this is larger than the core energy, and so depends on the value that must be taken for r in eq. 2.5. For example, for a wavy dislocation straightening under the influence of line tension, a reduction in energy is associated with the elimination of waviness and the line tension derives from this. However, at large distances the strain field of a wavy dislocation must be the same as that of a straight one, and the extra strain energy of a wavy one is therefore limited to a region of radius approximately equal to the wavelength of the waves. Thus this is approximately the value to take for r in such a case. This example makes it clear that the tension depends somewhat on circumstances. But the energy is not very sensitive to the value of r and it is usually good enough to take the tension as equal to $\frac{1}{2}Gb^2$.

The existence of the line tension has two consequences.

1. A uniform stress τb on the dislocation will bend it into an arc of radius

$$R \sim \frac{Gb}{2\tau} \qquad (2.7)$$

just as a uniform pressure bends a soap film into a spherical shape.

2. Where three or more dislocations meet in a point, the angles at which they meet must be such that the line tensions are in equilibrium. In addition, of course, the sum of their Burgers vectors must be zero, and only dislocations having Burgers vectors which satisfy this requirement can join in this way.

A large Peierls force may modify both these consequences because it tends to fix the dislocations in certain crystallographic directions. Clearly a stress will not bow a dislocation subjected to a large Peierls force into an arc of a circle, but into a polygon, the sides of which are parallel to crystallographic directions such as AB in Fig. 2.9. Very clear examples of this have been seen in silicon.[29] Similarly, the angles at which dislocations meet must be influenced by the tendency of the dislocations to

[29] W. C. Dash, *J.A.P.*, 1958, **29**, 705.

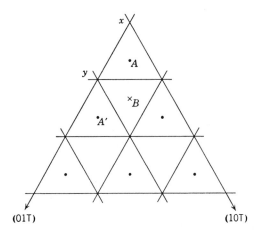

Fig. 2.11. (111) planes in an fcc lattice. One layer of atoms lies at the points of intersection of the full lines. The next lies at the positions indicated by the dots.

lie in certain directions, for a torque is needed to twist the dislocations away from these directions and has to be included in the equilibrium of forces. A dislocation lying in a preferred direction somewhat resembles a twin boundary in that it has a low energy and resists a torque.

(g) *Extended Dislocations and Stacking Faults.* Dislocations in some lattices can be *extended*. Figure 2.11 illustrates a simple example of this, which occurs in the fcc lattice. The figure shows atoms in two (111) planes, one above the other; X, Y, etc. are the positions of atoms in one of the planes and AA', etc., the positions in the other. AA' is one of the macroscopically observed slip directions. Slip will surely occur most easily, however, via the two saddle points, that is, $A \rightarrow B \rightarrow A'$, which implies that the $a/2 \langle 01\bar{1} \rangle$ dislocation AA' exists as two *partial* dislocations, namely, the $a/6 \langle 11\bar{2} \rangle$ dislocation AB and the $a/6 \langle \bar{1}2\bar{1} \rangle$ dislocation BA'. These repel each other to some extent and the original dislocation is said to be extended. Between the two partial dislocations is a layer across which the atoms misfit to some degree. This is called a *stacking fault* because it upsets the stacking sequence. Thus, in the particular case mentioned, the stacking sequence normal to a (111) plane in an fcc lattice, which can be represented by *abcabcabc*, etc., becomes *abcbcabc*, etc. Because of the atomic misfit, the stacking fault has an interfacial energy and tension; as a consequence the partial dislocations separate to a distance where, in the absence of other forces, their mutual repulsion is numerically equal to the stacking fault energy. A low stacking fault

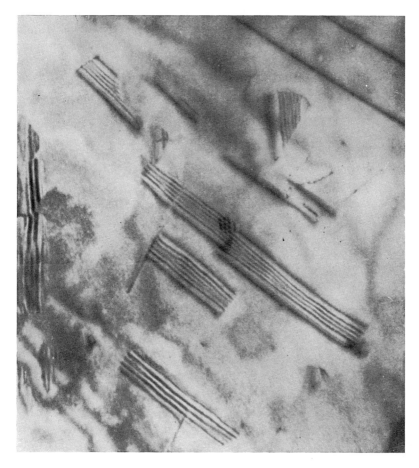

Fig. 2.12. Stacking faults in Nb lying on (112) planes. For electron-optical reasons connected with the lattice displacement at the stacking fault, each of the latter shows up as a set of fringes. × 20,000. (Ref. 30)

energy therefore goes with a wide stacking fault. Stacking faults have been seen with the electron microscope; Fig. 2.12 shows stacking faults in niobium (see also Fig. 5.26). It has also been found that solute alloying elements can alter the stacking fault energy; for example, stacking faults are frequently observed with the electron microscope in Cu–Al alloys but not in pure aluminium or copper[31]; this is discussed further in chapter 6.

[30] A. Fourdeux and A. Berghezan, *J.I.M.*, 1960–61, **89**, 31.
[31] A. Howie, Electron Microscope Conference, De Nederlandse Vereniging voor Electronenmicroscopie, Delft, 1960.

All the extended dislocations so far observed appear to involve stacking faults which upset the stacking sequence in the same kind of way as that referred to earlier. However, this is not an essential feature of an extended dislocation. Misfit layers which cannot be described as a fault in the stacking sequence are possible between the two partials provided that the energy of this layer is reasonably small. Because of this it seems possible that $\frac{1}{2}\langle 111 \rangle$ dislocations in bcc lattices may dissociate on (110) planes.[32]

Since the energy of a dislocation is nearly proportional to the square of its Burgers vector, it will always be possible to resolve a dislocation into two dislocations with smaller Burgers vectors and save energy. In fact, we can judge the likelihood of any dislocation reaction by comparing the squares of the Burgers vectors involved (square rule). But the resolution into two dislocations will only occur in practice if the stacking fault created has a reasonably small energy. For the stacking fault in the fcc lattice described previously, the misfit on either side of the fault plane (the centre "b" layer in the foregoing sequence) is the same geometrically as that at a twin boundary, so the fault energy should be very approximately twice that of a twin boundary. It is therefore generally taken that if annealing twins are common in a particular fcc metal, that metal has a lower stacking fault energy than an otherwise similar one in which annealing twins are scarce. This rule seems to be quite a good guide. Several fcc metals appear to have twin boundary energies of not more than a few tens of ergs/cm², and their properties (see below) indicate that they have stacking faults which are effective in the sense to be described. In aluminium, however, the twin boundary energy is large, and correspondingly the properties indicate that the dislocations are not seriously extended. In layered structures like graphite and MoS$_2$ wide stacking faults occur and correspondingly the fault energy is only about 1 erg/cm².[33]

Stacking faults affect the mechanical properties in two ways. One is that they affect the readiness of screw dislocations to cross slip. An extended screw dislocation, unlike an unextended screw, has a definite slip plane. To cross slip, that is, to transfer to another, intersecting plane, geometry requires that the dislocation first be compressed into an unextended dislocation. Energy is needed to force the partials together. This requires more energy when the partials are well separated, as in a metal with a low stacking fault energy. General experience supports this connection between stacking fault energy and cross slip, since in metals believed to have high stacking fault energies we can frequently see cross

[32] C. Crussard, *Compt. rend.*, 1961, **252**, 273.
[33] D. W. Pashley and A. E. B. Presland, Electron Microscope Conference, De Neder landse Vereniging voor Electronenmicroscopie, Delft, 1960.

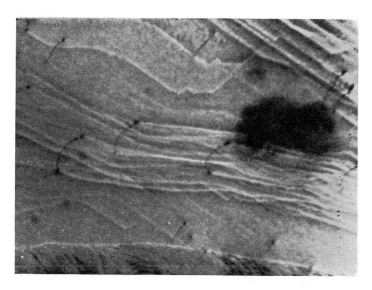

Fig. 2.13. Wavy slip in Al. Electron micrograph, ×28,000. (Hale; Crown copyright reserved.)

slip in the electron microscope and the wavy slip bands associated with cross slip. Figure 2.13 shows wavy slip in aluminium.

Theoretical estimates have been made of the stress needed for cross slip. An earlier treatment[4] assumed that the partials must combine along a length l given by the Frank-Read equation, $l = Gb/\tau$, before being able to move in the new plane. The resultant activation energies are then rather high unless l is made small by applying a large stress, and cross slip is difficult. According to a more recent investigation[34] this assumption overestimates l. If account is taken of the fact that the combined portion can bow in the new slip plane to some degree, however short it is, the applied stress does work that helps stabilise the new system, in the sense that its energy is beginning to fall, when l is much smaller than the value given by the foregoing expression. This lowers the stress for cross slip into the region where experiment shows it to occur. In either case, an activation energy is involved, so that raising the temperature lowers the stress at which cross slip occurs.

Stacking faults are also believed to affect the readiness of edge dislocations to climb. There are two possibilities. One is that the partials come together at a jog. The energy of a jog is then higher the more

[34] J. Friedel, *Conference on Internal Stresses and Fatigue*, Elsevier publishing company, Amsterdam, 1959, p. 220.

extended the dislocation. Consequently we expect fewer jogs in thermal equilibrium the lower the stacking fault energy, and a slower rate of climb. The other is that the partials climb without coming together; however, to avoid serious atomic misfits they must climb together, and jogs opposite each other in both partials are necessary.[35] In either possibility, the stacking fault tends to impede climb. Although general experience supports this conclusion, the experimental observations are not entirely in agreement with expectation. Thus, copper polygonises more slowly than aluminium, but not as slowly as expected,[36, 37] and alpha brass polygonises faster than copper, although more twins form in it during annealing.[38]

(*h*) *Dislocation Networks.* Dislocations join at threefold nodes in ways satisfying line tension equilibrium and conservation of the Burgers vectors. For instance, in the fcc lattice in Fig. 2.14 the $\frac{1}{2}\langle 110 \rangle$ dislocations *CA* and *AD* can join to make the new $\frac{1}{2}\langle 110 \rangle$ dislocation *CD*, and in the bcc lattice the $\frac{1}{2}\langle 111 \rangle$ dislocations *AC* and *CB* can join to make the $\langle 100 \rangle$ dislocation *AB*. If all three dislocations have the same edge-screw ratio,

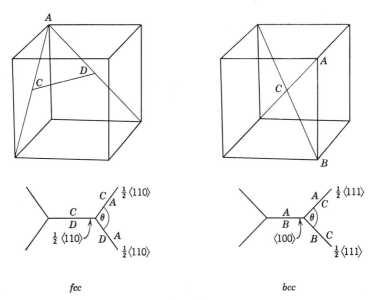

fcc   *bcc*

Fig. 2.14.

[35] R. S. Barnes, *Acta Met.*, 1954, **2**, 380.
[36] A. Franks and D. McLean, *Phil. Mag.*, 1956, **1**, 101.
[37] F. W. Young, *J.A.P.*, 1958, **29**, 760.
[38] V. Y. Doo, *Acta Met.*, 1960, **8**, 106.

in the first case they all have equal line energies, and the junction angle θ is 120°; in the second case it is 96°. Many dislocations can join up in this way to make networks, which can be either flat two-dimensional ones or three-dimensional ones. Figure 2.2 is an example of a two-dimensional network and Fig. 2.4 that of a three-dimensional network.

The two-dimensional networks constitute subboundaries, and the theory of these is well advanced. The misorientation between the parts of the crystals on the two sides of the network is connected with the Burgers vectors of the dislocations in the network through the basic equation of network theory.[39]

$$d = r \times l \cdot 2 \sin \phi/2 \qquad (2.8)$$

where d is the total Burgers vector intersected by the unit vector r lying in the subboundary and l is the axis and ϕ the amount of the misorientation. According to eq. 2.8, the misorientation ϕ determines the spacing of the network, and the Burgers vectors of the dislocations in it determine the axis of misorientation l; the exact shape of the individual meshes is controlled by the junction angle θ in Fig. 2.14. Although once the Burgers vectors of the dislocations are fixed l is also fixed, there is no restriction on the plane in which the net lies. What happens if the net is rotated from one plane into another is that the edge-screw ratio changes, and with this the angle θ and the mesh shape alter. A consequence is that a given net can, as it were, be wrapped around a piece of crystal causing it to be rotated bodily with respect to its environment, and everywhere the boundary is satisfactory when the adjustments of θ and mesh shape have taken place. Furthermore, if each parallel set of dislocations have all the same Burgers vector, a line r drawn to cut only one set is perpendicular to this Burgers vector according to eq. 2.8. By determining the crystallographic directions of such lines, we can therefore determine the Burgers vectors. In this way, the joining in the bcc lattice of two $\frac{1}{2}(111)$ dislocations to make a (100) dislocation, as illustrated in Fig. 2.14b, has been experimentally verified.[40]

However, if the parallel dislocations do not all have the same Burgers vector, the *stranger* dislocations may cause the appearance of meshes of distinctive shape. Such figures can be investigated readily with the aid of a lettering convention such as the following which ensures continuity of Burgers vector at a node. Trace out a circular track around a junction point. The dislocations must be so lettered that they make a continuous path in the upper part of Fig. 2.14; for example, AC, CB, BA, not AC, CB, AB. They can, however, lie in any order along the circular track— for example, CB, AC, BA or BA, AC, CB—because change in the order

[39] F. C. Frank, Symposium on Defects in Crystalline Solids, Physical Society, London, 1955, p. 159.
[40] W. E. Carrington, K. F. Hale, and D. McLean, *P.R.S.*, 1960, **A.259**, 203.

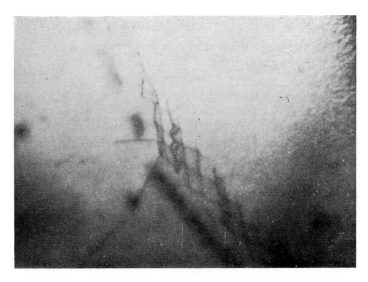

Fig. 2.15. Repeated irregularity in two-dimensional network due to "stranger" dislocations. Fe, × 44,000. (Carrington, Hale, and McLean; Crown copyright reserved.)

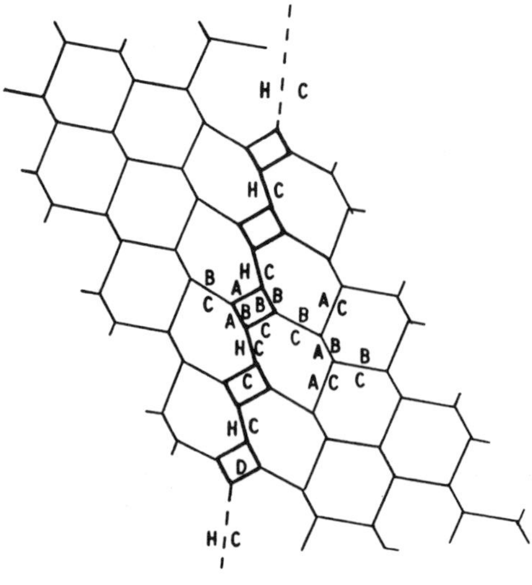

Fig. 2.16. Interpretation of Fig. 2.15. (Carrington, Hale, and McLean; Crown copyright reserved.)

does not affect vectorial addition of the Burgers vectors. Such a convention has been used to analyse networks in ionic crystals and in metals.[40, 41] Figure 2.15 shows irregularities along the paths of stranger dislocations in a network in iron and Fig. 2.16 shows the interpretation obtained in this way.

The three-dimensional network fills the spaces between the subboundaries and seems to be joined to the latter. In Fig. 2.2, for instance, dislocations flow out of the subboundary in a few places, evidently becoming part of a three-dimensional network. To judge from etch pit patterns, probably all ordinary polycrystalline metals contain a three-dimensional network. At each junction the same conditions apply separately as for two-dimensional networks, but no general theory like that for the latter has yet been worked out.

(*i*) *Intersection of Dislocations.* Since most metals have slip planes mutually inclined to each other, a very common event during deformation must be the intersection of dislocations with different Burgers vectors.[34, 40, 42, 43] There are two main situations. Suppose in Fig. 2.17 P and Q are two slip planes on which move towards each other under an applied stress the dislocations XX' and YY'. One situation occurs if the dislocations attract each other and form a junction dislocation. If climb is excluded, this necessarily lies along the line of intersection $P'Q'$ of the slip planes and the arrangement taken up is that shown in Fig. 2.17.

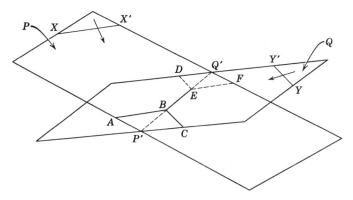

Fig. 2.17.   Intersection of dislocations.

[41] S. Amelinckx, *Dislocations and Mechanical Properties*, John Wiley and Sons, New York, 1957, p. 2.
[42] P. B. Hirsch, *Conference on Internal Stresses and Fatigue*, Elsevier Publishing Company, Amsterdam, 1959, p. 139.
[43] Z. S. Basinski, *Phil. Mag.*, 1959, **40**, 393.

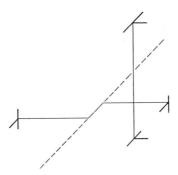

Fig. 2.18. Jog produced by intersection of two dislocations.

The other situation occurs if the dislocations repel each other. It can be seen from the lettering convention of the previous subsection that changing the sign of one of the dislocations (e.g. from AC to CA) converts an attractive arrangement into a repulsive arrangement and vice versa. Both kinds of intersection impede the motion of dislocations; their strength is discussed in section 4.7.

In addition, if the two intersecting dislocations have nonparallel Burgers vectors, a step known as a jog is necessarily produced in one of the dislocations; the process is depicted in Fig. 2.18. If both Burgers vectors are parallel, glide can immediately eliminate the step, which does not effectively exist. As a jog is in effect a short length of dislocation which has energy, the geometrical necessity for the production of jogs gives rise to an extra resistance to intersection which is also discussed in section 4.7.

An intersection which has played an important part in the theory of strain hardening is the Lomer-Cottrell intersection,[44] which occurs in fcc lattices in the following way. Suppose that in Fig. 2.17, P is a (111) plane and XX' is the dislocation $\frac{1}{2}a$ (10$\bar{1}$), and Q is the plane (11$\bar{1}$) and YY' is the dislocation $\frac{1}{2}a$ (011). The junction dislocation is then $\frac{1}{2}a$ (110), a Burgers vector that lies in the (001) plane which bisects the angle between planes P and Q. Therefore, the junction dislocation probably cannot glide easily. In any event, it can decompose with a saving of energy by the reaction:

$$\tfrac{1}{2}a\,(110) \rightarrow \tfrac{1}{6}a\,(11\bar{2}) + \tfrac{1}{6}a\,(112) + \tfrac{1}{6}a\,(110)$$

The $\frac{1}{6}a$ (11$\bar{2}$) dislocation is repelled by the others and runs up the plane P away from the intersection line $P'Q'$, and the $\frac{1}{6}a$ (112) dislocation similarly

[44] W. M. Lomer, *Phil. Mag.*, 1951, **42**, 1327; A. H. Cottrell, *Phil. Mag.*, 1952, **43**, 645.

runs up the plane Q, both leaving a sheet of stacking fault joining them to the dislocation $\frac{1}{6}a$ (110), which remains along the line $P'Q'$. This group of dislocations is clearly tied together and cannot glide. It is "sessile." Because of this it has been used in some theories of strain hardening as a barrier which is bound to form when there is multiple slip and which stops further slip on either of the intersecting planes. But as it now appears, this particular junction dislocation can be undone like any other junction dislocation from its ends in the way discussed in section 4.7b, in which case it loses its effectiveness as a barrier.

Another intersection with special properties occurs if the two dislocations have equal but opposite Burgers vectors, which must lie along $P'Q'$. The junction dislocation is then nonexistent, and there is nothing to stop the pieces ABC and DEF in Fig. 2.17 from straightening out and sliding apart to take up positions such as $AP'C$ and $DQ'E$. The original dislocations XX' and YY' have now both been cut in two and joined up in a new way. At P' and Q' they now change from one slip plane to another as though cross slip had occurred, although there has been no cross slip in the ordinary sense. Moreover, the total length of dislocation has been reduced, so that this process is a recovery process that occurs during straining. This rearrangement probably happens frequently during straining. For example, as there are eight different slip Burgers vectors in the bcc lattice, the "cutting" intersection should occur once in every seven intersections during ordinary, multiple slip, assuming that a dislocation does not cut another with the same Burgers vector but pushes it ahead instead. Consequently, before a dislocation has travelled very far, it probably changes slip planes frequently, loses its original identity, and causes a reduction in total dislocation density, which has to be offset by production of fresh dislocation if strain hardening is to occur. Cross slip must help the cutting intersection to occur more frequently than it otherwise would, since dislocations of opposite Burgers vector will be particularly strongly attracted toward each other and may be able to intersect by cross slipping when they would not otherwise have done so.

(j) *Origin of Dislocations.* In the early years of dislocation theory, one school of thought, believing that because dislocations are thermodynamically unstable they would not be present in annealed metals, sought for ways in which they could be made by a stress. This view overlooked the fact that grain boundaries are also thermodynamically unstable and yet are present, so the existence of unstable features is quite familiar. Another school of thought adopted the intuitive argument that because the dividing line between a slipped and an unslipped part of a crystal is precisely a dislocation, dislocations could reasonably be present.

Although this view is now known to be correct, it is not certain where all the dislocations come from. One clear mechanism arises from the fact that the equilibrium concentration, or solubility, of vacancies increases with temperature. During cooling the supersaturated vacancies precipitate, often as discs like Guinier-Preston zones, and the disc is necessarily bounded by a dislocation. Dislocation loops evidently formed in this way have been seen,[45-47] and are discussed in section 4.6c. It has been suggested that dislocations form on freezing from the melt in a similar way but on a bigger scale, the volume contraction on freezing providing large numbers of vacancies.[48] Dislocations might also be produced during freezing by plastic deformation caused either by mechanical disturbance, uneven cooling, or segregation when the lattice parameter varies with concentration.[49] Dislocations are evidently also produced, or at least persist, during recrystallisation, but nothing is understood about this.

A second problem is the origin of the numerous extra dislocations formed during cold work. This is really a problem of plastic yielding and strain hardening, and is discussed in chapters 4 and 5.

(k) *Effects of Dislocations on Physical Properties.* Dislocations affect several physical properties: density, electrical and thermal resistivity, and the internal energy. Both edge and screw dislocations produce a volume expansion through second-order elasticity effects. Calculation gives the expansion as about 2 atomic volumes per atomic length of dislocation.[50, 51] Since both sorts of dislocation are irregularities in the crystal lattice, they scatter electrons and phonons and lower the electrical and thermal conductivities. It is customary to express their influence on physical properties in terms of the effect when 1 at % of the defect is present. According to calculation, when 1 at % of atoms sites are occupied by dislocations (equivalent to a density of about $1\frac{1}{2} \times 10^{13}$ dislocations cm^2), the increase in electrical resistivity is between 0.1 and 1.0 microhm/cm.[52-54]

[45] P. B. Hirsch, J. Silcox, R. E. Smallman, and K. H. Westmacott, *Phil. Mag.*, 1958, **3**, 897.
[46] J. Silcox and P. B. Hirsch, *Phil. Mag.*, 1959, **4**, 72.
[47] R. E. Smallman and K. H. Westmacott, *J.A.P.*, 1954, **30**, 603.
[48] F. C. Frank, *J.I.M.*, 1956–7, **85**, 581.
[49] W. A. Tiller, *J.A.P.*, 1958, **29**, 611.
[50] W. M. Lomer, *Phil. Mag.*, 1957, **2**, 1053.
[51] A. Seeger and P. Haasen, *Phil. Mag.*, 1958, **3**, 470.
[52] S. C. Hunter and F. R. N. Nabarro, *P.R.S.*, 1953, **A.220**, 542.
[53] A. Seeger and H. Stehle, *Z. Physik.*, 1956, **146**, 242.
[54] W. A. Harrison, *J. Phys. Chem. Solids*, 1958, **5**, 44.

Measurements have been made of these effects as well as of the increase in internal energy when dislocations are introduced. Large numbers of dislocations are necessary to produce measurable effects and are introduced by cold working; the difference between the cold worked and the annealed condition is measured. One way of comparing the results is to apply the theoretical values to the experimental measurements and derive dislocation densities from the different property changes. This is done in Table 2.1. For comparison, direct counts with the electron microscope of dislocation density in cold worked metals are shown in Fig. 5.28. These densities range from about 10^{10} to 10^{12}.

The outstanding conclusion from these comparisons is clearly that electrical resistance measurements greatly overestimate the dislocation content on this simple basis, whereas the other methods give a rough and ready agreement among themselves. To explain the electrical resistance discrepancy efforts have been made to calculate the contribution from stacking faults,[67] with the conclusion that these help to account for the discrepancy. The error with the estimates from thermal conductivity at low temperature[66, 68] is probably to be explained in the same way, as these measurements were made on alloys based on either copper or silver, and a large area of stacking fault could be expected after cold work.

(*l*) *Concentrations of Dislocations after Different Treatments.* The density of dislocations in a substance is expressed either as the number intersecting unit area of a random section or as the total length of dislocation line per unit volume. The second measure gives a somewhat larger figure since most dislocations will not be normal to the random surface.

Densities up to about $10^9/cm^2$ can be determined fairly accurately by etch pit methods and up to $10^{10}/cm^2$ or more with the electron microscope.

55 H. Kangaki, *J. Phys. Soc. Japan*, 1951, 6, 90.
56 H. A. Aström, *Acta Met.*, 1955, 3, 508.
57 M. Wintenberger, *Compt. rend.*, 1957, **244**, 2800.
58 J. Molenaar and W. A. Aarts, *Nature*, 1950, **166**, 690.
59 L. M. Clarebrough, M. E. Hargreaves, and G. W. West, *Acta Met.*, 1957, **5**, 738.
60 L. M. Clarebrough, M. E. Hargreaves, D. Mitchell and G. W. West, *P.R.S.*, 1952, **A.215**, 507.
61 P. Gordon, *T.A.I.M.E.*, 1955, **203**, 1043.
62 W. B. Pearson, *Phys. Rev.*, 1955, **97**, 666.
63 Metals Handbook, A.S.M., 1948, p. 903.
64 Metals Handbook, A.S.M., 1948, p. 428.
65 H. M. Rosenberg, "Point Defects in Metals and Alloys," *Inst. Metals*, 1958, in discussion.
66 P. G. Klemens, *P.P.S.*, 1955, **A.68**, 1113.
67 A. Howie, *Phil. Mag.*, 1960, **5**, 251.
68 W. R. G. Kemp and P. Klemens, *Australian J. Phys.*, 1960, **13**, 247.

Table 2.1

Comparison of Dislocation Densities Deduced from Measurements of Physical Properties

Assume the following: energy per atom length of dislocation is 8 ev, electrical resistance per 1 at % of dislocation (1.5×10^{13} cms of dislocation per cc) is 0.1 microhm-cm, and volume expansion per atom length of dislocation is 2 atomic volumes.

Metal	Method	Per Cent Cold Work	Dislocation Density $\times 10^{-11}$	Ref. (See p. 35)
Al	Stored energy	70	2.2	55
	,,	45	0.5	56
	Electrical resistance	10	52	57
Ag	Electrical resistance	8	$\sim 50(1*)$	58
	Stored energy	30	0.7 ⎫	
	,,	55	0.9 ⎬	59
	,,	70	1.1 ⎭	
	,,	65	3.5	55
	,,	—	2.4	60
	,,	39	0.7	61
Cu	Density	30	1	⎫
	,,	55	1.5	⎪
	,,	70	2	⎪
	Electrical resistance	30	30(0.6*)	⎬ 59
	,,	55	42(0.8*)	⎪
	,,	70	54(1.1*)	⎭
	,,	60	64(1.1*)	62
	,,	80	122(2.4*)	63
	,,	8	51(1*)	58
Fe	Electrical resistance	99.8	860	64
Ni	Density	~ 100 (torsion)	1.6	⎫
	Electrical resistance	~ 100 (torsion)	320(6.4*)	⎬ 62 ⎭
Brass	Thermal conductivity	10	1	65
Cu-10% Ni	,, ,,	—	⎫	
Ag-2% Pd	,, ,,	—	⎬ 6–20×10^{12}	66
Ag-2% Cd	,, ,,	—	⎪	
Ag-20% Cd	,, ,,	—	⎭	

* Dividing by 50 to allow for contribution of stacking faults (see p. 35).

Larger densities have been determined with less accuracy through effects on physical properties as explained in section 2.1k. Densities present under different conditions are roughly as follows.

Very carefully grown, very pure single crystal 0–10^3
Average annealed single crystal 10^5–10^6
Annealed polycrystal specimen 10^7–10^8
Heavily cold worked metal 10^{11}–10^{12}

With ordinary polycrystalline metals the final annealing treatment probably has an important influence on dislocation density within something like the range quoted, just as it has on grain size.   A high annealing temperature may be expected to anneal out dislocations, enlarging the network size.   Climb of dislocations should be an important element in this process, and it depends on volume diffusion.   On the other hand grain growth depends on grain boundary diffusion, which is considerably less sensitive to temperature.   Consequently, changes in the annealing temperature may be expected to cause larger changes in dislocation network size than in grain size.

2.2   Grain Boundaries

Grain boundaries have been known to occur in metals since the beginning of scientific metallurgy, unlike the other defects discussed whose existence has been demonstrated experimentally only comparatively recently.   A grain boundary is now known to be a layer of atomic misfit two or three atoms wide, as shown by the field-ion micrograph Fig. 2.19, which illustrates a grain boundary in tungsten.

There are many analogies between grain boundaries and dislocations. Except in a very special case, grain boundaries raise the total free energy and a single crystal has lower free energy than a polycrystal.   The free energy per atomic area of boundary varies for different metals over the range 0.1–0.4 ev (250–1000 ergs/cm^2 of boundary area) for ordinary boundaries and over the range 0.002–0.1 ev (5–250 ergs/cm^2 of boundary area) for boundaries of special orientation such as twin boundaries.   In single phase metals grain boundaries are present only because they anneal out so slowly.   They exist as a three-dimensional network which satisfies surface tension equilibrium and the geometrical rules of space filling and resembles the three-dimensional dislocation network.   On thermodynamical grounds it is to be expected that there will be ledges in grain boundaries analogous to jogs in dislocations; the ledges are presumably preferred sites for absorbing or emitting point defects.   There is evidence that precipitates impede migration of grain boundaries, and solute

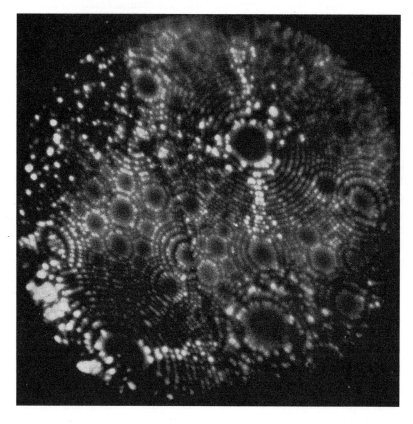

Fig. 2.19. Field-ion micrograph of grain boundary in tungsten. The grain boundary is 2 to 3 atoms wide.   × ∼ 5,000,000.   (D. G. Brandon)

segregation to boundaries should do so too.   This is equivalent to the restraining effect of solutes and precipitates on the climb of edge dislocations.

The grains in a polycrystal may contain subgrains, the subboundaries being the two-dimensional arrays of dislocations such as that in Fig. 2.2. "Veins" in alpha iron are subboundaries, the oldest known.   The misorientation across a subboundary in an annealed metal ranges up to about 1°.   Subboundaries seem to be commoner in metals with unextended dislocations, as might be expected, since such dislocations can climb and cross slip into arrays easily.   Not all etching reagents reveal subboundaries, and probably they are really present much oftener than they are seen on optical microsections.   Subboundaries exert some stiffening effect on a crystal, but apart from this do not have direct influence on the mechanical properties.

The effects of grain boundaries on mechanical properties are partly due to the change in orientation at a grain boundary and partly due to their special properties. For example, the change in orientation results in dislocations being held up, and makes it necessary for several slip systems to operate in most grains. These factors both accelerate the rate of strain hardening. The special properties of grain boundaries manifest themselves at high temperature when they in effect become glissile and grains can slide over each other. This not only gives an extra shearing mechanism but also helps to form cavities in the boundaries which eventually lead to the typical creep fracture. Grain boundaries may also be paths for easy propagation of cracks as a result of weak intergranular cohesion, leading to hot and cold shortness. These various effects of grain boundaries are discussed in the appropriate chapters.

2.3 Vacancies and Interstitials

The known "point defects" in pure metals are empty lattice sites or vacancies, interstitial atoms, and groups of these. Vacancies have been seen with the field ion microscope and their number counted[9]; in the field ion micrograph of Fig. 2.20 a vacant lattice site is illustrated. Since single vacancies and interstitials constitute point irregularities in the crystal lattice, they resemble solute atoms in some respects. Vacancies in particular resemble solute atoms of large size factor. Their energy of formation is typically about 1 ev compared with, for instance, 0.42 ev for the heat of solution of carbon in alpha iron. Their mobility is similar to that of interstitial solute atoms, the activation energy for migration being also about 1 ev. As will be shown, their effect on mechanical properties is similar to that of such solutes.

The experimental data about interstitials is less extensive and also less certain. They are often believed to have energies of formation of about 5 ev and correspondingly larger mobilities with activation energies of migration of the order of $\frac{1}{10}$ ev, but there is some evidence in favour of a larger migration energy of about $\frac{1}{2}$ to 1 ev.[69, 70] Because of the large misfit energy, for equal concentration their effect on mechanical properties ought to outdo any solute atom. When vacancies or interstitials are present in excess of the equilibrium concentration, that is, when the metal is supersaturated with either, it is possible for them to precipitate much as a supersaturated solution of foreign atoms does. In one point

[69] J. C. Meechan and J. A. Brinkman, *Phys. Rev.*, 1956, **103**, 1193.
[70] A. Seeger, P. Schiller and H. Kronmüller, *Phil. Mag.*, 1960, **5**, 853.

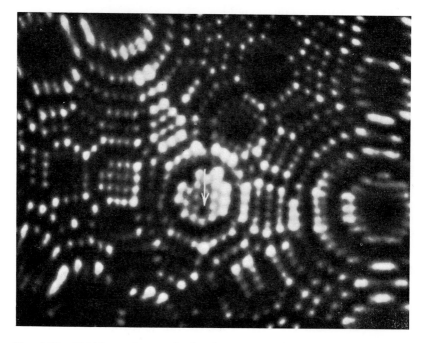

Fig. 2.20. Field-ion micrograph showing vacancy in Pt. × 10,000,000. (E. Müller)

in particular, however, vacancies and interstitials differ from solute atoms. This difference is in their interaction with dislocations and arises from the fact that they can disappear, whereas solute atoms cannot.

It is convenient to treat vacancies and interstitials together since their properties are qualitatively so similar. Although it is geometrically incorrect to regard them as the same "particle" with positive and negative sign, the opposite sign of matter involved does reflect itself as a reversal of direction of some of the processes in which they take part.

(a) *Concentrations of Point Defects.* Both vacancies and interstitials can be formed or absorbed in several ways. Thermal equilibrium is believed to be maintained by their formation and disappearance at jogs in edge dislocations and at corners of incomplete planes on the crystal surface, but there is convincing evidence that they can also form at grain boundaries,[71, 72] presumably at the corners of ledges. These three kinds of site all have the property that emission or absorption of either a vacancy

[71] R. S. Barnes, G. B. Redding, and A. H. Cottrell, *Phil. Mag.*, 1957, **3**, 97.
[72] R. S. Barnes, *Phil. Mag.*, 1960, **5**, 635.

or interstitial does not alter the site but merely moves it forward or back-ward one atomic distance. Consequently, the energy of formation is the same at all three sites. In all except the thinnest samples, however, surface sources are probably unimportant.

There are a number of nonequilibrium processes occurring during deformation and irradiation which generate or absorb point defects and upset the equilibrium concentration, for experiment shows that point defects are produced during these processes. With irradiation the position is basically simple (but complicated in detail), since irradiation knocks atoms into interstitial positions, each time leaving a vacant site behind (chapter 11). With deformation the position is uncertain, for although several possible processes for producing point defects during de-formation have been described, there are difficulties about each.

The most favoured process is the movement of a jog in a screw disloca-tion produced by cutting another screw dislocation; such a jog is an edge dislocation one atom long with Burgers vector parallel to the dislocation line, since the Burgers vector has to be the same as that of the screw dislocation. Consequently, if the screw moves forward dragging the jog with it, the extra half plane of this is either lengthened or shortened so that a row of vacancies or interstitials is produced. This kind of process has been seen with the electron microscope in zinc[73] and magnesium oxide.[74] Large jogs were involved in these two cases and, in the way depicted in Fig. 2.21, dislocation loops equivalent to platelets of point defects rather than isolated point defects were produced. Moving screw dislocations in silicon have also been seen to leave in their wake some kind of trail, believed to be a similar ribbon of point defects left behind large jogs many atoms long which condenses into separate platelets.[29] It

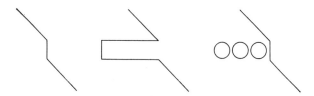

Fig. 2.21. Successive stages in the creation of platelets of point defects in the wake of a suitable jog.

[73] P. B. Price, Electron Microscope Conference, De Nederlandse Vereniging voor Electronenmicroscopie, Delft, 1960.

[74] G. K. Williamson, J. Washburn, G. W. Groves, and A. Kelly, Electron Microscope Conferences, De Nederlandse Vereniging voor Electronenmicrosopie, Delft, 1960.

has, however, been objected that these jogs will not always produce point defects (or loops) on the grounds that they will be able to glide along their dislocation under some circumstances, producing fewer or no defects. To understand this, suppose Fig. 2.22 represents the cusp in a dislocation caused by the drag of a jog at J and let JT be the direction of the Burgers vector of the jog (and of the dislocation), that is, it is that direction in which the jog must move if it is to create no point defects. The smaller is the angle θ at the cusp, and the slower the dislocation moves as a whole, the more chance the jog has of gliding in the direction JT. (A consequence is that point defects are more likely to be created after the strong attractive type junction than after the repulsive type, since the angle θ is larger for the former. Moreover, as will be clearer after the discussion in section 4.7b, the piece of dislocation containing the jog may move forward rapidly immediately after an attractive junction is broken,[75] giving the

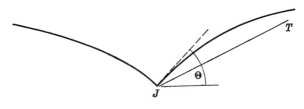

Fig. 2.22.

jog little opportunity to glide sideways.) The jog mechanism for producing point defects also seems to meet another objection, namely, that according to a detailed analysis[76] of the geometry of deformation, most jogs will be of the interstitial producing type, at least in fcc lattices, whereas more vacancies than interstitials are produced during deformation.

However, a detailed study suggests that the original view is the correct one, at least for the fcc lattice. From a study of their detailed geometry it appears that large jogs in the fcc lattice[77] do not move sideways easily. Extrapolating to jogs of atomic length, the conclusion is reached that a vacancy jog will move forward creating vacancies more easily than it will move sideways, but that an interstitial jog at ordinary temperatures will move sideways more easily than it will move forwards. However, in the case of interstitial jogs, there is a stress-aided activation energy involved in moving sideways, so that the stress required for this movement increases as the temperature falls.

[75] G. Saade, Doctoral Thesis, University of Paris, 1960.
[76] A. H. Cottrell, *Dislocations and Mechanical Properties*, John Wiley and Sons, New York, 1957, p. 509.
[77] P. B. Hirsch, quoted by N. F. Mott, *T.A.I.M.E.*, 1960, **218**, 962.

Other mechanisms that have been suggested for producing point defects do not seem likely to produce enough of either type. Thus, although several hundred electron volts may be liberated when an attractive junction forms, analysis indicates that not much of this is likely to be used up in producing point defects. Nor is a normal stress acting on an edge dislocation likely to produce many point defects at room temperature. Point defects will be produced if two edge dislocations, one above the other as shown in Fig. 2.23, are close enough; their mutual attraction will pull them together, a ribbon of vacancies of interstitials is produced, and the dislocations disappear. It is uncertain just how close the dislocations have to be for this to happen, but if they are on adjacent planes a row of vacancies or interstitials is produced as soon as they come into the position where one is above the other. Edge dislocations of opposite sign on consecutive planes should be produced each time an edge dis-

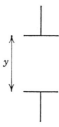

Fig. 2.23. Edge dislocations close together, one above the other, are equivalent to a row of vacancies (as in this sketch) or a row of interstitials (if of opposite sign to here).

location wraps around a screw dislocation. However, they will break through the screw dislocation long before the angle θ (see Fig. 2.22) is near 90°, so that the edge dislocations do not come into the required position. Nor does there seem to be any other frequent circumstance which brings the edge dislocations into the required relative positions.

Estimates of the concentration of point defects present can be made from their influence on physical properties. Although this is qualitatively similar to that of dislocations, the effects of interstitials, vacancies, and dislocations are often separable because of their very different mobilities. It is often believed that interstitials anneal out at temperatures greater than about $\frac{1}{20}$ of the melting point on the absolute scale, vacancies at about $\frac{1}{5}$ and dislocations at about $\frac{1}{2}$. Theoretical estimates of the effect of vacancies and interstitials have been made; for many metals the calculated effects of vacancies on electrical resistance, stored energy, and density are about 1 microhm-cm per 1% concentration, 1 ev per vacancy, and 1 atomic volume per vacancy, respectively. The corresponding values for interstitials are about 1 microhm-cm per 1%, 5 ev per interstitial, and an increase of 3 atomic volumes per interstitial. Electrical resistance measurements have been mainly used in experimental studies of point defects, and the sensitivity is increased by making measurements at low temperatures. To take a particular example, since the electrical resistance of copper due to thermal scattering falls from 2×10^{-6} ohm-cm at 300°K to 1×10^{-10} at 4.2°K, by measuring at liquid helium temperature we see that there is a gain in sensitivity of about 10^4 times, and a concentration of 10^{-3} % of vacancies shows up strongly.

The thermal equilibrium concentration of vacancies in some metals has been determined by quenching from high temperature and then measuring the decrease in resistance as the vacancies anneal out. It was found[78] in this way with gold that the electrical resistance "quenched in" from temperature T owing to retained vacancies was $\Delta\rho = 3.5 \times 10^{-4}$ exp $-0.95/kT$ ohm-cm. If we assume the preceding value for the effect of vacancies on resistance the concentration of vacancies as a function of temperature is therefore $C = 3.5$ exp $-0.95/kT$ atom fraction. Other workers[79] have obtained with gold the very similar result $C = 4.9$ exp $-0.98/kT$ atom fraction. These results imply an energy of formation of close to 1 ev per vacancy and also, since the frequency factor is near to unity, only a small entropy of formation. At the melting point of gold, the concentration works out to 0.1%. These and other results are collected in Table 2.2, from which it will be seen that the concentration deduced to exist in thermal equilibrium at the melting point is usually about 0.1%. None of the effects observed in these experiments is ascribed to interstitials, both because interstitials have such a large energy of formation that the concentration present in thermal equilibrium is negligible by comparison with that of vacancies, and because they should anneal out relatively quickly.

A possible source of error in the quenching type of experiment is that vacancies may aggregate during quenching. For example, the experimental observation that when specimens of gold were quenched from above 800°C the resistance annealed out much faster than when they were quenched from lower temperatures pointed to this conclusion, since calculation indicates that di-vacancies should migrate faster than single vacancies. A detailed analysis in this case showed that a consistent interpretation of the results was possible if the energy of migration of

[78] F. J. Bradshaw and S. Pearson, *Phil. Mag.*, 1957, **2**, 379.
[79] J. E. Bauerle and J. S. Koehler, *Phys. Rev.*, 1957, **107**, 1493.

Table 2.2

Energies and Concentrations of Vacancies in Thermal
Equilibrium

Q_f = energy of formation in ev
$c\%$ = concentration in atomic percent at the melting point

Metal	Q_f	$c\%$	Ref.
Al	0.75	0.039	80
Al	0.79	0.1	81
Al*	0.61	0.13	82
Au	0.95	0.097	78
Au	0.98	0.11	79
Pt	1.4	0.52	83
Pt	1.23	0.12	84
Pt†	1.15	—	9

* The vacancy concentration was deduced from a comparison of the density and lattice parameter of quenched samples, the assumption being that the vacancies do not affect the parameter although they reduce the density.

† Determined by counting the number seen with the field ion microscope.

single vacancies was 0.8 ev, of di-vacancies 0.6 to 0.7 ev, and the binding energy of di-vacancies was 0.1 to 0.2 ev.

Studies have also been made of the behaviour on annealing of the supersaturated vacancy concentration produced by quenching, for example. [81, 84, 85, 86] The results are complicated because several annealing processes are possible, such as collecting into clusters, migrating to dislocations, and disappearing at grain boundaries, which have different time constants and somewhat different consequences. There are still further complications when solute atoms are present. Thus, delayed annealing and other effects [87, 88] have then been observed and have been interpreted as meaning that solute atoms can act as temporary traps for vacancies. A value for the binding energy between a vacancy and an

[80] F. J. Bradshaw and S. Pearson, *Phil. Mag.*, 1957, **2**, 570.
[81] W. De Sorbo and T. Turnbull, *Acta Met.*, 1959, **7**, 83.
[82] S. Nenno and J. W. Kauffman, *Phil. Mag.*, 1959, **4**, 1382.
[83] F. J. Bradshaw and S. Pearson, *Phil. Mag.*, 1956, **1**, 812.
[84] A. Ascoli, M. Asdente, E. Germagnoli, and A. Manara, *Phys. Chem. Solids*, 1958, **6**, 59.
[85] C. Panseri and T. Federighi, *Phil. Mag.*, 1958, **3**, 1223.
[86] M. Wintenberger, *Acta Met.*, 1959, **7**, 549.
[87] C. Panseri, F. Gatto, and T. Federighi, *Acta Met.*, 1958, **6**, 198.
[88] L. A. Neimark and R. A. Suelin, *T.A.I.M.E.*, 1960, **218**, 82.

impurity atom estimated from such results is some tenths of an electron volt. The vacancy concentrations introduced by cold work have also been measured through the effect on physical properties. Some results are given in Table 2.3. In the final column the vacancy concentration is given as a function of the percentage deformation, making the assumption that the relation is a linear one. The concentration in per cent is of the order

Table 2.3

Concentrations of Point Defects Produced during Deformation, Deduced from Effects on Physical Properties

Assuming: energy per vacancy of 1 ev volume expansion per vacancy of 1 atomic volume, electrical resistance change of 1 microhm-cm per 1% point defect

Metal	Method	Elongation $(E\%)$ and Temperature ($°K$) of Cold Work	Concentration C of Point Defects %	Coefficient α in $c\% = \delta$ $\alpha E\%$	Ref.*
		Vacancies			
Cu	Stored energy	71(90°K)	0.035	4.9×10^{-4}	89
	Electrical resistance	8(77°K)	0.005	5×10^{-4}	58
Ni	Stored energy	100 (rt)	0.049	4.9×10^{-4}	90
	Density	80 (rt)	0.04	5×10^{-4}	91
	Electrical resistance	100 (rt)	0.15	1.5×10^{-3}	90
		Interstitials			
Cu	Electrical resistance	18(4°K)	0.001 (annealed 100°K)	5.6×10^{-5}	92
Au	Electrical resistance	21(4°K)	0.0011 (annealed 80°K)	5.2×10^{-5}	92

* See facing page for table references.

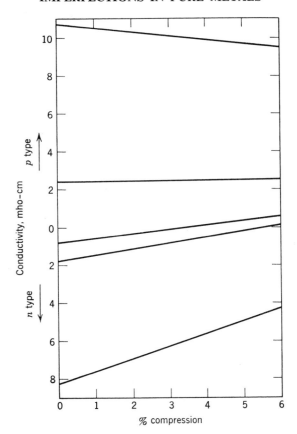

Fig. 2.24. Effect of compression on the room temperature conductivity of germanium having various initial conductivities (Ref. 96).

of 10^{-3} to $10^{-4}E$, with E also in per cent. Various theoretical estimates give the concentration in per cent as 10^{-4} to $10^{-5}E$.[93]

Attempts have been made to obtain similar data for interstitials by cold working at a very low temperature followed by annealing at a temperature so low that only interstitials are mobile. Any change in the electrical resistance is then ascribed to the disappearance of interstitials. This probably oversimplifies the situation, however, for reasons mentioned in the next paragraph. Some low temperature data obtained by the

[89] J. W. Henderson and J. S. Koehler, *Bull. Am. Phys. Soc.*, 1958, **1**, 204.

[90] L. M. Clarebrough, M. E. Hargreaves, and G. W. West, *P.R.S.*, 1955, **A.232**, 252.

[91] L. M. Clarebrough, M. E. Hargreaves, and G. W. West, *Phil. Mag.*, 1956, **1**, 528.

[92] C. J. Meechan and A. Sosin, *J.A.P.*, 1958, **29**, 738.

[93] A. H. Cottrell, "Point Defects in Metals and Alloys," *Inst. Metals*, 1958, p. 1.

resistance method and apparently relating to interstitials are included in Table 2.3. There is similar data on platinum,[94] titanium and zirconium.[95] As far as these data go they suggest that about $\frac{1}{10}$th as many interstitials are made as vacancies. Some supporting evidence that interstitials are produced during deformation is provided by observations on germanium.[96] The conductivity of germanium is affected by compression according to type, n or p, in the way shown in Fig. 2.24. There seems no explanation of the reversal between low and high conductivity p type if only vacancies or only interstitials are produced by the deformation; but by an argument that assumes different electron levels around interstitials and vacancies, and hence assumes that both are created, a self consistent explanation can be produced.

However, quantitative conclusions about interstitial concentrations obtained from annealing data should be regarded with caution since their annealing behaviour is likely to be at least as complex as that of vacancies. For example when an interstitial anneals it might migrate to a vacancy, when both disappear, or it might exist as a crowdion,[93] that is, a row of $(n + 1)$ atoms squashed into the length normally occupied by n atoms. It seems reasonable to expect that a crowdion should diffuse much more easily along its axis than in any other direction. If so, it would then move along the preferred direction and stop at the nearest point to a trapping centre, such as a vacancy or a dislocation, without actually being eliminated. The strain field and effects on physical properties would be weakened, but would be restored if the crowdion became parted from the trapping centre, for example by thermal agitation. The possibility of this kind of trapping makes the theoretical value for a physical property change on annealing at low temperature uncertain. It also adds some vagueness to the vacancy annealing range, since some crowdions may be left over until vacancies become mobile and can move to them, annihilating both; if this happens, the electrical resistance, energy, and density changes associated with the disappearance of a vacancy is somewhat indefinite.

(b) *Effect on Mechanical Properties.* Some measurements of the effect of vacancies on yield stress have been made by introducing them by quenching or irradiation. The yield stress of aluminium is raised by 0.3 kg/mm^2[97, 98] at room temperature by quenching from 600°C, which,

[94] G. R. Piercy, *Phil. Mag.*, 1960, **5**, 201.
[95] E. Smith and M. S. Stagg, Cambridge Conference on Lattice Defects, 1960, paper S.2.53.
[96] J. N. Hobstetter and P. Breidt, *J.A.P.*, 1957, **28**, 1214.
[97] R. Maddin and A. H. Cottrell, *Phil. Mag.*, 1955, **46**, 735.
[98] M. Wintenberger, "Point Defects in Metals and Alloys," *Inst. Metals*, 1958. In discussion.

according to the data given earlier, should introduce a concentration of about 0.03%. (Evidence that the increase in yield stress was not due to quenching strains was that the full rise in yield stress only occurred after some ageing, and that up-quenching did not produce the effect.) Irradiation with 4.4×10^{18} neutrons/cm^2 has been found to raise the yield stress of copper by 1.5 kg/mm^2 at room temperature; a vacancy concentration of about 0.15% would be expected. If the assumption is made, reasonable for low concentration, of a linear relation between concentration and yield stress, the increase in yield stress for 1% of vacancies given by both experiments is close to 10 kg/mm^2. For comparison, 1 at % antimony raises the yield stress of copper by 7 kg/mm^2 and 3 at % magnesium raises that of aluminium by 12 kg/mm^2. The effect of vacancies on yield stress is therefore somewhat greater than that of solutes of large size factor but of the same order. These figures show that the effect on strength of the vacancies produced during straining is minute in ordinary polycrystalline samples. Thus, from the figures given earlier, after 30% cold work a typical vacancy concentration is 0.003%, which raises the flow stress by only about $\frac{1}{30}$ kg/mm^2 compared with a typical flow stress of, say, 10 kg/mm^2.

These effects on mechanical properties are probably due to vacancies which are not uniformly dispersed. Being present in great supersaturation at room temperature (0.01% vacancies at room temperature is a supersaturation of about 10^{13}-fold) they will have a strong tendency to precipitate. One possibility is that they precipitate on dislocations. In quenched or irradiated, but perhaps not in deformed, metals there should be many vacancies to every atom on a dislocation; for example, if there are 10^8 cm of dislocations per cc, a concentration of 0.01% vacancies provides 4000 vacancies to every such atom. Consequently, we may expect unextended edge dislocations to become very joggy and unextended screws to be turned into helical dislocations in quenched or irradiated metal, and both these effects will produce some hardening. The effect is analogous to that of a solute atmosphere (chapter 5), but point defects permanently alter the dislocation, which cannot recover its original easy gliding condition by breaking away and leaving the vacancies (or interstitials) behind. Furthermore, since movement of jogs from one equilibrium position to the next presents a resistance of short wavelength, hardening due to this effect should be appreciably affected by temperature; the yield stress of specimens hardened by quenched-in vacancies is in fact somewhat temperature dependent.[93] The possibility also exists of a moving dislocation sweeping up point defects if it moves through a supersaturation of them and acquiring fresh jogs.[97] Possibly similar effects happen with extended dislocations, although a detailed picture is lacking.

But since there are so many more vacancies than dislocation sites, many vacancies must hit each other before they hit a dislocation, and precipitate just as supersaturated solutes do. As already mentioned, this is known to occur and there is some discussion of the geometry of the clusters in section 4.6c. Insofar as their effect on density disappears, they cannot precipitate as spherical cavities. They may instead collect into platelets like Guinier-Preston zones, for with vacancies the opposite faces can cave in, leaving the circumference of the site marked by a ring of dislocations. Platelets of interstitials would also resemble Guinier-Preston zones. A concentration of 0.1% of vacancies, collected into platelets 100 atoms in diameter, would form in this way 10^{10} cm of dislocation line per cc, which should be enough to produce some general lattice hardening. Experiments on irradiated lithium fluoride show in fact that dislocations experience more resistance to moving through the lattice after irradiation than before.[99]

To conclude this chapter, we find the proportion of energy expended during cold work in creating defects. According to the data given, 100% deformation should produce about 3×10^{11} dislocations/cm^2 (0.013% atoms on dislocations), 0.05% vacancies, and perhaps 0.005% interstitials. The energy, per cc, of these defects at 8 ev per atom length of a dislocation, 1 ev per vacancy, and 5 ev per interstitial is 1.5, 0.7, and 0.4×10^8 ergs for dislocations, vacancies, and interstitials respectively, making a total of 2.6×10^8 ergs. Measured values of total stored energy confirm this estimate since they give about the same result. The total work done by the applied stress is typically 5×10^9 ergs/cc, or twenty times larger. Consequently, during cold deformation most of the work is dissipated as heat.

[99] A. D. Whapham, "Point Defects in Metals and Alloys," *Inst. Metals*, 1958. In discussion.

3

Anelasticity

When a solid is vibrated there are several processes which may occur that affect the elastic modulus and may dissipate energy, even at low amplitudes of vibration. The effect on modulus and the ratio of the energy dissipated to the peak elastic energy are usually quite small; their main significance is that they can give information about the processes involved. At large amplitudes the proportion of energy dissipated is often much larger, but these amplitudes belong to the realm of fatigue, which is discussed in chapter 10.

The most important process is the vibration of dislocations. The movement of dislocations produces a strain additional to the elastic strain and hence lowers the effective modulus, and any energy the dislocations dissipate while vibrating manifests itself as "internal friction." There are also several *relaxation* processes which contribute to the internal friction but do not involve dislocations. They are called relaxation processes because they cause the metal to change shape under load and because each has a certain characteristic "relaxation time." Such processes are grain boundary sliding, thermal diffusion, atomic diffusion, and magnetostriction. They have been fully reviewed;[1, 2, 3] only the first two are relevant to this book and are discussed here.

[1] C. Zener, *Elasticity and Anelasticity of Metals*, University of Chicago Press, Chicago, 1948.

[2] A. S. Nowick, *Progress in Metal Physics*, Vol. 4, Pergamon Press, London and New York, 1953, p. 1.

[3] A. S. Nowick, *Creep and Recovery*, A.S.M. Symposium, 1957, p. 146.

The relaxation processes were called *anelastic* by Zener, who first interpreted them fully.[1] They give a peak in the curve of internal friction against frequency of vibration at a frequency approximately equal to (relaxation time)$^{-1}$. The magnitude of the internal friction is independent of the amplitude of vibration, at least to a first approximation. The most important sort of dislocation process is somewhat different in that it gives no such peak until megacycle frequencies are reached, and the magnitude of the associated internal friction is not so independent of the amplitude of vibration. To differentiate it from the relaxation processes it has been called a process of static hysteresis.[2] For simplicity, all the processes will be called anelastic in this chapter.

The usual measure of the effect on modulus is the fractional drop in modulus, called the "modulus defect." A frequent measure of the internal friction is the decrement, that is, the fractional drop in amplitude of free resonant vibration of a specimen on successive cycles. When the internal friction is small the decrement = log decrement = πQ^{-1}, where Q is the ratio of strain in phase with the stress to strain out of phase with the stress.

3.1 Thermal Anelasticity

Equation 1.4 shows that energy is dissipated in a vibrating bar as a result of the finite rate of thermal diffusion. For it indicates that heat flows from the compressed part to the stretched part, and, unless the rate

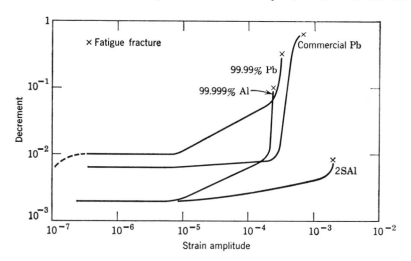

Fig. 3.1. Relation between decrement and strain amplitude for Pb and Al polycrystals. Frequency 17 kc, longitudinal vibration (Ref. 4).

[4] W. P. Mason, *J. Acoust. Soc. Am.*, 1956, **28**, 1207.

of heat conduction is so fast compared with the rate of vibration that the temperature is kept the same everywhere, the heat flow produces a component of strain that is out of phase with the elastic strain. There is hence a dissipation of energy and a lowering of the modulus. In polycrystalline specimens of elastically anisotropic metals, each grain is strained differently from those around it, and anelasticity then arises from thermal diffusion across grain boundaries.

Thermal anelasticity is therefore a universal phenomenon. However, it is normally a small effect. The internal friction, or decrement, arising from it in the experiments described in this chapter is probably not greater than 10^{-5}. Because specific heats tend to zero at $0°K$, thermal elasticity does also. This may explain why in Fig. 3.3 the decrement of lead falls steeply when the temperature is reduced below that of the Bordoni peak (see below).

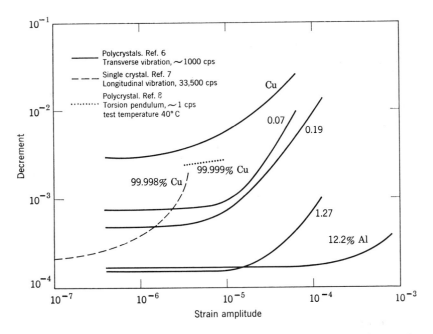

Fig. 3.2. Effect of Al additions to Cu on the curves of decrement against strain amplitude.

[5] D. H. Niblett and J. Wilks, *Adv. in Phys.*, 1960, **9**, 1.
[6] S. Takahashi, *J. Phys. Soc. Japan*, 1956, **11**, 1253.
[7] T. A. Read, *T.A.I.M.E.*, 1941, **143**, 30.
[8] S. Weinig and E. S. Machlin, *Acta Met.*, 1956, **4**, 262.

3.2   Dislocation Anelasticity*

The internal friction typically varies with the amplitude of vibration in the way shown in Fig. 3.1. Up to a strain amplitude of about 10^{-5} in this figure the internal friction is independent of amplitude ("amplitude-independent" range), then commences to increase with amplitude ("amplitude-dependent" range); at very large amplitudes in the fatigue range it increases still faster, and the test ends with a fatigue fracture.†

The following evidence shows that most of this internal friction is connected with the movement of dislocations.

1. Even small amounts of second elements impede the movement of dislocations but can hardly affect other possible causes of internal friction significantly. Figure 3.2 shows the effect of additions of aluminium on the internal friction of copper. In the alloys the internal friction does not start to rise until larger strain-amplitudes are applied, and the amplitude-independent internal friction is lowered to less than $\frac{1}{10}$ of its value in pure copper. Both these results therefore indicate strongly that most of the original internal friction was due to dislocation movement. Point defects, whether introduced by neutron irradiation, gamma ray irradiation, or rapid cooling from a high temperature, have an effect[9, 10] similar to that of second elements.

2. Other causes of internal friction are expected to be nearly independent of amplitude of vibration; only dislocation movement can explain the large increase commencing at a low stress. Accordingly this stress (from Fig. 3.1 and 3.2, 10^{-5} to $10^{-6} \times G$), which is considerably lower than the ordinarily determined yield stress of a single crystal, marks the point at which a significant number of dislocations move appreciable distances.

3. The internal friction is affected by cold work (section 3.2d).

4. In zinc single crystals the curves of decrement against strain amplitude vary with orientation in such a way that the larger the resolved shear stress on the basal plane the larger the decrement.[7] The same is true of the modulus defect. In other work,[11] longitudinal pulses transmitted parallel to the hexagonal axis suffered an attenuation very close to that calculated for the thermal-anelastic loss, and a shear wave along the hexagonal axis, with therefore the shear direction in the basal slip plane,

---

* A recent review is contained in Ref. 5 (see p. 53).

† In two investigations[7, 9] both on copper single crystals, a fall at low strain amplitude such as that indicated by the dashed line in Fig. 3.1 has been found. In the former investigation it commenced at a strain amplitude of 5×10^{-6} and in the latter at a strain amplitude of 4×10^{-8}.

[9] D. O. Thompson and D. K. Holmes, *J.A.P.*, 1956, **27**, 713.
[10] R. S. Barnes, N. H. Hancock, and E. C. H. Silk, *Phil. Mag.*, 1958, **3**, 519; *ibid.*, 527.
[11] K. Lücke, *J.A.P.*, 1956, **27**, 1433.

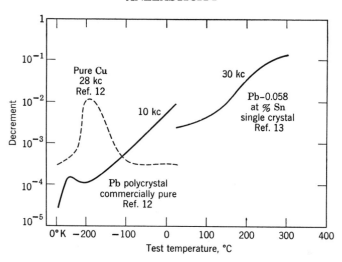

Fig. 3.3. Effect of temperature on decrement of Pb and Cu. Longitudinal vibration, amplitude between 10^{-8} and 10^{-7}.

suffered a much larger attenuation, presumably due to dislocation movement.

5. Germanium has a decrement of only 1.2×10^{-7} when measured at 100 kcs and 85°C.[14] A very low decrement from dislocation movement is to be expected in germanium at such a temperature because the dislocations are immobile, as the plastic properties indicate.

Thus, provided the chosen conditions do not excite a relaxation peak, most of the internal friction in metals is connected with dislocation movement.

Besides the amplitude of vibration, temperature and frequency may affect the internal friction. Examples of the way the internal friction varies with temperature are shown in Fig. 3.3 and 3.4. In lead (Fig. 3.3) the decrement increases almost continuously as the temperature is raised from 4°K and reaches a very high value near the melting point even in a single crystal. These measurements were made at an amplitude of vibration low enough to be in the amplitude-independent range at all temperatures, although raising the temperature has the same effect as improving the purity in reducing the amplitude at which the decrement starts to rise.[13, 15] At low temperature the curve is interrupted by a

[12] P. G. Bordoni, *J. Acoust. Soc. Am.*, 1954, **26**, 495.
[13] J. Weertman and E. L. Salkowitz, *Acta Met.*, 1955, **3**, 1.
[14] P. D. Southgate, *Phys. Rev.*, 1958, **110**, 855.
[15] A. S. Nowick, *Phys. Rev.*, 1950, **80**, 249.

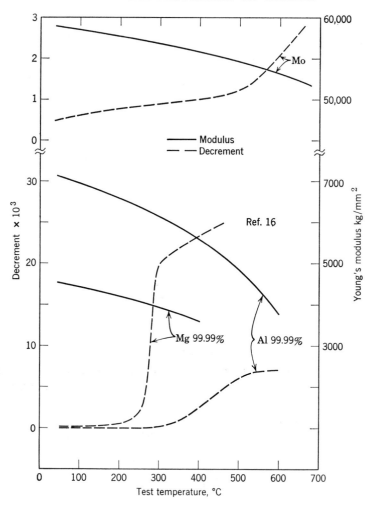

Fig. 3.4. Effect of temperature on modulus and decrement. Measured at temperature of abscissa. Specimen annealed before test. Transverse vibrations.

peak ("Bordoni peak," section 3.2c) for example in the curves for lead and copper in Fig. 3.3. In nickel a high-temperature peak has been discovered[17] which occurs between 630 and 800°C. Its exact cause is uncertain, but since it was affected by deformation, being lowered in height and in temperature by prior cold work and recovering on annealing, and because impurities suppressed it, it is probably due to

[16] F. Förster and W. Köster, Z. Metallk., 1937, **29**, 116.

[17] O. I. Datsko and V. A. Pavlov, Fiz. Metal. Metalloved. Akad. Nauk S.S.S.R., 1958, **6**, 900.

dislocation movement rather than to one of the other internal friction mechanisms mentioned earlier. Lowering the frequency increases the internal friction in tests at high temperatures. For example, when measured at a frequency of 30 kcs, the decrement of lead is about 0.1 near the melting point (Fig. 3.3) whereas at an oscillation speed of one cycle in 15 sec the decrement of aluminium near the melting point is 0.8 and at an oscillation speed of one cycle in 45 min is 0.9.[18] At lower temperatures, frequency seems less important, apart from two effects mentioned later. For example, in Fig. 3.2 there is little difference between the two results for polycrystalline copper specimens at 1 cps and 1000 cps.

There is a modulus defect in both the amplitude-dependent and amplitude-independent ranges, and the ratio of the modulus defect to the decrement is considerably smaller in the former than in the latter range. Three measurements of this ratio in the amplitude-dependent range are collected in Table 3.1. In this range the ratio is determined by simply changing the amplitude and measuring the change in modulus defect

Table 3.1

Ratio of Change in Decrement to Change in Young's Modulus E in the Amplitude-Dependent Region

(Changes produced by altering the amplitude)

Metal	Zn* Single Crystal	Cu Single Crystal 99.998% pure	Cu-1.38% Al Polycrystal
Frequency of vibration	39 kc	33.5 kc	1000 cps
Amplitude range (strain)	$\sim 5 \times 10^{-8}$ to 5×10^{-7}	$\sim 2 \times 10^{-8}$ to 10^{-6}	$\sim 5 \times 10^{-7}$– to 5×10^{-4}
Corresponding decrement range	2×10^{-4} to 2×10^{-3}	1.5×10^{-4} to 7×10^{-4}	6×10^{-5} to 8.3×10^{-3}
Corresponding modulus defect range	2×10^{-5} to 3.2×10^{-4}	zero to 1.3×10^{-4}	zero to 4×10^{-3}
$\dfrac{\text{Decrement}}{\Delta E/E}$	6	4.2	2.05
Ref.	7	7	6

* Longitudinal wave propagated through a crystal having basal plane at 61.3° to longitudinal axis—that is, considerable shear component in basal plane.

[18] J. Friedel, C. Boulanger, and C. Crussard, *Acta Met.*, 1955, **3**, 380.

and decrement.[7, 6, 13] The ratios lie between 2 and 6. In the amplitude-independent range, as the internal friction and modulus are independent of amplitude, some other way of producing simultaneous changes of decrement and modulus has to be used. Such changes are produced in an irradiation experiment. If it is accepted that irradiation affects damping and modulus mainly through the dislocation contribution to internal friction, by causing extra resistance to the movement of dislocations for example, the relation between decrement and modulus change in the amplitude-independent range is that occurring during the irradiation experiment. Table 3.2 gives some results obtained in this kind of way. The ratios are smaller than in Table 3.1.

Table 3.2

Ratio of Change in Decrement to Change in Modulus M in the Amplitude-Independent Range

(Changes produced by irradiation or annealing)

Substance	Cu Single Crystal		NaCl Single Crystal	
Modulus measured	E		S_{11}	
Frequency	10 kc		85 kc	
Temperature of measurement	21°K		Room temperature	
Nature of experiment	Neutron irradiation at 21°K	Specimen of column 1 annealed at 55°K after the neutron irradiation	Irradiated with 39 kv X rays	
Amplitude (strain)	About 10^{-7}		2×10^{-6}	7×10^{-8}
Change in decrement	1.28×10^{-3} to 0.3×10^{-3}	0.3×10^{-3} to 0.11×10^{-3}	1.1×10^{-2} to 7×10^{-4}	2.4×10^{-3} to 1.8×10^{-3}
$\Delta M/M$	4×10^{-3}	4×10^{-3}	1×10^{-2}	1×10^{-2}
$\dfrac{\text{Decrement}}{\Delta M/M}$	0.24	0.05	1.0	0.18
Ref.	19		20	

[19] D. O. Thompson, T. H. Blewitt, and D. K. Holmes, *J.A.P.*, 1957, **28**, 742.
[20] R. B. Gordon and A. S. Nowick, *Acta Met.*, 1956, **4**, 514.

Simultaneous changes in modulus and decrement are of course also produced by altering the temperature, but the relative effect on the modulus is so much greater than in Table 3.1 and 3.2 that a new factor must be involved. Measurements of Young's moduli of aluminium, magnesium, and molybdenum as a function of temperature are included in Fig. 3.4, and it can be seen that the ratio of change in decrement to the modulus defect that occurs on altering the temperature is minute except at temperatures high enough for creep to help produce an exceptionally large decrement. The new factor is simply thermal expansion, which has the effect of lowering the modulus but does not necessarily affect the decrement.

(a) *Theories of Dislocation Anelasticity.* Theories of dislocation anelasticity assume that the anelasticity is connected with a stress-strain hysteresis diagram like one of those shown in Fig. 3.5a, b, or c, in which for clearness in the diagrams E_a, the anelastic strain, has been made similar in magnitude to E_e, the elastic strain, although in practice E_a is usually very much smaller than E_e. The elastic modulus actually observed corresponds to BD in each diagram and the energy loss per cycle to the area of the loop. Since the decrement is equal to the loss per cycle divided by twice the potential energy at peak amplitude, it has an upper limit which occurs for a flat-topped curve of the shape $OABCD$ in Fig. 3.5c, for which the width of the loop $w = E_a$, and this upper limit is closely equal to $\tau E_a / \tau E_e = E_a / E_e$, which of course is the fractional drop in modulus. Normally, therefore, the decrement should be less than the modulus defect, as it is in Table 3.2. The reason why in Table 3.1 the decrement exceeds the modulus defect is presumably connected with the fact that *changes* in these quantities are there in question.

With hysteresis loops like Fig. 3.5a or b, in which the width w of the hysteresis loop is less than E_a, the decrement is less than the modulus defect, so these diagrams both correspond to the amplitude-independent range. However, they require different behaviours from the dislocations. The loop in Fig. 3.5a is the more likely and has been observed in sensitive direct stress-strain tests on zinc employing stresses up to $10^{-5}G$ (chapter 4). It would result if the dislocations were opposed by a nonuniform friction stress arising, for example, from solute atoms or uneven dislocation density, so that some dislocations move easily at low stress and others only at higher stress. The unloading curve would not then retrace the loading curve since a suitable friction stress would oppose the movement backward as well as the movement forward, although at this point the same difficulty is encountered concerning the actual distance a dislocation moves that is referred to below. Fig. 3.5b requires, on the other hand,

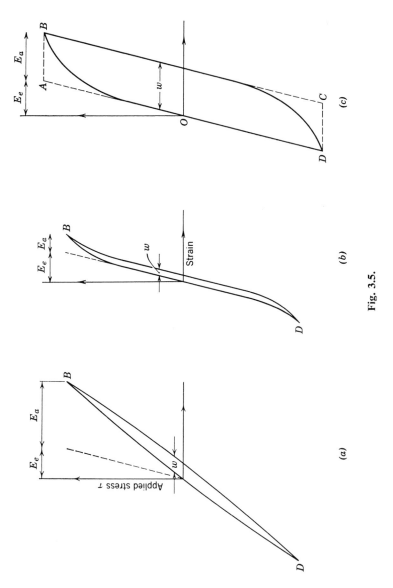

Fig. 3.5.

that dislocations recoil rapidly when the stress is reversed, and a satisfactory model for this is hard to find. In the amplitude-independent range, w must increase in a manner approximately proportional to E_a. When it starts to increase faster than E_a, the amplitude-dependent range has been entered.

Since the hysteresis is believed to be associated with the oscillation of dislocation loops, a calculation of the order of magnitude of the modulus defect this would cause will be helpful before we go any further. Each length L of dislocation between anchoring points, for example dislocation junctions, is bowed out by an applied stress into an arc of a circle. If the line tension is $Gb^2/2$, the middle of the loop moves a distance $L^2\tau/4Gb$, where τ is the applied shear stress. The area swept by the moving loop in one-half cycle is thus about $L^3\tau/5Gb$, and the associated anelastic strain is b times this. With n loops per cc, the anelastic strain E_a is therefore $nL^3\tau/5G$. The elastic strain E_e is equal to τ/G, so

$$\frac{\delta G}{G} = \frac{E_a}{E_e} = \frac{nL^3}{5} = \frac{NL^2}{5} \qquad (3.1)$$

where N is the total length of dislocation per cc. Since for dislocations arranged in a network $N \sim L^{-2}$, $\delta G/G \sim 0.2$. This is much larger than the values usually found. With dislocation loops which end at attractive junctions at the equilibrium angle the modulus defect is still greater, since such junctions commence to undo at vanishingly small stress. From eq. 3.1 it can be seen that such a loop of length L would move a distance equal to $2L^2\tau/Gb$. This is about ten times larger than for a loop whose ends are rigidly held in position.

Explanations of dislocation anelasticity therefore assume that the movement of dislocations is normally impeded more strongly by impurities than by the restoring force of line tension. Two such theories have been developed. In one,[13, 21, 22] the dislocations are assumed to be impeded by the stress fields around solute atoms as in the theory of solute hardening described in section 6.6. As explained there, a dislocation loop finds equilibrium positions separated by the mean spacing between solute atoms. In moving from one equilibrium position to another, the loop as a whole rides over many solute atoms and so experiences an oscillating stress. In applying this concept to explain internal friction behaviour, we employ a statistical argument to show that the fraction of the total line length of dislocation that is faced by a stress field from the solute atoms equal to the applied stress τ is proportional to τ/τ_b, where τ_b (eq. 6.3) is the height of a main internal stress peak, that is, the yield stress. From this linear dependence on applied stress the amplitude-independence of the damping is derived. Amplitude-dependent anelasticity is supposed to set in when τ exceeds τ_b; the dislocations then move through much larger distances, being limited only by particularly high internal stress peaks.

[21] J. Weertman, *J.A.P.*, 1955, **26**, 202.
[22] J. Weertman and E. I. Salkovitz, *J.A.P.*, 1956, **27**, 1251.

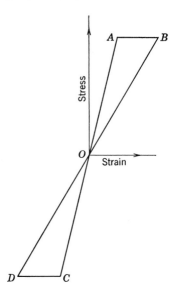

Fig. 3.6.

A criticism made of this theory is that at the low strains in question, pinned dislocations will not bow out far enough to encounter solute atoms,[23] and so will not dissipate energy. The distances moved by a dislocation anchored at each end will indeed be small; the foregoing expressions give a maximum movement in the middle of a loop 10^{-4} cm long whose ends are pinned of 1A at a strain amplitude of 10^{-7}, and of about 10A for the same loop held at attractive junctions. However, whether these small permitted movements calculated for an ideally homogeneous situation mean that the loop cannot dissipate energy at solute atoms perhaps depends on exactly what happens. The loop is in a heterogeneous situation, having to thread its way between many impurity atoms even in quite pure metal, and may at places move over a solute atom even though the average displacement is less than an atomic diameter. If so, these parts will dissipate energy.

The other theory[23, 24] describes a somewhat different way in which solute atoms can cause a hysteresis loss. The solute atoms are supposed to anchor the dislocations at a number of points, allowing the lengths in between to vibrate freely. Small stresses move these parts against line tension; the stress strain relation follows OA in Fig. 3.6. When the stress

[23] A. Granato and K. Lücke, *J.A.P.*, 1956, **27**, 583.
[24] J. S. Koehler, *Imperfections in Nearly Perfect Crystals*, John Wiley and Sons, New York, 1952, p. 197.

is large enough to tear the dislocation away from the solute atoms, the effective loop length becomes the larger value of the dislocation network spacing, and the displacement of the dislocation suddenly increases by a corresponding amount; the strain jumps from A to B in Fig. 3.6. As the stress is reduced the strain starts to recover along BO in a metal which contains no other impurities or defects, but in practice probably along a line that is steeper than BO. It is therefore not difficult to imagine that the hysteresis loop shown in idealised fashion as OAB would in practice resemble that in Fig. 3.5a. The process described is supposed to occur in the amplitude-dependent range, and clearly accounts for the amplitude dependence of the decrement. Quantitative expressions for the decrement and modulus defect have been worked out, a random distribution of locking points being assumed. For the amplitude-independent damping, this theory falls back on the radiation damping discussed below.

In addition to these losses caused by solutes, the way internal friction increases with purity up to the highest purities obtained suggests that there are mechanisms of dissipating energy which do not involve solutes. For example, purifying a copper single crystal by prolonged heating in vacuum has been found to raise the decrement to 0.02 at a strain of only 2×10^{-9} (Ref. 10).

(b) *"Radiation" Damping of Dislocations.* A dislocation passing over a row of atoms sets them in motion somewhat like a violinist's bow sets a violin string in motion. The dislocation loses energy in this and other ways.[25, 26, 27] The corresponding resistive force due to this "radiation damping" has been estimated[26, 27] for metals to be approximately 10^{-4} dyne per cm length of dislocation per cm/sec velocity of the dislocation.

To estimate the damping which comes from this frictional force, we have to take into account the resonant behaviour of the dislocation arising from its line tension and effective mass. A dislocation loop resembles a damped, elastic string. The effective mass M per unit length is approximately equal to that of a row of atoms of unit length (since the sum of the distances moved by all the atoms traversed by a moving dislocation is approximately equal to the distance moved by the dislocation) and the restoring force C on a loop of length L displaced by an amount x at its centre is $8Gb^2x/L$ per cm length. The equation of motion of the dislocation is therefore the simple harmonic motion equation

$$M\ddot{x} + B\dot{x} + Cx = \tau \sin 2\pi \, ft$$

[25] J. D. Eshelby, *P.R.S.*, 1949, **A197**, 396.
[26] G. Leibfried, *Z. Physik*, 1949, **127**, 344.
[27] F. R. N. Nabarro, *P.R.S.*, 1951, **A209**, 278.

where B is the resistive force due to radiation damping and τ is the applied stress oscillating at frequency f. Expressions for the resulting decrement and modulus defect have been derived[23]:

$$\text{Decrement} = \frac{\varrho F_n L^2 B}{f_0^2 M} \left[\frac{f/f_0}{(1 - f^2/f_0^2)^2 + B^2 f^2/A^2 f_0^4} \right] \quad (3.2)$$

$$\frac{\delta G}{G} = \frac{\varrho F_n L^2}{\pi} \left[\frac{(1 - f^2/f_0^2)}{(1 - f^2/f_0^2)^2 + B^2 f^2/A^2 f_0^4} \right] \quad (3.3)$$

where ϱ is the dislocation density, F_n is an orientation factor of about $\frac{1}{4}$, and f_0 is the resonant frequency of about $(1/2L)\sqrt{C/M}$. The resonant frequency works out to about $10^5/L$, that is, in the high-megacycle region. Measurements[28] of the attenuation in germanium over a frequency range of 5 to 300 megacycles when compared with eq. 3.2 lead to a value for B of 1.1×10^{-4}, which is in close agreement with the theoretical value. Accepting this value of B, at a frequency of 10^5 cps the decrement according to eq. 3.2 is 10^{-5} and at 1 cps is 10^{-10}.

It was mentioned in section 3.2a that the amplitude-independent damping discussed there has been ascribed to radiation damping. If this is correct, the change in the ratio of decrement—modulus defect between the two ranges can then be readily accounted for in principle, as internal friction in the two ranges arises from two distant mechanisms. There is, however, the difficulty raised by the discrepancy between a prediction from eq. 3.2, namely, that the decrement is proportional to frequency well below resonance and is very small at kilocycle frequencies and below, and the experimental result that in this frequency range the decrement is always significant in magnitude and not obviously dependent on frequency. An attempt has been made to explain away this difficulty[29] by noting the dependence of the damping on loop length in eq. 3.2, and combining this with the argument that the lower the frequency the more time there is for weakly pinned points to give way. The effective loop length therefore increases as the frequency decreases and counteracts the fall in decrement that would otherwise occur. The increase with temperature of the decrement in the amplitude-independent range has been explained in the same way, since thermal agitation will break more pinning points the higher the temperature.

(c) *The Bordoni Peak.* At a temperature of 50–100°K a peak has been found in the curves of internal friction against temperature of some fcc metals and is called the Bordoni peak after its discoverer.[12] Figure 3.3

[28] A. Granato and R. Truell, *J.A.P.*, 1956, **27**, 1219.
[29] J. Wilks, *Phil. Mag.*, 1959, **4**, 1379.

shows examples of the Bordoni peak. The relation between the temperature at which the peak occurs and the vibration frequency used can be expressed in the form

$$f = f_0 e^{-Q/RT}$$

according to some measurements on copper (frequency range 380[30] to 30,000 cps[12]) and germanium, T being the temperature at which the peak occurs at the applied frequency f. For copper the values of f_0 and Q are 10^{10} and 2000 cal/mol respectively; for germanium they are[31] 2.5×10^{11} and 20,400 cal/mol. Sometimes the Bordoni peak consists in reality of two peaks.[30] In two bcc metals, iron and niobium, investigated over the temperature range -269 to 77°C, no peak was found.[17]

At such a low temperature as 50°K presumably only dislocations, interstitial atoms, and electrons are mobile enough to give rise to energy losses. Studies of the dependence of the peak on conditions suggest that it is due to dislocations. Thus, the height of the peak is increased by small amounts of cold work and is decreased not only by impurities but also by neutron irradiation,[30] which seems to eliminate interstitial atoms as a cause since neutron irradiation would increase the concentration of these. Moreover, to eliminate entirely the increase in the peak height caused by cold working it is necessary to anneal at temperatures causing recrystallisation, which suggests directly that the peak is connected with dislocations.

It has been proposed[32] that the Bordoni peak is due to those parts of the dislocations that lie parallel to a simple crystallographic direction vibrating over the Peierls hills. The Bordoni peak has only been investigated so far in metals believed to have low Peierls forces, in which thermal agitation is presumably large enough at temperatures above 50–100°K to overcome the Peierls force. If this theory is right the peak should occur at higher temperatures in materials like iron and germanium that are believed to have large Peierls forces. The fact that in iron and niobium no peak has been found up to 77°C, and that in germanium a peak occurs in the region of 420°C, is thus support for this theory.[14]

(d) *Effect of Cold Work and Annealing on Dislocation Anelasticity.* The internal friction changes rapidly after, as well as during, plastic deformation, but approaches a stable value after straining has stopped. If attention is concentrated on these stable values, on cold working a metal the internal friction first rises, but often begins to decrease after a few per cent strain; the modulus varies in the reverse way. The rapid

[30] D. H. Niblett and J. Wilks, *Phil. Mag.*, 1957, **2**, 1427.

[31] J. O. Kessler, *Phys. Rev.*, 1957, **106**, 646.

[32] A. Seeger, H. Donth, and F. Pfaff, *Discussions Faraday Soc.*, 1957, **23**, 19.

changes are also interesting, and were followed in some experiments[33] on brass. In these experiments, the internal friction could be determined either without removing the load or after the load was removed. It was found that, with the load kept on, the internal friction was already falling fast after 10 sec (the earliest time a measurement could be obtained). Removing the load was equivalent to increasing it as far as the immediate changes in internal friction were concerned, for the internal friction was thereby increased and was again rapidly falling 10 sec after removal. These rapid changes immediately after a strain are presumably associated with exhaustion creep, the dislocations which are least firmly locked after the strain moving to more stable positions. Fairly steady values were always reached after a few hours.

The steady values are altered by annealing. The effect of annealing on the modulus and decrement of cold worked brass is shown in Fig. 3.7 for initial strains of 10% and 60%; the changes are larger and clearer for an initial strain of 60%. Starting with this initial condition, about half the modulus defect was recovered progressively before recrystallisation, and the remaining half during recrystallisation at 270–300°C, with which was associated a rapid drop in hardness. On the other hand, nearly all the increase in decrement was recovered after heating at only 150°C, and, as the inset shows, the very small remaining amount recovers during recrystallisation. With both modulus and decrement there are further changes on annealing at higher temperatures. Modulus changes in the annealed state have already been referred to in chapter 1.

There are two points about results such as these. One is that the discrepancy between the recovery of modulus and decrement shows again as noted in connection with the dependence on amplitude that these two properties are not uniquely related. Probably much of the modulus defect which recovers during recrystallisation is due to the higher internal stress with many dislocations present. In addition, it seems quite likely that the short dislocation loops which are characteristic of cold worked material do not experience so much interference from solute atoms simply because they do not move so far for a given oscillatory stress in the anelastic experiment. Both factors would, of course, reduce the ratio of decrement to modulus defect. The other point is that the large number of dislocations present until the recrystallisation temperature is reached cause little more internal friction than the far smaller number present after recrystallisation has occurred. Two factors must conduce to this result. In the first place, insofar as other restraints on dislocation movement become unimportant when there are many dislocations present, eq. 3.1 becomes correct, and gives a modulus defect and decrement independent

[33] W. Köster and E. Stolte, *Z. Metallk.*, 1954, **45**, 356.

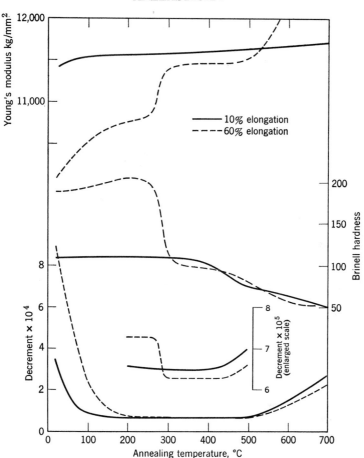

Fig. 3.7. Effect of annealing stretched brass containing 72% Cu. Time of anneal, 2 hr. Measurement at room temperature. Modulus and decrement measured in transverse vibration (Ref. 34).

of the dislocation density. In the second place, since each dislocation must tend to lie in a valley of the stress field due to the other dislocations, on bowing out it experiences a restraining force due to this.[35] The restraint is not easy to calculate as the other dislocations move at the same time, so the stress field moves, but if the effect is inversely proportional to the square of the mesh size of the net, it also leads to a decrement and modulus defect independent of dislocation density.

[34] W. Köster and K. Rosenthal, *Z. Metallk.*, 1938, **30**, 345.
[35] J. Weertman and J. S. Koehler, *J.A.P.*, 1953, **24**, 624.

3.3   Grain-Boundary Anelasticity

In a plot of internal friction against temperature, polycrystalline specimens usually show a peak of internal friction that is not found with single crystal specimens of the same metals.[36]   The temperature at which the peak occurs is always in the region where grain-boundary sliding takes place at a perceptible rate, and the peak has consequently been ascribed to this.   The mechanism envisaged is that at the small stresses applied in these experiments the grain boundaries slide a small amount and are stopped by the elastic stresses set up at grain corners.   This is a typical relaxation process; at low temperatures it does not occur and at high temperatures does not dissipate energy because the necessary energy can be supplied by thermal agitation.   The peak decrement varies considerably from metal to metal[37]; it is 5×10^{-3} in tin and $\frac{1}{4}$ in aluminium. The associated modulus defect has been measured in a few metals and is about $\frac{1}{4}$.

It has not been shown whether the effect is solely due to a sort of viscous sliding at grain boundaries or whether there is a large contribution from the movement of dislocations in the adjoining parts of the grains that probably accompanies grain-boundary sliding.   However, in an alpha-beta brass it has been possible to associate three separate peaks with the three different interfaces present, that is, alpha-alpha, alpha-gamma, gamma-gamma.[38]

[36] T. S. Kê, *Phys. Rev.*, 1947, **71**, 533.
[37] D. McLean, *Grain Boundaries in Metals*, Oxford University Press, London, 1957, p. 271.
[38] L. M. Clarebrough, *Acta Met.*, 1957, **5**, 413.

4

Plastic Yielding
in Metals of Good Purity

4.1 Yield by Slip

As far as yield stress is concerned, metals of good purity can be divided into a soft group and a hard group. The soft group includes fcc metals and also hcp metals oriented for basal glide. The hard group includes bcc metals and also hcp crystals oriented for other than basal glide (and also many ionic crystals). With good single crystals of the soft group, plastic yield on the macroscopic scale occurs at a stress of about $10^{-5} \times$ shear modulus (i.e., about $0.1 \ \mathrm{kg/mm^2}$ or less), and, as internal friction experiments show, there is some plastic contribution to the strain at stresses at least as small as $10^{-6} \times$ shear modulus (e.g. Fig. 3.2). The mechanical usefulness in engineering of pure metals such as copper and aluminium is entirely due to the fact that in the polycrystalline form in which they are used, the grain boundaries give rise to the most rapid kind of strain hardening known in metallurgy, and this raises the practical yield stress many times. With single crystals of the hard group, much larger stresses ($1 \ \mathrm{kg/mm^2}$ or more) are needed for yield and larger stresses again for these metals in polycrystalline form.

Usually, with single crystals, there is a fairly clearly marked yield stress, but with the softer group in particular, this is preceded by a small and gradual plastic strain. The typical yield behaviour of a single crystal of

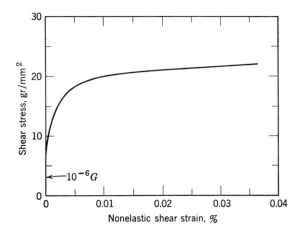

Fig. 4.1.   Yield in basal glide of Zn single crystal (Ref. 1).

the soft group is shown in Fig. 4.1 on a sensitive strain scale and well illustrates how gradual yield really is in this group. The macroscopic yield stress here is about 20 g/mm², but the first departure from elastic behaviour occurs at about 6 g/mm². It should be added, however, that a good deal of the nonelastic strain is recovered on unloading, part of it immediately and part of it gradually; for instance, in Fig. 4.1 the strain at a stress of 15 g/mm² is 0.002%, but on unloading the permanent set was only about $\frac{1}{10}$ of this. With the softer group, at least, the yield stress is probably still a structure-sensitive property even in the best experiments to date, for over a period of decades lower and lower values have been found for the yield stress of single crystals of a particular metal as purity and crystalline perfection have improved. There is no reason to believe that a limiting value corresponding to an intrinsic property like the Peierls force has yet been reached. The yield stress appears (section 4.7) to depend rather on dislocation density, and the gradual onset of yield in this group is therefore ascribable to an uneven density of dislocations in the crystal. With the hard group, yield is sharper and probably does depend on some intrinsic property.

A clearly marked macroscopic yield requires that in the vicinity of the yield stress either the speed of dislocations or the multiplication of dislocations or that both are sensitive to stress. Experiments with silicon-iron[2] and lithium fluoride,[3] which both belong to the hard group (probably

[1] J. M. Roberts and N. Brown, *T.A.I.M.E.*, 1960, **218**, 414.
[2] D. F. Stein and J. R. Low, *J.A.P.*, 1960, **31**, 362.
[3] W. G. Johnston and J. J. Gilman, *J.A.P.*, 1959, **30**, 129.

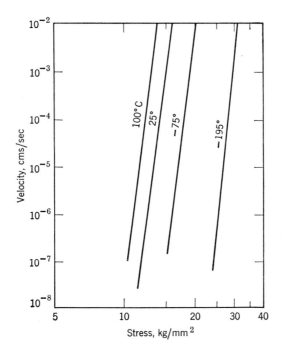

Fig. 4.2.   Influence of stress and temperature on the velocity of edge dislocations in Fe–3¼% Si alloy (Ref. 2).

in the case of lithium fluoride because of impurities present), show that both speed and multiplication are indeed sensitive to stress.   The experiments consisted of applying a stress pulse of known duration and determining, by etch pitting, the positions of dislocations before and after the pulse, which was possible provided the grown-in dislocation density was sufficiently small.   Figure 4.2 illustrates how the velocity depends on the applied stress in silicon-iron, and similar results were obtained with the lithium fluoride.   In Fig. 4.2 the dislocation velocity is approximately proportional to stress[40] (stress to the power forty); it also increases greatly with temperature at a given stress.   The sharpness of the macroscopic yield was greatly accentuated by the fact that moving dislocations evidently multiplied immensely, since many others appeared in their wake and often to their side, forming a band well populated with dislocations, such as the slip bands in silicon-iron shown in Fig. 4.3.

In the silicon-iron, no dislocation movement at all was observed until a stress equal to about three-fourths of the macroscopic yield stress was

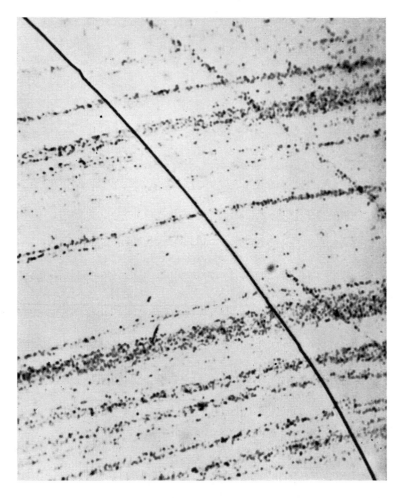

Fig. 4.3. Slip bands in Fe–3% Si alloy revealed by etch-pitting. × 1500. (Crown copyright reserved.)

applied, so that the yield process is sharper than for the single crystal of Fig. 4.1 besides occurring at a much higher stress. Since the dislocations were freshly introduced for the experiments to escape complications from impurity locking, and since grown-in dislocations were too scarce for resistance to motion by processes depending on dislocation density (intersection and stress field—section 4.7) to be significant compared with the yield stress found, uneven initial distribution of dislocations can have had no substantial influence in the direction of spreading out the onset of yield.

Whatever was the important resistive force (e.g., Peierls force or defect production—section 4.7) must have been similar for all the moving dislocations.

It is fairly certain that similar multiplication of dislocations to that implied by Fig. 4.3 occurs in all metals, and the discussion of yield processes in section 4.7 indicates that dislocation velocity in the soft group of metals should still be more sensitive to stress than it is in Fig. 4.2. Yield in the soft group therefore should be sharper than in the hard group, provided the dislocation density were uniform. As already intimated, the dislocation density is evidently sufficiently uneven to make the onset of yield in this group more gradual than in the hard group.

Polycrystals never yield as suddenly as single crystals, unless one of the impurity locking mechanisms discussed in chapter 6 is present. Figures 4.4 and 4.5 show, for aluminium and copper respectively, typical stress-strain curves up to 1% elongation of polycrystals and of single

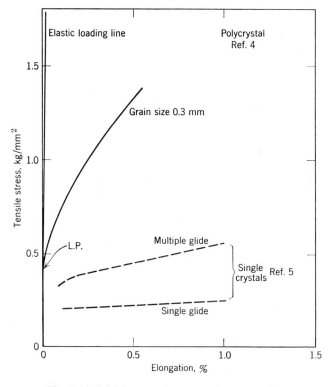

Fig. 4.4.   Initial parts of stress-strain curves of Al.

[4] N.P.L. Data.
[5] K. Lücke and H. Lange, *Z. Metallk.*, 1952, **43**, 55.

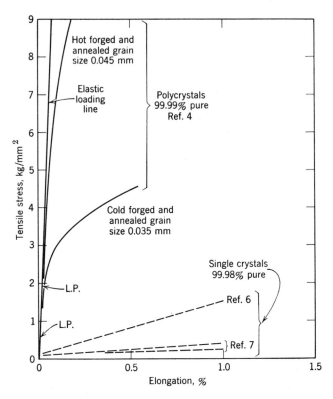

Fig. 4.5. Initial parts of stress-strain curves of Cu.

crystals of two different orientations—one oriented for "easy glide" and one for "multiple glide" as explained in chapter 5. With copper in particular, the curves for the polycrystals rise far above the yield stress of the single crystals before yielding appreciably. Sensitive tests show, however, that plastic deformation can be detected in polycrystals at stresses only a few times greater than the yield stress of single crystals. For example, some shear yield stresses for copper single and polycrystals are given in Table 4.1.

Yield in polycrystals is thus very gradual indeed. Elastic anisotropy will be a factor, but in this context only a small one. The gradualness must be mainly due to extremely steep strain hardening in the polycrystals occasioned by the presence of grain boundaries. (As the two curves for differently treated polycrystals of about the same grain size in Fig. 4.5 show, other factors such as the degree of preferred orientation—that is the

[6] F. D. Rosi, *T.A.I.M.E.*, 1954, **200**, 1009.
[7] J. Diehl, *Z. Metallk.*, 1956, **47**, 331.

Table 4.1

Yield Stress of Single and Polycrystals of Copper

	Single Crystals		Polycrystals		
Purity claimed, %	99.98	99.999	99.99 +	99.999	tough pitch
Shear yield stress g/mm²	94	65	300	350	400
Ref.		7	8	9	10

amount of misorientation at each boundary—also affect the result.) Strictly, therefore, yield of polycrystals belongs to the next chapter on strain hardening. However, it is conventional to count the first few tenths of a per cent of plastic strain of a polycrystal as part of the yielding process.

Because of the extremely gradual nature of yielding in polycrystals, the yield stresses quoted for them in Table 4.1 are very likely over estimates of the stress which first makes dislocations move through the lattice. There is thus no reason to suppose that dislocations do not begin to move at about the same stress in polycrystals as in single crystals. Indeed, as elastic anisotropy causes the stress to concentrate on those grains oriented to have the direction of largest modulus parallel to the stress, and near grain boundaries elastic discontinuity must also give rise to stress concentrations, dislocations may move at some places in a polycrystal at a lower applied stress than they would in a single crystal.

In order to have a reasonably definable and observable value to deal with in the case of polycrystals, a "proof stress" is defined as the stress which produces a given strain—for example, the 0.1% proof stress is the stress which produces 0.1% plastic deformation. The ratio of the 0.1% proof stress of a polycrystal to that of a single crystal varies considerably from one metal to another. For example, Fig. 4.4 and 4.5 show that the ratio is considerably higher for copper than for aluminium, being about 15 to 3. Figure 4.6 shows that the proof stress depends also on grain size, since it is proportional to (grain size)$^{-\frac{1}{2}}$. This kind of dependence on grain size occurs a number of times in this book. It arises very simply in the way discussed in section 4.7c.

Subgrain boundaries have an effect similar to that of grain boundaries. Attempts have been made to isolate the influence of subboundaries from that of grain boundaries by taking material of given grain size, strain-

[8] N.P.L. Data.
[9] D. A. Thomas and B. L. Averbach, *Acta Met.*, 1959, **7**, 69.
[10] C. S. Smith and C. van Wagner, *A.S.T.M.*, 1941, **41**, 825.

ing at different temperatures to produce different subgrain sizes, then annealing at a temperature too low to cause recrystallisation but high enough to substantially reduce the dislocation density inside each subgrain. Re-straining might then be expected to reveal any effect of subboundaries per se. Tests of this nature on aluminium,[12] copper,[13] and iron[14] (the copper specimens were not given the final anneal) have shown that subboundaries raise the yield stress in much the same way that grain boundaries do. The yield stress is again proportional to (sub-

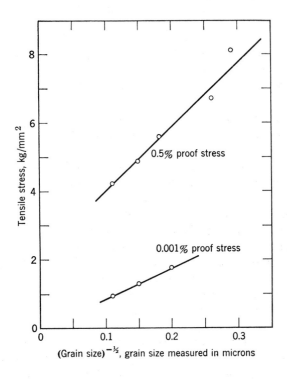

Fig. 4.6. Variation of proof stress of Cu with grain size. Measured at room temperature. (Ref. 9, lower curve; 11, upper curve.)

grain size)$^{-\frac{1}{2}}$. Figure 4.7 illustrates the relation for aluminium and copper.

The yield stress also depends on temperature, strain rate, and purity in

[11] R. P. Carreker and W. R. Hibbard, *Acta Met.*, 1953, **1**, 654.
[12] C. J. Ball, *Phil. Mag.*, 1957, **2**, 1011.
[13] D. H. Warrington, Electron Microscope Conference, Delft, 1961.   de Nederlandse Vereniging Voor Electronenmicroscopie.
[14] C. J. Ball, *J.I.S.I.*, 1959, **191**, 232.

both single and polycrystals. The variation with temperature is considerably weaker in metals of the soft group than in those of the hard group. Figures 4.8 and 4.9 illustrate some results for the soft group and Fig. 4.10*a* and 4.10*b* (the curve for prismatic slip) illustrate some results for the hard group. Figure 4.2 also illustrates the temperature sensitivity of this group. In the soft group the yield stress varies even at its steepest by less than 0.05 kg/mm² (shear stress) per 100°C temperature change for

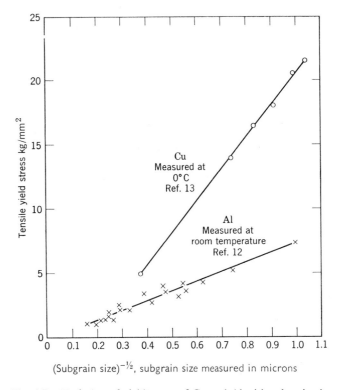

Fig. 4.7. Variation of yield stress of Cu and Al with subgrain size.

the single crystals and by only 0.5 kg/mm² per 100°C for the copper polycrystals of Fig. 4.9, but in the hard group it varies by as much as 40 kg/mm² per 100°C temperature change for molybdenum polycrystals (Fig. 4.10*a*). Perhaps the clearest contrast is in Fig. 4.10*b*, which includes results for basal slip (soft group) and prismatic slip (hard group) in single crystals of magnesium. The temperature sensitivity of the yield stress in the latter case is approximately two orders of magnitude greater than in the former.

There are the following several pieces of evidence to show that the steep

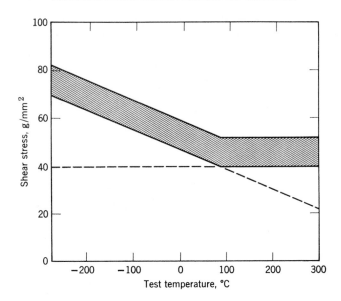

Fig. 4.8a. Yield stress of Mg single crystal; variation with temperature. All results fell in the shaded band (Ref. 15).

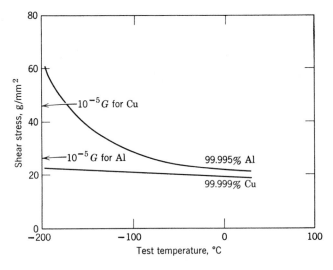

Fig. 4.8b. Stress required to produce 0.0002% permanent set in single crystals at different temperatures (Ref. 16).

[15] W. F. Sheely and R. R. Nash, *T.A.I.M.E.*, 1960, **218**, 416.
[16] A. R. Rosenfeld and B. L. Averbach, *Acta Met.*, 1960, **8**, 625.

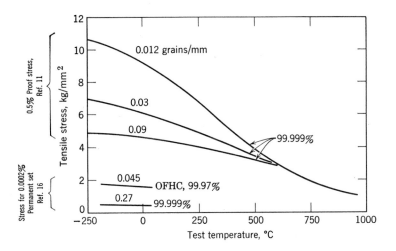

Fig. 4.9. Variation of yield stress of copper polycrystals with temperature.

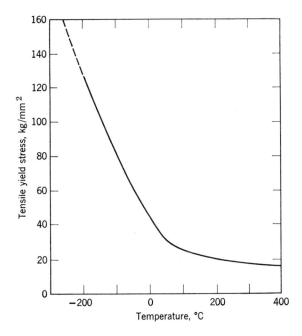

Fig. 4.10a. Variation with temperature of yield stress of Mo polycrystals. Compression tests (Ref. 17).

[17] G. A. Alers, R. W. Armstrong, and J. H. Bechtold, *T.A.I.M.E.*, 1958, **212**, 523.

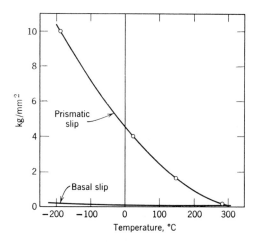

Fig. 4.10b. Variation with temperature of the critical resolved shear stress of Mg for "prismatic" slip along prism plane $\{10\bar{1}0\}$ in $\langle 11\bar{2}0 \rangle$ direction and for "basal" slip along basal plane $\{0001\}$ in $\langle 11\bar{2}0 \rangle$ direction (Ref. 18, upper curve; 19, lower curve)

temperature sensitivity of the hard group is not due to an impurity locking mechanism, as has sometimes been thought to be the case.

1. The high temperature sensitivity revealed in Fig. 4.2 relates to unlocked dislocations, as already mentioned, and virtually the same temperature sensitivity for molybdenum as that shown in Fig. 4.10a was obtained when the specimens were purified or slightly strained to unlock dislocations.[17]

2. The yield stress of bcc iron has a steep temperature coefficient irrespective of purity, alloy content, or whether a single crystal or a polycrystal is tested.[20, 21]

3. Iron always has a relatively large yield stress at room temperature, however well it is purified. Thus, zone refined polycrystalline iron and decarburised single crystals[22] both yield at about 7 kg/mm² tensile stress at room temperature.

The fact that the yield stress of metals of the hard group is always large and sensitive to temperature over a considerable range, irrespective of

[18] R. E. Reed-Hill and W. D. Robertson, *T.A.I.M.E.*, 1957, **209**, 496.

[19] E. Schmid and W. Boas, *Plasticity of Crystals*, Hughes and Co., London, 1950, p. 148.

[20] N. P. Allen, *J.I.S.I.*, 1959, **191**, 1.

[21] H. Conrad, *Phil. Mag.*, 1960, **5**, 745.

[22] R. L. Smith and J. L. Rutherford, *T.A.I.M.E.*, 1957, **209**, 857; H. Schwartzbart and J. R. Low, *T.A.I.M.E.*, 1949, **185**, 637.

purity and grain size, and that it derives from a resistance to dislocation movement that is much the same for all dislocations, points rather conclusively to its depending on an intrinsic property of dislocations. The intrinsic property in question has the characteristics of a Peierls force. From (3) above, the Peierls force in iron at room temperature is therefore about $3\frac{1}{2}$ kg/mm^2 shear stress. In the next chapter it will be seen that experiments on the flow stress of the hard group after plastic strain show that deformation has little effect on either the temperature sensitivity or the strain rate sensitivity, implying that the measured effects are inherent properties of the dislocations. However, they also make it uncertain whether the relatively temperature-insensitive part of the yield stress above room temperature where the yield stress is still large (e.g. Fig. 4.10a) is due to the Peierls force. With this proviso, yield in the hard group is therefore inherently a rather sharp phenomenon, since it is large and the small, uneven dislocation density that is characteristic of annealed metals cannot spread it out, as it evidently does in metals of the soft group.

The individual curves in Fig. 4.8–4.10 reveal some further points. Figure 4.8a shows how the yield stress of a magnesium single crystal varies with temperature. The different temperature sensitivity here in different temperature ranges points to there being two yield mechanisms "in series," that is, each follows the dashed line in the temperature range where the other controls and is there the weaker and ineffective mechanism. Figure 4.10a has the same feature. This is a point of great theoretical interest and is discussed in section 4.7. Figure 4.8b shows how the stress for 0.0002% permanent set in aluminium and copper single crystals varies with temperature. The curve here for aluminium could also be divided into branches like that in Fig. 4.8a, and thus illustrates that the same considerations apply to the beginning of yield, as of course they should, whereas the flatness of the curve for copper shows that members of the soft group may have a markedly temperature-insensitive mechanism, at least when in the form of single crystals. The curves in Fig. 4.8b are similar in shape to those for the macroscopic yield stress of these metals, but lie at about $\frac{1}{3}$ the stress. In Fig. 4.9 are curves for the 0.5% proof stress of copper polycrystals of various grain sizes. They illustrate the fact that grain size affects the temperature dependence of the initial strain hardening that really determines the proof stress of polycrystals. The curves in the lower part of this figure showing the relatively low stress required for a 0.0002% permanent set bring out again the steepness of the initial strain hardening in polycrystals.

Provided the temperature sensitivity of the yield stress arises because the yield process is a thermally activated one, the dependence of the yield stress on temperature and its dependence on strain rate are connected through eq. 4.10c (section 4.7), according to which a high temperature sensitivity goes hand in hand with a high strain rate sensitivity, other things being equal.   General experience supports this conclusion, for the yield stress and also the flow stress (section 5.5) of the metals which are being called the hard group in this chapter have the higher sensitivity to strain rate as well as to temperature.   For example, in Fig. 5.15 the yield stress of tungsten is evidently much more sensitive than that of copper to rate of strain.   For the flow stress there are, in fact, some fairly specific data on this point which are discussed in sections 5.4 and 5.5.   As a

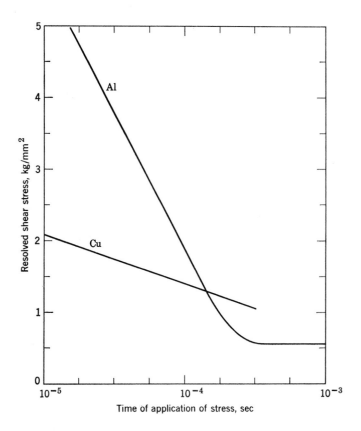

Fig. 4.11. Delay time for yield on {111} planes at −196°C of Al and Cu single crystals which had been strained 1% at room temperature.   Undeformed crystals showed no observable delay time.   To the left of each curve some slip occurred on {123} planes (Ref. 23).

[23] I. R. Kramer, *T.A.I.M.E.*, 1959, **215**, 226.

result of the strain rate dependence of the yield stress, the yield stress is higher for short stress pulses than for a steady stress; the effect of shortening the time of application of the stress is illustrated for aluminium and copper in Fig. 4.11.   By comparing this figure with Fig. 6.18a and 6.18b which show similar results for other metals, it can be seen that for equal effects on the yield stress the pulses must be particularly short with pure soft metals.   This point is discussed further in section 6.7b.   Figure 4.2 also bears on the strain rate sensitivity.   It shows about the same sensitivity in silicon-iron for individual dislocations as is found for bulk strain in iron itself; for example, according to Fig. 4.2 a 10:1 increase in dislocation velocity at room temperature requires an increase in tensile stress of 2.2 kg/mm^2, and a 10:1 increase in bulk strain rate in iron needs a 2.5 kg/mm^2 increase in tensile stress (section 5.5).

Three miscellaneous points which should be made are the following. (a) There is evidence[24, 25] that large hydrostatic stresses (up to 3000 kg/$mm^2 \equiv$ 290,000 atmospheres) raise the yield stress substantially (e.g. 12-fold in a soft metal and 30-fold in steel) in polycrystalline specimens. (b) There is a special feature about the onset of yield in polycrystals of alpha uranium in that it starts at vanishingly small stresses.   Alpha uranium is exceedingly anisotropic in its coefficient of thermal expansion. As a result, it appears that some grains are inevitably strained beyond the yield stress whenever the metal is cooled to room temperature, and yield as soon as any small stress is applied.   (c) It is general experience that impurities raise the yield stress, and the data for two grades of copper in Fig. 4.9 illustrate this tendency.   It does not, however, follow that the yield stress is determined by some mechanism directly involving impurities, at least in the soft group.   In this group the impurities could exert their effect by, for example, causing there to be more dislocations after the preparation heat treatment.

4.2 Slip Bands

Ever since slip bands were discovered, slip has featured prominently in discussions of mechanical behaviour.   For a long time it was accepted that slip occurs on a single plane.   The frequent straightness of slip lines as seen with the optical microscope has encouraged this view.   However, this straightness usually hides a lot of irregular movement on the atomic

[24] L. F. Vereschagin and V. A. Shapochkin, Fiz. Metal. i Metalloved. Akad. Nauk S.S.S.R., 1959, 7, 479. English Translation in Physics of Met. & Metallog., 1959, 7, 166.

[25] L. F. Vereschagin and V. A. Shapochkin, Fiz. Metal. i Metalloved. Akad Nauk S.S.S.R., 1959, 7, 479. English translation in Physics of Met. & Metallog., 1959, 7, 168.

scale which occurs because dislocations cross slip frequently and rarely lie in one plane over a long length. The old concept should be replaced by one in which little patches of slip occur on numerous adjacent planes. Such a concept makes the cold worked structure as faulty as it really is.

However, numerous investigations have shown that slip directions are definite, and in a few cases these directions have been confirmed by evidence about the Burgers vector of the slip dislocations. These directions are given in Table 4.2. Observed slip planes are also included in

Table 4.2

Slip Systems

Lattice or Metal	Directions and Planes
fcc	[1Ī0] (111)
bcc*	[111] (110), (112), (123)
Hexagonal† (Mg, Zn, Cd, Be, Ti, Zr, Re‡)	[11Ī0] (0001), (10Ī1), (10Ī0)
Sn	[001] (110), (100). [011] (100) [101] (10Ī), (121).
α-U	[100] (010).

* In many bcc metals, slip is believed to occur on many planes containing a ⟨111⟩ slip direction. This behaviour gives rise to the term "pencil glide," that is, glide on many planes containing a ⟨111⟩ direction.

† The ratio of the critical shear stress for slip on different planes varies considerably with metal and temperature. The [Ī Ī23] (11Ī2) system has also been identified in zinc.

‡ These are the probable systems for rhenium.

Table 4.2. There is, however, nothing to prove that a portion of slip does not take place on other planes on which short lengths of dislocations happen to lie. In this connection, an observation related to Fig. 4.11 is interesting. Although it is widely believed that fcc metals slip only on (111) planes, when such slip was suppressed in Fig. 4.11 by using short enough stress pulses, a small amount of slip on (123) planes was observed.[23]

Observationally, slip markings are often divided into two sorts. There are thick, emphatic bands called slip bands, coarse slip or slip zones, and finer lines called slip lines, fine slip or elementary slip.

4.3 Yield in Whiskers

The yield stress of thin whiskers about 1 micron in diameter is very high. Table 4.3 gives some of the largest stresses reported. As far as can be told, the deformation up to these stresses is perfectly elastic; the elastic loading line of an iron whisker is illustrated in Fig. 1.1. The stresses in

Table 4.3

Highest Strengths of Whiskers (kg/mm^2)

Material	Fe	Cu	Ag	Sn	Si	Glass fibre
Diameter, micron	1.6	1.25	3.8	1.8	~1	3
Tensile yield strength	1340	300	176	—	390*	345*
Resolved shear yield strength	364	82	72	—	—	—
Elastic strain, %	6†	2.2†	3.1†	3‡	(2‡)	(3.4‡)
Ref.	26	26	26	27	28	29

* Breaking strength. ‡ Elongation.
† Shear strain. The elongations in parentheses are estimates.

Table 4.3 range up to $\frac{1}{20}$ the elastic modulus, which is as high as the theoretical strength of a perfect crystal.

There is an interesting difference between whiskers of different metals at the limiting stress, which recalls the behaviour of bulk metals at much lower stresses. When the limiting stress is reached, copper sometimes, and silver always, deform before breaking, but, according to some experiments,[26] iron whiskers invariably break without plastic deformation. Similarly, bulk specimens of copper and silver are of course, ductile, whereas iron in bulk form is liable to behave in a brittle way (chapter 7).

With the whiskers which deform, there is a huge drop in stress to about $G/1000$ when yield begins and a Lüders band (chapter 6) propagates along the specimen, the strain in this band varying from 1 or 2 to about 100%. The large, sudden drop in stress is very evident in Fig. 4.12, which shows the stress-strain curve of a copper whisker. Similarly, tin whiskers tested in bending[27] deform plastically by kinking sharply like a mild steel wire, which is indicative of a sharp yield. The yield elongation is frequently jerky.

[26] S. E. Brenner, *J.A.P.*, 1956, **27**, 1484.
[27] C. Herring and J. K. Galt, *Phys. Rev.*, 1952, **85**, 1060.
[28] R. L. Eisner, *Acta Met.*, 1955, **3**, 414.
[29] A. A. Griffith, *Phil. Trans. Roy. Soc. London*, 1921, **221**, 163.

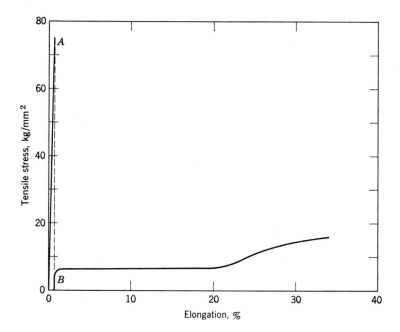

Fig. 4.12. Stress-strain curves of Cu whiskers. [111] direction parallel to stress. The whisker yielded suddenly at point A and relaxed the load. The load was re-applied at point B (Ref. 30).

It appears that the high yield stress of whiskers is sometimes a consequence of the difficulty of operating or making sources of dislocations and sometimes a consequence of the difficulty of moving dislocations already present. In copper whiskers (e.g. Fig. 4.12), substantial locking seems ruled out both because the whiskers can be too pure for locking of the necessary strength to be conceivable[30] and because they can support a stress of 50 kg/mm² at 900°C without deformation.[26] This shows that the initiation of slip is not appreciably affected by thermal agitation, as strong atomic locking mechanisms at least are expected to be (chapter 6). Another instance of the same sort is that tin whiskers support the large stress of 0.006 × Young's modulus at room temperature without creeping. In these two metals, therefore, high strength must be the result of the difficulty of making dislocations. On the other hand, the yield stress of silicon whiskers falls several fold as the temperature is raised from 500°C to 800°C. In addition, silicon whiskers exhibit the process of ageing; when strained through the upper yield stress they have been found to

[30] S. Brenner, *J.A.P.*, 1957, **28**, 1023.

recover much of their original strength on ageing at 800°C.   Little crystals of the same size, but obtained by cutting from large crystals, showed qualitatively similar behaviour, although they had generally lower yield strengths and different rates of recovery.[31]   These observations suggest that the main reason for the high yield strength of these silicon whiskers was impurity locking.   A large Peierls force could also account for the temperature dependence of the yield stress, but to account for recovery on ageing the dislocations would have to adjust themselves to crystallographic directions of low energy and high Peierls force, which is perhaps an unlikely explanation of the ageing behaviour.

The yield and fracture strengths of whiskers depend on their size. With copper and iron whiskers the strength for a given length is, with a fair amount of scatter, inversely proportional to the diameter.[26]   In the experiments in question, the weakest iron and copper whiskers were the largest ones of 15 microns diameter and had strengths of 70 and 35 kg/mm^2 respectively; these figures may be compared with the figures of 1340 and 300 kg/mm^2 in Table 4.3 for whiskers of about $\frac{1}{10}$ the diameter since they were measured in the same experiments.   A similar dependence of the fracture strength on the reciprocal of the diameter was found much earlier for glass fibres[29] and recurs in silicon rods.[31]   Moreover, when one of the two pieces of a broken whisker is retested the strength is usually higher than that of the original complete specimen.[26, 28]

The dependence of the strength on size as well as its variability suggests that some kind of randomly distributed defect prevents the full theoretical strength being reached in all except the smallest whiskers.   Inclusion particles are one source of weakness according to Fig. 2.5.   The large influence of surface contamination on ionic crystals (section 7.12) points to another kind of explanation.   Still another is the vacancy platelet, which could act as a source of dislocations at the stresses in question if its diameter exceeded about 50 atoms.   Such platelets would have to be spaced some microns apart to give a good chance that none would be found in the smallest whiskers; the same remark applies to inclusion particles.

4.4   Yield by Twinning

Mechanical twinning is sufficiently distinct from ordinary slip as to be regarded as a separate mode of deformation.   Like slip, it consists of a shear on a definite plane in a definite direction, with only a few exceptions to this rule in metals, for example, alpha uranium.   But the shear consists

[31] G. I. Pearson, W. T. Read, and W. L. Feldmann, *Acta Met.*, 1957, **5**, 181.

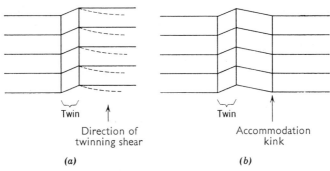

Fig. 4.13.

of only a fraction of the repeat distance and follows uniformly on successive planes in the commoner lattices with some elaboration in other lattices. In all cases the macroscopic result is a homogeneous shear as depicted in Fig. 4.13a. The crystallography of, and atomic movements in, mechanical twinning have been discussed.[32, 33, 34] Twinning planes and directions are listed in Table 4.4.

Table 4.4

Twinning Planes and Directions

Lattice in Metal	Twinning (shear) plane and direction
fcc	(111) [11$\bar{2}$]
bcc	(112) [11$\bar{1}$]
hcp (Mg, Zn, Cd, Be, Ti*)	(10$\bar{1}$2) [10$\bar{1}$1]
Rh	(11$\bar{2}$1), (11$\bar{2}$2), (10$\bar{1}$2) direction not known.
Sn	(301) [$\bar{1}$03], (101) [10$\bar{1}$]
α-U	(130) [3$\bar{1}$0], —†[312], (112)—†, (121)—†

* Other twinning systems have also been reported.
† Irrational.

The stress for twinning tends to be large at room temperature and below, with the result that twinning occurs under conditions where the yield stress is high, for example, particularly at low temperatures or fast

[32] E. Schmidt and W. Boas, *Plasticity of Crystals*, Hughes and Co., London, 1950, p. 69.

[33] C. S. Barrett, *Structure of Metals*, 2nd edition, McGraw-Hill, New York, 1954.

[34] E. O. Hall, *Twinning and Diffusionless Transformations in Metals*, Butterworth, London, 1954.

rates of strain in bcc metals, in orientations unfavourable for basal glide in hcp metals, and consequently in many grains of a polycrystalline hexagonal metal. It has been found in fcc metals at low temperature after strain hardening has raised the flow stress.[35, 36] Under all these conditions twinning occurs suddenly, as though the stress to propagate twinning is less than the stress needed to initiate it. Mechanical twinning also occurs slowly in polycrystalline hexagonal metals in creep.[37]

In single crystals of hcp metals, twinning nevertheless often occurs at stresses of about 0.1 to 0.2 kg/mm^2. This happens when stress raisers are present. For instance, in experiments with zinc and cadmium single crystals when care was taken to avoid stress concentrations, for example by electropolishing the surface, twinning did not occur until much higher stresses were applied.[38] Twinning then occurred at stresses of about 2 kg/mm^2 if the crystal were indented while under stress, and without an externally applied stress concentration not until a stress of 3 kg/mm^2 or more was reached. At this stress, prismatic slip occurred and evidently acted as an internal stress concentration. Avoiding any such slip by using whiskers has the effect of raising the twinning stress to 50 kg/mm^2.[39] However, once twins exist in zinc, they may spread at stresses below $\frac{1}{2}$ kg/mm^2.

The concentrated shear in a mechanical twin engenders big strains around it as suggested by the curved dashed lines in Fig. 4.13a, which may be partly relieved by a kink band called an "accommodation kink" depicted in Fig. 4.13b. A twin may be stopped by another twin or by a grain boundary. Figure 2.3 shows two twins stopped by a grain boundary and the shower of dislocations in the next grain, revealed as etch pits, which are generated by the stress concentration at the end of each twin. As shown in Fig. 2.3, the end of a twin is pointed to minimize the strain. The row of etch pits stretching to the bottom right from the tip of each twin in Fig. 2.3 is probably an accommodation kink.

It is difficult to believe that twinning does not occur by the movement of dislocations and, although twinning dislocations have not been identified experimentally, a feasible dislocation twinning mechanism has been suggested for some lattices.[40, 41] For example, to produce a twin in the

[35] T. H. Blewitt, R. R. Coltman, and J. K. Redman, Conference on Defects in Crystal Solids, *Phys. Soc.*, 1955, p. 369.
[36] I. A. Gindin, V. I. Khothevich, and Ya. D. Stavodubor, *Fiz. Metal. i Metallovdenie*, 1959, **7**, 794.
[37] A. R. Chaudhuri, N. J. Grant, and J. T. Norton, *T.A.I.M.E.*, 1953, **197**, 312.
[38] R. L. Bell and R. W. Cahn, *P.R.S.*, 1957, **A.239**, 494.
[39] P. B. Price, Electron Microscope Conference, Delft, 1960.
[40] A. H. Cottrell and B. A. Bilby, *Phil. Mag.*, 1951, **42**, 573.
[41] N. Thompson and D. J. Millard, *Phil. Mag.*, 1952, **43**, 422.

bcc lattice a dislocation is needed lying in a (112) plane (see Table 4.4), with a Burgers vector along $[11\bar{1}]$, but of magnitude only $\frac{1}{6}[11\bar{1}]$, as this is the magnitude of the twin shear per (112) plane. If such a dislocation rotates round another which has a screw component of $\frac{1}{6}[112]$, which is the spacing of (112) planes, it will spiral upward by one layer for each revolution and so repeat the twinning shear on successive planes. Such an arrangement is geometrically possible. Suppose a $\frac{1}{2}[\bar{1}1\bar{1}]$ dislocation lying in the plane $(\bar{1}12)$ dissociates in the following way:

$$\tfrac{1}{2}[\bar{1}1\bar{1}] \rightarrow \tfrac{1}{3}[\bar{2}1\bar{1}] + \tfrac{1}{6}[11\bar{1}]$$

the dissociation presumably being assisted by a suitable stress. The $\frac{1}{6}[11\bar{1}]$ dislocation can move in the $(\bar{1}12)$ plane, and transfer to a (112) plane by becoming parallel to the line of intersection of these two planes. It is therefore the mobile dislocation required. The $\frac{1}{3}[\bar{2}1\bar{1}]$ dislocation cannot move because there would be a serious atomic misfit in its wake. This dislocation is called a sessile dislocation (for another example of a sessile dislocation see section 4.6c) and acts as an anchor line about which the $\frac{1}{6}[11\bar{1}]$ dislocation can rotate. As both the $\frac{1}{3}[\bar{2}1\bar{1}]$ dislocation and the undissociated $\frac{1}{2}[\bar{1}1\bar{1}]$ dislocation have screw components of $\frac{1}{6}[\bar{1}\bar{1}2]$, the rotation is accompanied by the necessary spiralling from one plane to the next. In the fcc lattice the corresponding dissociation is

$$\tfrac{1}{2}(110) \rightarrow \tfrac{1}{3}(111) + \tfrac{1}{6}(11\bar{2}).$$

The $\frac{1}{6}[11\bar{2}]$ dislocation produces the twinning shear, and the $\frac{1}{3}[111]$ is a sessile dislocation. Both it and the $\frac{1}{2}[110]$ dislocation have screw components of $\frac{1}{2}[111]$, which produces the necessary spiralling effect. In hcp metals a dislocation with Burgers vector along the c axis and equal to [0001] can be resolved, in the twinned part, into two basal slip dislocations and two twinning dislocations.[41] As the screw component normal to the composition plane is equal to twice the spacing normal to the composition plane, the twinning dislocations spiral upward at the correct speed as they rotate.

4.5 Surface Effects

There are three somewhat distinct surface effects on yield behaviour.

1. The Rehbinder effect—an effect whereby the flow stress is reduced on immersing the specimen in a solution containing a surface active agent. This effect, discovered by Rehbinder[42] (a review of this work in English

[42] P. Rehbinder, V. I. Lichtman, and V. M. Maslennikov, *C.R. Acad. Sci. U.S.S.R.*, 1941, **32**, 25.

is given in ref. 42a), has been confirmed by others,[43, 44] although further precise work implies that it is really the rate of strain hardening that is affected by the surface active agent.[45] Two explanations have been proposed. One is that the surface active agent penetrates and opens up minute cracks in the specimen surface. The other is that the effect is due to a reduction of the surface energy of the metal when in contact with the surface active agent, which presumably facilitates the creation of a slip step at the surface. However, as surface energies are of the order of 1000 ergs/cm^2, the latter effect should only provide a reduction in yield strength of about 1 g/cm^2.

2. Surface films on single crystals raise the yield strength, [45, 46, 47, 48, 49] in some cases at least apparently by simply acting as a barrier to slip.[50] The film then acts like another grain of different orientation.

3. For copper single crystals there is evidence that slip sources near the surface require lower stresses to operate them than do sources in the interior.[51] The evidence is that by diffusing zinc into the surface layers the yield stress can be raised considerably. For example, the yield stress of pure copper in these experiments was 56 g/mm^2, but with $\frac{1}{3}$ at % zinc in a surface layer about 10 microns thick it was 75 g/mm^2, with 1% Zn 101 g/mm^2, and with 8% Zn 150 g/mm^2. This is not simply a barrier effect because a "yield drop" occurs, indicative of source locking by the zinc (chapter 5). When the surface layer was removed, the original yield stress of pure copper was restored. Similar effects have also been found when silver is diffused into copper to produce an alloy layer 30 microns thick.[52] Presumably the dislocation network pattern is more open near the surface than in the interior.

4.6 Sources and Multiplication of Dislocations during Plastic Strain

The numerous dislocations produced on straining a metal originate at certain sources and are also believed to multiply as they travel through

[42a] V. I. Lichtman, P. Rehbinder, and G. V. Karpenko, *Effect of a Surface-Active Medium on the Deformation of Metals*, English translation published H.M. Stationery Office, London, 1958.

[43] W. Klinkenberg, K. Lücke, and G. Masing, *Z. Metallk.*, 1953, **44**, 362.

[44] A. Pfützenreuter and G. Masing, *Z. Metallk.*, 1951, **42**, 361.

[45] I. R. Kramer and L. J. Demer, *T.A.I.M.E.*, 1961, **221**, 780; I. R. Kramer, *ibid.*, 999.

[46] R. Roscoe, *Phil. Mag.*, 1936, **21**, 399.

[47] A. H. Cottrell and D. F. Gibbons, *Nature*, 1948, **162**, 488.

[48] S. Harper and A. H. Cottrell, *P.P.S.*, 1950, **63B**, 331.

[49] M. Metzger and T. A. Read, *T.A.I.M.E.*, 1958, **212**, 236.

[50] C. S. Barrett, *Acta Met.*, 1953, **1**, 2.

[51] M. A. Adams, *Acta Met.*, 1958, **6**, 327.

[52] F. D. Rosi, *Acta Met.*, 1957, **5**, 348.

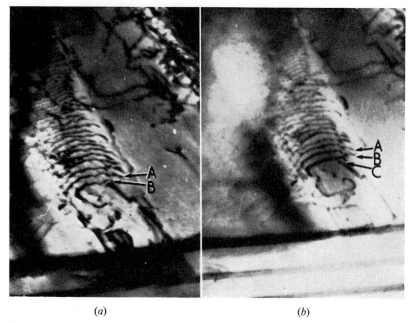

(a)   (b)

Fig. 4.14. Two successive photographs, showing operation of a source of dislocations during straining. Dislocation C was seen to follow dislocations A and B. In the right-hand micrograph, another dislocation can be seen growing at the source and will follow C. The nature of the source is unknown. Material, 18/8 stainless steel. × 70,000. (R. M. Fisher)

the crystals. Dislocation sources have been seen in action with the electron microscope, and Fig. 4.14a and 4.14b are two successive photographs from a sequence showing a source in action. In this case it was not possible to identify the nature of the source. There are, however, some ideas and some evidence about both sources and multiplication. Several features appear to be called into play.

(a) *Particles of Precipitate or Impurity.* The dislocations around precipitates (Fig. 2.5) can evidently act as sources, for slip bands have been observed to spring out from particles [2, 53, 54]; an example of a particle acting as a source of slip bands is shown in Fig. 4.15.

To account for the number of dislocations in this and other slip bands there must be some multiplication process. One simple multiplication process [55] is that illustrated in Fig. 4.16a and 4.16b. A piece AB of the original loop which is of screw type cross slips because of some local stress

[53] J. Gilman, *J.A.P.*, 1959, **30**, 1584.
[54] J. Holden, *Acta Met.*, 1960, **8**, 424.
[55] J. S. Koehler, *Phys. Rev.*, 1952, **86**, 52.

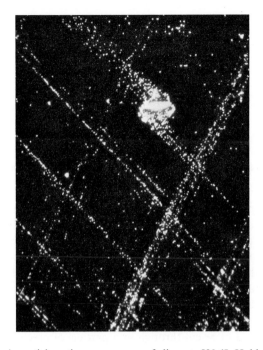

Fig. 4.15. A particle acting as a source of slip. × 500 (J. Holden, Ref. 54)

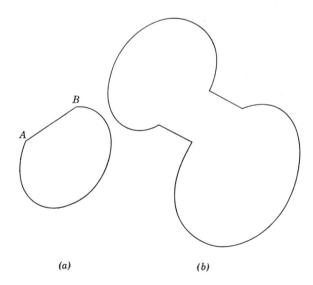

(a)   *(b)*

Fig. 4.16. Multiplication of moving dislocation.

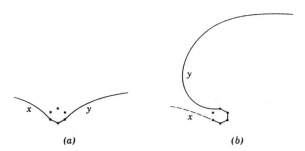

(a) (b)

Fig. 4.17. Growth of dislocation line at an obstacle.

on to another plane. The new pieces of dislocation so made are believed sometimes to act as anchors. If so, the portion of dislocation in the original plane and that in the new plane can proceed to multiply by the Frank-Read mechanism of repeated looping. This cross-slip process accounts for the fact that slip bands often grow in width as well as in length, and that at an early stage one side may extend further than the other. Another process is that shown in Fig. 4.17a and 4.17b. At a a dislocation meets an obstacle which may be simply a group of dislocations too closely spaced to be cut through or a particle of precipitate, and loops round this as shown at b; for clarity only one arm y is shown looping in b. If now the two arms x and y are on planes separated by more than one or two atomic distances, they will not join up as they cross each other, and both can go on looping indefinitely. Both these multiplication mechanisms apply equally to dislocations produced by any of the methods (a) to (d).

(b) *Grain Boundaries and Surfaces.* Grain boundaries and twin boundaries have been seen to act as sources in foils thin enough to be examined in the electron microscope. Figure 4.18 shows an example of such a boundary source in a commercial mild steel. The dislocations emitted in foils are presumably screw dislocations,* involving sliding at the grain boundaries; there seems no reason why a similar process should not occur in a bulk metal.

(c) *Vacancy Platelets.* It is geometrically possible for the vacancy platelets referred to in chapter 2 to act as sources although, as originally

---

* The stress system in a foil under electron microscope examination, arising either from electron beam heating or a surface contamination film, is a radially symmetrical direct stress. The shear stress thus acts through the foil thickness and can move a screw dislocation parallel to the foil plane, but it can move an edge dislocation only out of the foil.

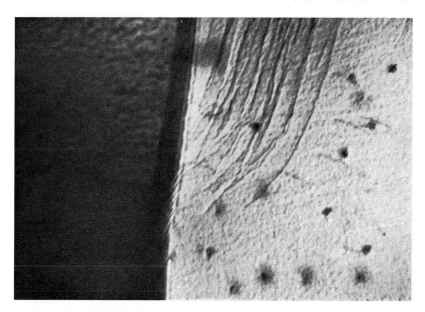

Fig. 4.18. Slip traces made by dislocations which were observed to emerge from the grain boundary.   × 50,000.   (J. D. Baird; Crown copyright reserved.)

formed, they are sessile dislocations.   The idea is as follows.[56]   Consider an fcc metal.   Figure 4.19a shows the dislocation loop lying in a (111) plane with the pieces AB and CD supposed to be parallel to a $\langle 110 \rangle$ direction.   Figure 4.19b illustrates the crystallography of the situation. OPQ is the (111) plane in which the single-layer vacancy platelet lies, and ORQ and so on are the other {111} planes.   The Burgers vector of the dislocation loop is necessarily $SR = \frac{1}{3}[111]$.   A dislocation with such a Burgers vector cannot move without trailing serious atomic misfit behind it and is therefore expected not to move.   It is an example of a sessile dislocation. SO, etc., represent the Burgers vectors $\frac{1}{6}\langle 112 \rangle$ of slip dislocation partials.   If a shear corresponding to the partial PS takes place in the faulted layer $ABCD$, the Burgers vector of the dislocation $ABCD$ becomes $PS + SR = PR$, which is a normal $\frac{1}{2}[110]$ slip dislocation.   The lengths AB and CD lying parallel to a $\langle 110 \rangle$ direction can now glide as indicated by the dashed loops in Fig. 4.19a and multiply as in Fig. 4.16b.   This kind of behaviour has been seen with the electron microscope.[57]   A similar sequence of events is geometrically possible in the

[56] D. Kuhlmann-Wilsdorf, *Phil. Mag.*, 1958, **3**, 125.
[57] K. H. Westmacott, D. Hull, R. S. Barnes, and R. E. Smallman, *Phil. Mag.*, 1959, **4**, 1089.

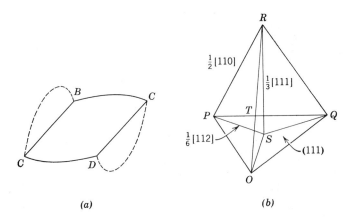

(a)   *(b)*

Fig. 4.19.   Vacancy platelet.   (*a*) The platelet itself; (*b*) the Burgers vectors involved.

bcc lattice.   For example, suppose vacancies precipitate on the (112) plane, removing two layers—since the layers are not densely packed this does not involve an excessive number of atoms—to produce a loop of sessile dislocation of Burgers vector $\frac{1}{3}[112]$.   A shear across the plane of the loop of $\frac{1}{6}[11\bar{1}]$ gives the reaction $\frac{1}{3}[112] + \frac{1}{6}[11\bar{1}] = \frac{1}{2}[111]$ and the loop becomes a loop of the normal slip dislocation for the bcc lattice.   It has the same possibility of glide as indicated in connection with Fig. 4.19*a*. There are, of course, other possibilities in both lattices.   In the fcc lattice, suppose vacancies precipitate on a (100) plane followed by a shear of $\frac{1}{2}[010]$.   The result is $\frac{1}{2}[100] + \frac{1}{2}[010] = \frac{1}{2}[110]$.   In the bcc lattice, suppose vacancies also precipitate on a (100) plane followed by shear of $\frac{1}{2}[011]$; the result is $\frac{1}{2}[100] + \frac{1}{2}[011] = \frac{1}{2}[111]$.   In both cases, a loop of slip dislocation is produced.

For completeness it should be mentioned that there is an alternative way in which the $\frac{1}{3}[111]$ dislocation SR in Fig. 4.19*b* may lower its energy. It can break down into $ST + TR$, where T is the mid-point of OPR; this is the reaction $\frac{1}{3}[111] \rightarrow \frac{1}{6}[011] + \frac{1}{6}[211]$.   Suppose that the vacancy platelet is triangular, with sides parallel to the $\langle 110 \rangle$ directions OP, PQ, and QO.   If this reaction occurs on the side parallel to OP, the $[01\bar{1}]$ direction, then the $\frac{1}{6}[211]$ dislocation TR, which is the ordinary partial slip dislocation in the fcc lattice, can slip in the $(\bar{1}11)$ plane OPR.   As it is the ordinary partial slip dislocation, in so doing it leaves the normal stacking fault in its wake; let it glide away from OP to take up the position ORP, so that the area ORP is a piece of stacking fault.   Suppose now that similar decompositions occur along PQ and OQ.   Then along OR, for example, the dislocations $\frac{1}{6}[211]$ and $\frac{1}{6}[\bar{1}\bar{1}2]$ meet and unite to form

$\frac{1}{6}[10\bar{1}]$ since the square rule shows that energy is thereby saved.   There is now left a tetrahedron, the edges of which consist of $\frac{1}{6}\langle 110 \rangle$ type dislocations and the faces of stacking fault.   As far as the dislocations are concerned the total energy saved is $3 \times \frac{1}{3} - 6 \times \frac{1}{18} = \frac{2}{3}$ of the original energy.   A relatively large area of stacking fault has, however, been created, so that breakdown into a defect tetrahedron is only to be expected in metals of low stacking fault energy.   They have been observed in quenched gold,[58] which is such a metal.

On the other hand, a large stacking fault energy should encourage the type of reaction depicted in Fig. 4.19.   Here, before the shear *PS* occurred, the area enclosed by the dislocation loop consisted of stacking fault which is eliminated by the shear *PS*.   The energy of the stacking fault tends to provoke the shear, and must be one factor determining the course of events.   Consequently, it would seem that vacancy platelets are more likely to act as sources of slip in metals of high than in metals of low stacking fault energy.

(*d*) *The Grown-In Networks.*   There is no evidence that the grown-in networks do act directly as multiplying sources in the sense that nodes in the network act as pinning points for the loop between them, enabling it to multiply by the Frank-Read mechanism.   The evidence is rather that most grown-in dislocations are rather firmly anchored in position, presumably either by point defects, foreign atoms, or by being on unfavourable planes for slip.

4.7   Processes Determining the Yield Stress

Several forces must contribute to the yield stress, but to different extents in different metals.

(*a*) *The Peierls-Nabarro Force.*   It is easy to see why the Peierls force is highly sensitive to atomic structure and also why there is difficulty in making an accurate theoretical estimate of its magnitude.   It is closely connected with the variation in the core energy as a dislocation moves from one atomic position to the next.   As one atomic length of dislocation moves to the quarter-way position between successive equilibrium positions a Burgers vector apart, which is the position where the Peierls force probably reaches its maximum, a stress τ does work approximately equal to $\frac{1}{4}\tau b^3$.   Dislocation core energies are about 1 ev per atomic length, so that a stress of 10 kg/mm^2 is needed to overcome a variation of only 1% in the core energy.   It is therefore very difficult to calculate sufficiently precisely to obtain a reliable estimate of the Peierls force.   The calculation is further complicated by another factor.   Except at absolute zero, it is

[58] J. Silcox and P. B. Hirsch, *Phil. Mag.*, 1959, **4**, 72.

not necessary for a long length of dislocation to jump forward simultaneously from one atomic position to the next. If a small loop is thrown forward with the help of thermal agitation (cf. Fig. 6.17) it can drag the rest of the dislocation line forward provided it is greater than a certain critical size.[59] Raising the temperature increases the assistance from thermal agitation and reduces the measured yield stress.

Because of these complexities it is not yet possible to decide from theory in any particular case whether the Peierls force is the cause of the yield stress. As already intimated, however, the experimental evidence enables a decision to be made about the magnitude of the Peierls force in different metals, and this evidence is briefly collected together in section 4.7*f*.

(*b*) *Intersection of Dislocations.* With the dislocation density normal for a well-annealed metal, very little plastic deformation can take place without there being very numerous dislocation intersections. Moving dislocations intersect the existing network, member dislocations of which may also be in motion, and also intersect other dislocations newly created by the deformation. A system is thus formed of some attractive junctions, as at *A* in Fig. 4.20*a*, and some repulsive junctions as at *R*. Figure 4.20*a* is intended to represent the situation if the stress is removed so that the attractive junctions can form fully. Figure 4.20*b* represents the situation when a stress nearly large enough to break the junction at *A* is applied, and shows how the junction shrinks; other junctions may shrink as well.

The sequence of events envisaged when an attractive junction forms and breaks can be gathered from Fig. 2.17, supposing now that the dislocations have different Burgers vectors. When they meet they quickly move to the

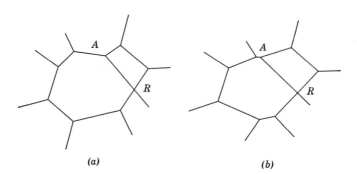

(*a*)   (*b*)

Fig. 4.20. Part of the three-dimensional dislocation network. An attractive intersection is represented at *A* and a repulsive one at *R*.

[59] A. Seeger, *Handbuch der Physik*, vol. 7, part 1, Springer, 1955, p. 383.

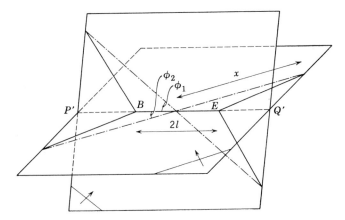

Fig. 4.21.   An attractive dislocation intersection in the absence of stress.

position in which the junction dislocation has its full length *BE*, and the energy thereby saved is carried away by atomic motion as heat.   This energy is large, being in the region of hundreds of electron volts.   For the junction to be broken again and the dislocations to continue moving, this energy must be supplied once more by the stress.   In this way attractive junctions give rise to a resistance to flow.

Accurate estimation of the resistance to flow arising in this way is complicated, not only because there are many situations to consider such as different angles of meeting, different intersecting planes, and different resolved shear stresses, physically different events—for example, in Fig. 2.17 the junction dislocation increases in length and the arms *PE* shrink as the meeting dislocations continue moving, whereas in Fig. 4.21 the junction dislocation shrinks to zero during this movement—but also because the behaviour of one junction depends on how much movement occurs at its neighbours.   Estimates have been made only for isolated junctions with arms having fixed outer ends.   We can make a simple estimate from Fig. 4.21 by following the argument just outlined and equating the change in dislocation line energy as the junction dislocation closes up to the work done by the stress.[60, 61]   In Fig. 4.21 the change in line energy as the junction dislocation shrinks by dl, assuming a symmetrical situation in which all arms are of equal length x and $\phi_1 = \phi_2 = \phi$, is

$$dE = (4W_1 \cos \phi - 2W_2) \, dl \qquad (4.1)$$

[60] J. Friedel, Conference on Internal Stresses and Fatigue, Elsevier, 1959.
[61] W. E. Carrington, K. F. Hale and D. McLean, *P.R.S.*, 1960, **A.259**, 203.

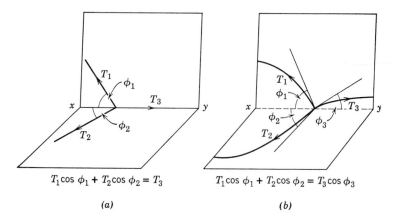

$$T_1 \cos \phi_1 + T_2 \cos \phi_2 = T_3 \qquad T_1 \cos \phi_1 + T_2 \cos \phi_2 = T_3 \cos \phi_3$$

(a)   (b)

Fig. 4.22. Line tension equilibrium of a node: (a) in the absence of stress; (b) in the presence of a stress.

where W_1 and W_2 are the line energies of the original and junction dislocations respectively. Supposing that for this same movement each of the four arms moves a distance kdl under the applied stress τ, the work done by the stress is

$$dW = 4\tau bxk \, dl \qquad (4.2)$$

Equating dE to dW gives an equation of the form

$$\tau = \frac{\alpha G b}{x} \qquad (4.3)$$

with $\alpha = 0.2$ to 0.3, for the breaking stress of the junction, that is, the contribution to the flow stress offered by attractive intersections. More accurate estimates[62, 63] have been made based on the principle illustrated in Fig. 4.22a and 4.22b, namely, that at each node there must be line tension equilibrium. The dislocations bend to achieve this, and the curvatures and consequently the complete shape of the network can be calculated, which leads to an estimate of the breaking stress. The resulting expressions are of the same form as eq. 4.3 and yield values of α between 0.2 and 0.4. As, in practice, not all arms will be anchored, real values of α are probably somewhat smaller.

A feature of these calculations is illustrated in Fig. 4.23, in which the ordinate represents applied stress and the abscissa the distance between the approaching nodes. Although some junctions offer a resistance that rises continuously until the nodes meet, at others the stress reaches a peak

[62] G. Saada, Doctoral Thesis, University of Paris, 1960.
[63] J. D. Baird and B. Gale, unpublished work.

before the nodes have come together. Another seemingly reliable property of an attractive junction, which is almost a geometrical necessity, is that they are relatively weaker in bcc than in fcc metals. This is clear from eq. 4.1, for in bcc metals W_2 represents a [100] dislocation so that $W_2 > W_1$, but in fcc, $W_2 = W_1$.

The strength of a repulsive intersection is also difficult to estimate, for similar reasons. It necessarily varies inversely as x and so has the same form as eq. 4.3. According to one estimate,[64] α is approximately equal to 0.1, so that the repulsive intersection is weaker than the attractive. For this there is a simple physical reason. One type is obtained from the other by simply reversing the sign of one of the dislocations. If the dislocations were rigid the two types of junction would therefore be equally strong. However, the dislocations bend as they approach each other. In the attractive type they bend closer and finally unite, and so increase the attraction. In the repulsive type they bend away from each other and so decrease the repulsion. Consequently, the attractive type becomes the stronger.

In addition to these intersection processes, as mentioned in section 2.1i,

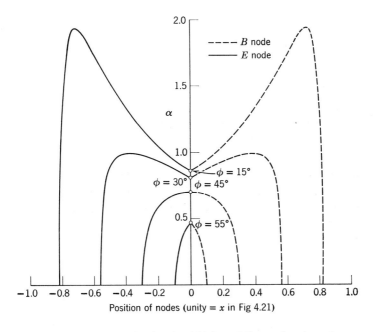

Fig. 4.23. Node separation in Fig. 4.21 (i.e., BE) as a function of stress.

[64] G. Saada, *Acta Met.*, 1960, **8**, 200.

jogs are made at many, and perhaps all, intersections. The resistance from this also is difficult to calculate, partly because, as intimated in section 2.1i, it is not certain how much of the jog is made in all cases, and also partly because the stress-strain curve of a jog, so to speak, is unknown. Presumably it has a form somewhat as in Fig. 4.24, in which the abscissa z represents the distance separating the dislocations from complete breakthrough. This kind of shape has been deduced from experiment.[65] For an extended dislocation, z presumably tends to be

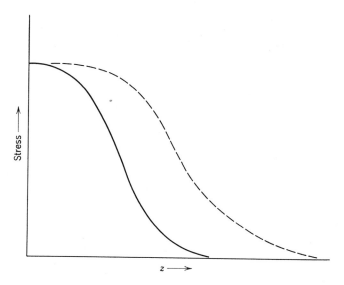

Fig. 4.24. Formation of a jog. Possible relation between stress and relative distance moved by the intersecting dislocations.

large as represented by the dashed curve. The form of the expression for the flow resistance due to jogs is readily obtainable, however, if the curve in Fig. 4.24 is replaced by a square topped one of width d and area W_j— W_j of course being equal to the energy of the jog. Then if the spacing between jogs is x

$$W_j = \tau x b d \tag{4.4}$$

or

$$\tau = \frac{W_j}{x b d} \tag{4.5}$$

$W_j \sim 0.1 G b^2 d$,[60] so that eq. 4.5 is similar to eq. 4.3 with $\alpha = W_j/bd$ in the region of 0.1.

[65] Z. S. Basinski, *Phil. Mag.*, 1959, **40**, 393.

Since jogs are made near rupture of an attractive intersection, to obtain the total resistance of the junction the curve for the jog in Fig. 4.24 must be superimposed on that for the attractive junction.   The combined effect is shown in Fig. 4.25, curve B representing the type of junction at which the stress rises to a peak before the nodes come together, that is, before the jog is formed.   Because the subsequent drop in stress is large, for this kind of junction the necessity of making a jog does not increase the resistance.   For the other kind of junction, curve A, the jog resistance

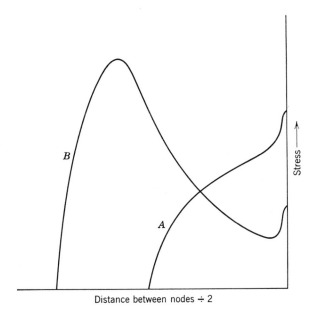

Distance between nodes ÷ 2

Fig. 4.25.   Curves of Fig. 4.23 modified to include the effect of making a jog.

simply adds on to the junction resistance.   According to the calculations referred to,[63] about half the junctions are of each kind.   In the writer's opinion, because the unstressed position of an attractive junction is symmetrically placed with respect to the position of the meeting dislocations just before they unite to make the junction and also with respect to their positions just after breaking, only half the jog energy is made during breaking, thus halving the value of α in eq. 4.5.

At repulsive junctions, as far as elastic forces are concerned, the dislocations repell both immediately before and immediately after breaking, but in opposite directions.   Consequently, the elastic repulsion already referred to drops to zero as the jog is being made.   As a result, the strength of a repulsive junction is whichever is the larger, the jog force or the junction force.

(c) *The General Stress Field: Groups of Dislocations.* All the dislocations, moving or static, combine to produce a stress field fluctuating in space and time, through which a moving dislocation travels. At some points the moving dislocation is helped and at others hindered by the stress field. To continue moving it must overcome the opposing stress peaks, which therefore are the contribution of the stress field to the yield stress. Traversing an opposing stress peak is essentially similar to intersection at a repulsive junction, since both concern elastic repulsive forces. A calculation[64] gives the result that the peak repulsion from dislocations not intersected is similar to that from those which are. Moreover, as elastic forces between dislocations are inversely proportional to their spacing, the stress peaks due to a network of dislocations will be inversely proportional to its spacing. Consequently the flow resistance arising from the stresses of all the other dislocations has the same form as eq. 4.3, probably with α in the region of 0.1 to 0.2.[64, 66]

Piled-up groups of like dislocations, produced when many dislocations from the same source are stopped by a strong barrier, create a particularly strong internal stress field. Strictly speaking, they occur after yield, but since even a large piled-up group requires only an insignificant amount of plastic deformation for its formation, they can reasonably be included in a discussion of yield stress, especially as they seem essential to the steep initial strain hardening of polycrystals. It can be shown[67] that the number n of dislocations which a shear stress τ can squeeze into a slip distance L between source and barrier is

$$n = \frac{k\pi\tau L}{Gb} \qquad (4.6)$$

where k is equal to unity for screw dislocations and to $1 - \nu$ (ν being Poisson's ratio) for edge dislocations. In other words, the n dislocations produce at the source a back stress τ opposing the applied stress and preventing the source emitting further dislocations. The shear strain ϵ produced by the n dislocations is equal[67] to that which they would have produced had they all travelled a distance of $3L/4$, and to harden the metal fairly uniformly the same event would have to occur at about $1/L^2$ places per unit area. It is then easily seen that the increase in $\tau \sim G/200$ per 1% strain. This accounts for the steep initial strain hardening of polycrystals, but may at first sight seem rather unrealistic for metals whose

[66] A. Seeger, *Conference on Dis. and Mechanical Properties of Crystals*, John Wiley and Sons, 1956, p. 243.

[67] J. D. Eshelby, F. C. Frank, and F. R. N. Nabarro, *Phil. Mag.*, 1951, **42**, 351.

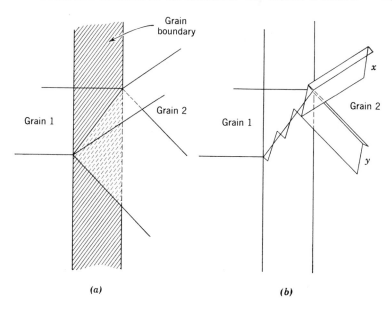

Fig. 4.26. Meeting of slip planes at a grain boundary. (*a*) The slip planes coincide exactly. (*b*) The slip bands do not coincide exactly. Slip in grain 2 tries to meet the slip band in grain 1 at the grain boundary by following the zig-zag line; parts of the slip bands in grain 2 are shown as *x* and *y*.

individual grains are quite soft, on the grounds that the high stress close to each piled-up group would cause other sources in the same or the neighbouring grains to emit dislocations of a Burgers vector that would reduce the high stress.   However, the effectiveness of a grain boundary as a barrier in a pure metal stems from the fact that the slip planes do not continue into the next grain.   The difficulty of continuing the slip into the next grain becomes particularly clear if we think of the whole slip plane in the initiating grain contacting the grain boundary.   The line of inter-section will not usually coincide with normal slip planes in the next grain. Nevertheless, a stress concentration where each initiating slip band contacts the grain boundary can only be avoided to the extent that slip is carried into the next grain.   Accordingly, in the next grain dislocations must attempt either to cross slip onto planes that do coincide, as indicated in Fig. 4.26*a*, or zig-zag frequently as in Fig. 4.26*b*.   The latter arrange-ment cannot avoid serious disturbance at the grain boundary; the former is presumably difficult and also leaves some disturbance because the vectorial sum of the slip on the two planes in the next grain can rarely exactly equal that in the initiating grain.   In practice, the problem is evidently solved by the slip band partially fading out as it nears the grain boundary, giving rise to a part of the large stress indicated by eq. 4.6. The fact that cross slip is required in the second grain means that the initial strain hardening should be more marked the more difficult this is, and explains why it is bigger in copper than in aluminium.

The large stress around the end of a slip band explains relations like those in Fig. 4.6 and 4.7 in which some critical stress, in this case the yield stress, is related to (grain size)$^{-\frac{1}{2}}$. It is not necessary to assume the existence of regular piled-up groups, which are in fact not frequently observed. The precise distribution of the dislocations is not particularly important. The important thing is the stress field around the end of a slip band. As far as stresses near its ends are concerned, a slip band is equivalent to a crack with friction between the two surfaces, differing from a crack only in that the faces do not decohere although they slip relatively to each other. Suppose the slip distance L is equal to the grain size, that a shear stress τ is applied, and that there is a resistance to slip from all the causes discussed in this section equal to τ_f. The effective shear stress on the slip band, regarded as a crack, is then $(\tau - \tau_f)$. The stress τ_s on the nearest source a distance l away from the head of the slip band, due to the stress concentration from the slip band acting like a crack, is then, somewhat approximately, $(\tau - \tau_f)(L/l)^{\frac{1}{2}}$. This source sends out dislocations of a sign that mitigates the stress around the end of the slip band; further slip can then occur in the slip band, and so on. Once the stress τ_s is reached, hardening due to the back stress consequently increases less rapidly. Assuming that this point is taken as the point at which observable yield occurs, the yield stress is

$$\tau = \tau_f + \tau_s \left(\frac{l}{L}\right)^{\frac{1}{2}} \tag{4.7}$$

and so depends on $L^{-\frac{1}{2}}$. Equation 4.7 is known as the Petch equation after its originator.

(d) *The Nonconservative Movement of Jogs.* It has already been explained (section 2.3a) that certain jogs may trail a row of point defects as their dislocation moves. As energy is needed to make the point defects, a stress has to act on these jogs and correspondingly they exert a restraining force on the dislocations. The estimate of this force follows the estimate given earlier for the production of jogs. From an equation similar to eq. 4.4, it follows that the stress is

$$\tau = \frac{Q_f}{byx} \tag{4.8}$$

where Q_f is the energy of formation of the defect and y is the distance the dislocation moves while the defect is being made.   As the kind of jog under consideration is most effective on a dislocation in pure screw orientation, the resistance arising in the way under discussion is a maximum for such dislocations and a minimum for those in pure edge orientations.

(e) *Influence of Temperature and Speed.*   Since in each of the processes (a) to (d) the stress has to overcome an energy barrier, thermal activation can assist these processes.   The degree to which it does so can be analysed in the following way.   It is convenient to use the jog of eq. 4.4 as an example, but to make the analysis in a general way.   The energy required from thermal activation is the jog energy less the work done by the stress; let this required energy be U, which is a function of stress.   Suppose also that there are N intersections at which a jog is being made at any one instant and that the slip distance moved by a length x of dislocation on completing the intersection is L.   Then the rate of flow $\dot{\epsilon}$ is

$$\dot{\epsilon} = \nu N x L b e^{-U/kT} \tag{4.9}$$

ν being a frequency factor smaller than the atomic frequency of vibration because the length of dislocation involved will usually be an appreciable number of atoms long.   By differentiating and recombining, it follows that

$$\left(\frac{\partial \tau}{\partial \dot{\epsilon}}\right)_T = -\frac{kT}{U'\dot{\epsilon}} \tag{4.10a}$$

$$\left(\frac{\partial \tau}{\partial T}\right)_{\dot{\epsilon}} = \frac{U}{U'T} \tag{4.10b}$$

$$\frac{(\partial \tau/\partial T)\dot{\epsilon}}{(\partial \tau/\partial \dot{\epsilon})_T} = \frac{\dot{\epsilon}}{T}\ln\frac{\nu N x L b}{\dot{\epsilon}} \tag{4.10c}$$

where $U' = \partial U/\partial \tau$ and τ is the applied shear stress.   For simplicity, any variation with temperature of U or N has been neglected here.   In practice, U at least will vary with temperature because atomic spacings and therefore elastic moduli vary; the error introduced by neglecting the variation is probably not greater than 10% (see appendix).   A simplifying assumption which is probably an approximation but which helps to bring out in a simple way the influence of the various factors is to suppose that the activation energy is a linear function of the applied stress.   Thus, using the "square-topped" jog assumed for eq. 4.4, $U = W_j - \tau x b d$.   Equations 4.10a and b become

$$\left(\frac{\partial \tau}{\partial \dot{\epsilon}}\right)_T = \frac{kT}{x b d \dot{\epsilon}} \tag{4.11a}$$

$$\left(\frac{\partial \tau}{\partial T}\right)_{\dot{\epsilon}} = -\frac{k}{x b d}\ln\frac{\nu N x L b}{\dot{\epsilon}} \tag{4.11b}$$

and eq. 4.10c remains unchanged.   With this assumption it also follows from eq. 4.9 that[68]

$$\tau = \frac{W}{xbd} - \frac{kT}{xbd} \ln \frac{vNxLb}{\dot{\epsilon}} \tag{4.12}$$

There are big differences among the processes (a) to (d) with regard to these equations.   For the intersection process, jogs apart, and for the internal stress field it can be seen that the energy required from thermal activation increases very rapidly as the applied stress is reduced below that which could produce flow unaided by thermal agitation.   In other words, thermal agitation makes little difference to the stress necessary.   In terms of eq. 4.12, W is very large, and so is d.   Consequently, the contribution to the yield stress from these processes is virtually unaffected by temperature (except for the influence of temperature on elastic modulus) or strain rate.   For the Peierls force, x and d are both small, and the sensitivity of this force both to temperature and strain rate is high, whereas the actual magnitude of the force will be large unless W is small.

For jog formation in unextended dislocations, both W and d will be smaller than for jog formation in extended dislocations; in the former sort of metal this process will therefore have the steeper temperature coefficient.   Whether or not the stress needed to produce point defects varies with temperature depends on circumstances.   If a vacancy is not separated immediately from the jog which has produced it, the stress is hardly sensitive to temperature as the following argument shows.   The frequency with which the dislocation jumps forward is proportional to

$$e^{-(Q_f - \tau x b d)/kT} \tag{4.13}$$

But as the vacancy is still in the next atomic position to the jog the dislocation can jump backwards, removing the vacancy, and the frequency of this movement is proportional to

$$e^{+(Q_f - \tau x b d)/kT} \tag{4.14}$$

Unless the stress term $\tau x b d$ is practically equal to Q_f there is no net movement forward.   Consequently, the stress is virtually insensitive to temperature under these conditions.   However, if the jog can move sideways and is immediately separated from the vacancy in this way, the restoring force implied by eq. 4.14 disappears and only the temperature sensitive force implied by eq. 4.13 remains.   This is also true if the vacancy can diffuse away, which requires a temperature high enough for self diffusion to take place, although then the energy Q_f in eq. 4.13 and also in eq. 4.8 must be replaced by the energy of self diffusion.   Consequently, if the jog

[68] A. Seeger, *Phil. Mag.*, 1955, **46**, 1194.

cannot move sideways, the flow stress is expected to be independent of temperature until the temperature is high enough to permit diffusion. Above this temperature the flow stress as measured at constant strain rate should fall linearly with rising temperature as indicated by eq. 4.12. The position is similar in principle for a jog which produces interstitials. Accepting in practice, however, that with this kind of jog the sideways movement is controlled by a moderate activation energy, as a cause of flow resistance its effectiveness should decline with rising temperature; possibly it declines from absolute zero and is ineffective at room temperature.

The slip distance L differs for the different processes when they are considered in isolation and affects the strain rate $\dot{\epsilon}$ (eq. 4.12). Both for intersection and jog production L is either equal to x or an integral number times x, since after one intersection the moving dislocation must move at least to the next dislocation, which is by definition a distance x away, and may make several intersections before being brought to rest. For defect production L is equal to d, the distance over which the defect is made, which should be considerably smaller. The Peierls force has the periodicity of the lattice, and for this $L = b$. If, as suggested by experiment, a curve of the shape shown in Fig. 4.24 is assumed instead of a "square-topped" curve, the effect in eq. 4.11 and 4.12 is to reduce d and W as the stress is increased. This can readily be seen from Fig. 4.24, for the energy required from thermal agitation decreases more rapidly with increase in stress than for a square-topped curve and the distance through which the stress moves during the thermal agitation also decreases. Some anomalies in the application of the analysis (e.g. logarithmic creep, section 9.2) are probably due to the inexactness of the linear assumption.

An interesting feature about eq. 4.10c should be noted. This is that the ratio of the temperature and strain rate sensitivities is independent of U or U' and so of the way in which the stress affects the activation energy.

(*f*) *Resultant Yield Stress.* All the processes which occur or are present simultaneously must add on to each other. The Peierls force is always present, although often very small. It can be argued that the other processes are most effective when occurring at an internal stress peak, so that this is also always present. If the jogs which produce point defects cannot move sideways, defect production occurs as well as intersection and all the resistances add up. The yield stress is then

$$\tau = P + S + I + J + D \tag{4.15}$$

where P is the Peierls force, S that due to the stress field of all the dislocations, I that due to intersection, J that due to production of jogs, and D

that due to production of defects. But if these jogs can move sideways the resistances arising from intersection and defect production do not necessarily add up, even though defects may be formed very frequently during a dislocation's movement. It seems that they should do so if defect production still provides the larger force and eq. 4.15 again applies. But if intersection provides the larger force, a dislocation is held up at the critical stage of intersection, that is, at the peak of the appropriate curve in Fig. 4.25, and during this time the jogs with the correct geometry for production of defects may escape doing so because the halt gives them time to move sideways, unless they chance to lie on a piece of dislocation in pure screw orientation. After the intersection has occurred, however, they presumably restrict the dislocation's speed. The yield stress is then

$$\tau_1 = P + S + I + J \qquad (4.16)$$

The temperature sensitive terms become evident at low temperature, so that in general a relation between yield stress and temperature like that in Fig. 4.8a is expected. Since P, J, and D may have different temperature sensitivities, and S and I are virtually insensitive to temperature, the curve could have several branches even in a pure metal.

   In trying to decide what proportion of the observed yield stress is contributed by each of these processes, a simplifying factor is that the dislocation pattern here in question is an annealed three-dimensional network that does not have the complicating irregularities met with in cold worked metal. The dislocation density should be fairly uniform locally as was tacitly assumed in deriving expressions for the strength of the resistance from each cause, so that these should apply directly. It can also be argued that in well-annealed metals, jogs should tend to be annealed out, indicating that D contributes little to the yield stress. It will be convenient to apply these considerations to the cubic metals. In the soft group P is evidently small and well below even the low yield stress of good crystals, for Fig. 4.1 and 4.9 show that dislocations begin to move at stresses considerably below the yield stress, which leaves as significant in this group the remaining three terms in eq. 4.15 or 4.16. The influence of temperature on the yield stress of aluminium and copper in Fig. 4.8b confirms this, as on account of difference in dislocation width J is expected to be more temperature sensitive in aluminium than in copper, and the other two terms are temperature insensitive in both. Moreover, in one investigation[69] the yield stress of aluminium single crystals was measured as a function of etch-pit density, each etch pit being taken to represent a dislocation. The shear yield stress was about $0.3Gb/x$, and thus varied with dislocation density in a way similar to that already estimated for

[69] M. Lauriente and R. B. Pond, *J.A.P.*, 1956, **27**, 950.

intersections plus internal stress. There is, however, a difficulty in accounting for so large a temperature variation as that for aluminium in Fig. 4.8b, but this is better discussed after considering strain hardening in chapter 5, as there is better data on temperature variation there.

Following the foregoing line of thought, we see that the large yield stress of the hard group is due to a large Peierls force, as being the only available source of a large yield stress, and of course the temperature and strain rate sensitivities as well as the evidence discussed in section 4.1 point also to this conclusion. There is, of course, no inconsistency in the Peierls force being large in one group and small in another because it is so sensitive to atomic structure. Because the dislocation density varies in practice as between one part of a crystal and another, all the terms in eq. 4.15 to 4.17 except P also vary. As a result, the soft group of metals effectively possess a distribution of yield stresses, which explains the gradual onset of yield in these metals. In the hard group, on the other hand, because the Peierls force is more or less constant wherever the dislocations are (doubtless varying somewhat with the ratio of edge to screw orientation and affected by elastic anisotropy), yield in these metals should be much sharper.

In the hexagonal metals, the same considerations apply to the soft glide systems as to the soft cubic metals. As regards difficult glide systems, a large Peierls force is a likely explanation, but there are two alternatives. Where nonbasal and basal glide both have a common slip direction it is possible that what is really being observed is the movement, by cross slip, of basal plane dislocations into nonbasal planes, and the cross slip stress is being measured.[60] Another possibility arises from the fact that the dislocations which do not lie in the basal plane have to intersect those which do, so that if these are more numerous the $(I + J)$ term is larger for the nonbasal dislocations. It hardly seems possible, however, that there are enough dislocations lying in the basal plane of well-annealed single crystals to produce the large shear stress for nonbasal yield usually found, for example, $1-1\frac{1}{2}$ kg/mm^2 for [$\bar{1}\bar{1}23$] ($11\bar{2}2$) slip in zinc,[38] since about 10^{10} cm/cc of basal plane dislocation would be needed.

These various sources of resistance to flow presumably also exist for twinning dislocations with, in addition, the possibility that nucleation of the twinning dislocations may require a still higher stress. The evidence for zinc mentioned in section 4.4, showing that a higher stress is needed to nucleate a twin in that metal than to make it grow, suggests that this is the situation in zinc.

5

Strain Hardening
in Pure Metals

The capacity of metals to strain-harden is the property determining the
course of stress-strain curves once plastic yielding begins and can thus be
studied through such curves.

5.1 Stress-strain Curves of Polycrystals

Once a metal yields, the elastic strain continues to increase as the stress
is increased, but is normally dwarfed by the plastic strain that takes place.
All metals harden when plastically deformed in the cold. In technical
tensile tests on polycrystalline samples, the rate of strain hardening falls
off with more and more plastic deformation, and a condition is reached in
a tensile test beyond which it no longer compensates for the decrease in
cross-sectional area. Thereafter, deformation concentrates at the place
along the specimen where this condition is first reached, and the specimen
grows steadily thinner at this place, that is, a "neck" begins to form.
At the same time the load required to continue straining begins to fall
and continues to do so until fracture occurs. Tensile stress-strain curves
for several metals are shown in Fig. 5.1, in which the nominal stress (i.e.,
the load divided by the original area) is plotted against elongation.
Several of the curves are taken up to fracture and show the eventual fall
in load. In compression tests, of course, this fall in load does not occur.

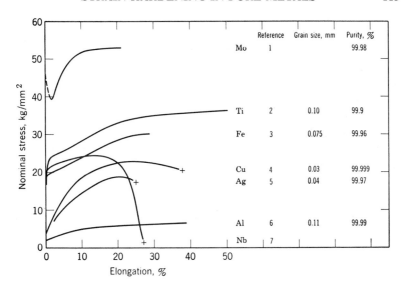

	Reference	Grain size, mm	Purity, %
Mo	1		99.98
Ti	2	0.10	99.9
Fe	3	0.075	99.96
Cu	4	0.03	99.999
Ag	5	0.04	99.97
Al	6	0.11	99.99
Nb	7		

Fig. 5.1. Nominal stress-strain curves of polycrystalline specimens. Tensile tests at room temperature. + indicates fracture.

The metals in Fig. 5.1 show very varied behaviour. Not only does the general stress level vary over a range of more than 10 : 1 but the curves have different shapes. These differences help to determine the uses of metals. For example, to be fabricated intensively as in deep drawing, a metal needs a long strain hardening range, whereas a low ratio of yield or proof stress to UTS* gives latitude for error. The ability to neck down considerably without fracture after the UTS point which comes from the possession of a large true fracture stress† provides a safeguard in operations involving tensile stress. On the other hand, a load-bearing piece needs a high yield or proof stress. Steel is the most used metal because

* Ultimate tensile stress, the peak stress in a diagram such as Fig. 5.1 of nominal stress against nominal strain, beyond which necking begins.

† Actual load divided by cross-sectional area at the place in the "necked" region where fracture occurs.

[1] J. H. Bechtold and H. Scott, *Metal Progress*, 1952, **61**, 82.
[2] F. C. Holden, D. N. Williams, W. E. Riley, and R. I. Jafee, Battelle Memorial Institute, Titanium Metallurgical Laboratory Report, No. 30, 1956.
[3] W. P. Rees, B. E. Hopkins, and H. R. Tipler, *J.I.S.I.*, 1951, **169**, 157.
[4] R. P. Carreker and W. R. Hibbard, *Acta Met.*, 1953, **1**, 654.
[5] R. P. Carreker, *T.A.I.M.E.*, 1957, **209**, 112.
[6] J. A. Dorn, P. Pietrokowsky and T. E. Tietz, *T.A.I.M.E.*, 1950, **188**, 933.
[7] E. T. Wessel, *T.A.I.M.E.*, 1957, **209**, 930.

it is the cheapest which has this property. At the same time, a UTS substantially higher than the yield or proof stress gives insurance against fracture; that is, the ratio of "yield" (or proof stress) to UTS should again not be too high.

Although the properties mentioned, together with elongation and reduction of area,* are those most often quoted from tensile tests and are used in engineering specifications, they are not simple properties since each is the resultant of more than one factor. For example, the UTS depends on how steep strain hardening is, and it and the uniform elongation† depend on how long strain hardening continues steeply enough to

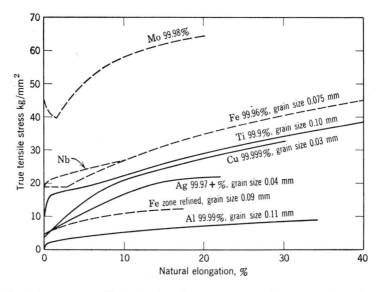

Fig. 5.2.   Curves of Fig. 5.1 replotted as true stress against natural elongation.

offset the accompanying reduction in section.   The value of these properties is that they provide a guide to service behaviour.   The two basic factors which completely determine the stress-strain curve after yielding are the strain-hardening behaviour and how soon fracture occurs.

In seeking reasons for the different strain-hardening behaviours in Fig. 5.1, it is helpful to replot the curves as *true stress*, that is, the load at any elongation divided by the cross sectional area at that elongation, against *natural strain* (also called *true strain* and *natural elongation*); the

---

* By this is always meant the reduction in area at the place in the necked region where the sectional area is reduced most.

† The "uniform elongation" is the elongation outside the necked region.

natural strain ϵ is defined as $\epsilon = \int_{l_0}^{l} \dfrac{dl}{l}$ where l is the actual length of the

specimen and l_0 is the original length, so that $E_{nat} \% = 100 \ln \left(1 + \dfrac{E}{100} \right)$

where E is the ordinary elongation.   Figure 5.2 shows the curves of Fig. 5.1 replotted as true stress against natural strain, and exhibits a similar wide range of behaviour.   Now, it is evident from the discussion in section 4.7 that the strength of all the dislocation interactions on which strain hardening can depend varies linearly as the shear modulus.   Other things being equal, therefore, the strain-hardening rates of two metals

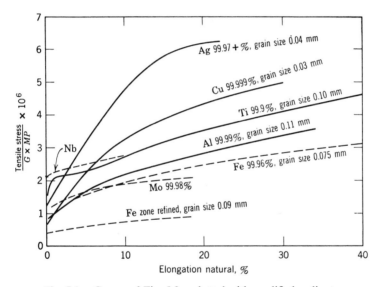

Fig. 5.3.   Curves of Fig. 5.2 replotted with modified ordinate.

will be proportional to their shear moduli.   Consequently, differences in Fig. 5.2 which are due to modulus differences can be eliminated by re-plotting against an ordinate of true stress/shear modulus.   It is also evident from sections 4.7 and 5.4 that temperature affects the strength of some dislocation interactions.   The correct way to eliminate temperature effects is to obtain data at or close to absolute zero.   In lieu of such data, an approximate alternative is to divide the ordinate in Fig. 5.2 by the absolute melting temperature.   Both adjustments are made in Fig. 5.3, and it will be seen that the ordinate range is compressed and the order is changed.   When the effects due to modulus and temperature are elimi-nated, or nearly eliminated, as in Fig. 5.3, the differences between the metals are not what they were before this was done.   Molybdenum is at the top in Fig. 5.2 but at the bottom in Fig. 5.3; silver is at the top in Fig. 5.3 but near the bottom in Fig. 5.2.   The differences in Fig. 5.3 do, however, reveal some system.   The three bcc metals, alpha iron, molybdenum, and niobium all strain harden at approximately the same rate (it is the slope of the curves that is here in question, not their height), which is less steep than that of any of the fcc metals.   The latter differ from the bcc metals in varying considerably among themselves.   Titanium, the only hexagonal metal included, strain hardens at a rate similar to that of aluminium, which has the slowest strain-hardening rate of the fcc metals included. As modulus and temperature effects have been largely eliminated, these differences must be caused primarily by the mechanism of strain hardening itself, and a theory of strain hardening should account for them.

5.2   Strain Hardening in Single Crystals*

If single crystals are used, by choice of orientation it can be determined

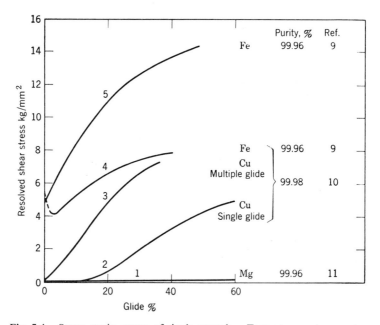

Fig. 5.4.   Stress-strain curves of single crystals.   Tests at room temperature.

* A full review of strain hardening in fcc and hexagonal metals is given in Ref. 8.
[8] L. M. Clarebrough and M. E. Hargreaves, *Prog. in Metal Phys.*, 1959, **8**, 1.
[9] B. Edmondson, *P.R.S.*, 1961, **A264**, 176.
[10] J. Diehl, *Z. Metallk.*, 1956, **47**, 331.
[11] H. Conrad and W. B. Robertson, *T.A.I.M.E.*, 1957, **209**, 503.

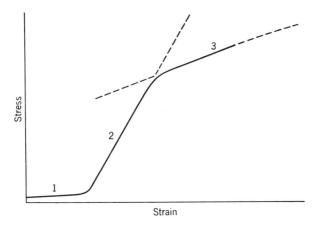

Fig. 5.5a. The three parts of the generic stress-strain curve of a single crystal.

which slip systems shall operate. Such experiments have shown that strain hardening is very slow unless there is slip on several systems. Figure 5.4, showing several stress-strain curves obtained from single crystals, illustrates this. Curves 1 and 2 show the slow initial strain hardening (easy glide) in hexagonal and fcc metals when oriented for single slip, that is for slip in one direction on a single plane. Curve 3 shows the more rapid hardening when oriented for multiple slip. Multiple slip eventually occurs also along curve 2 and causes the curve to bend upward and become approximately parallel to curve 3. Curves 4 and 5 show a similar difference—for the bcc metal alpha iron—between crystals oriented so that relatively simple slip (curve 4) and relatively complex slip (curve 5) would be expected, although, as will be explained, the detailed interpretation of these curves is somewhat different from that which applies to the fcc metals. The influence of multiple slip on hardening has also been shown by first straining a single crystal to activate one slip system, then straining in another direction to activate a second slip system, and finally straining in the original direction. The slip on the second system causes a relatively large increase in the stress needed to continue flow in the original direction. Such experiments have been made on fcc (aluminium[12]) and hexagonal (zinc[13]) metals.

All these results are consistent with the generic stress strain curve in Fig. 5.5a, in which three stages are distinguished: stage 1, consisting of easy glide, which only occurs if the crystal is initially oriented to favour single slip; stage 2, in which strain hardening is rapid, whose length varies

[12] D. B. Holt, *Acta Met.*, 1959, **7**, 446.
[13] E. H. Edwards and J. Washburn, *T.A.I.M.E.*, 1954, **200**, 1239.

greatly with temperature (section 5.4) and metal, and which has usually, but not always,[14] been found to be linear in a plot of resolved shear stress against resolved shear strain; and stage 3, in which the rate of strain hardening declines.

The sequence of events which leads from one stage to the next is as follows. In stage 1 there is slip on only one system, and strain hardening is therefore weak. This stage is longer the thinner the crystal, which implies that in this stage many of the dislocations run out of the crystal.[15] However, even in crystals oriented for single slip the rotation of the crystal axes that occurs during straining, together with accidental local stresses where dislocations occasionally get stuck, eventually causes slip on other systems, and stage 2 begins. Eventually, stage 2 gives place to stage 3. Since rapid hardening in stage 2 is due to interaction between dislocations belonging to different systems, it is believed that the slower hardening denoting stage 3 is due to the fact that at sufficiently high stress dislocations can cross slip, so that, on the one hand, they avoid doing things which provoke a resistance to flow such as intersecting other dislocations in the original slip path or collecting into a group that has a large stress field (e.g. a regular piled up group) and, on the other hand, strain hardening is positively reduced by one dislocation moving toward another dislocation of opposite sign and, for example, producing a cutting intersection (section 2.1i). Much experimental evidence confirms this interpretation that stage 3 coincides with the onset of cross slip, namely, observations on slip bands (section 5.9), the influence of temperature (section 5.4), and the influence of stacking fault energy (see below).

With fcc metals, all three stages can be experimentally realised in a test on one specimen. Examples are shown in Fig. 5.10. In stage 1 the strain-hardening coefficient is found to be variable as well as small, and ranges from $G/10^4$ to $G/10^3$ (G is the shear modulus). The higher values are probably the result of small amounts of multiple slip that are likely to occur in practice during stage 1. In stage 2 the strain-hardening coefficient is not only large but seems also to be much the same from one metal to another when expressed as a fraction of the shear modulus. It is close to $0.004 \times$ shear modulus for a number of fcc crystals on which experiments have been made, and appears to be independent of temperature and impurity content. It varies with orientation, however, by a factor[14] of about 2 (e.g., compare curves 2 and 3 in Fig. 5.4). For crystals pulled in tension, and representing the tension axis by a point in the stereographic triangle, the rate of strain hardening in stage 2 is at its largest when this point is near the [100]–[111] side of the triangle and

[14] W. F. Hosford, R. L. Fleisher, and W. A. Backofen, *Acta Met.*, 1960, **8**, 187.

[15] H. Suzuki, S. Ikeda, and S. Takeuchi, *J. Phys. Soc. Japan*, 1956, **11**, 382.

particularly if the point is close to one of these corners, and at its smallest when the point approaches the [110] corner.   In stage 3, strain hardening is approximately half as steep as in stage 2, but probably declines further at high strains.

Stage 3 is especially important because most of the stress-strain curve of a polycrystal belongs to this stage, particularly at room temperature, and consequently the differences between the strain-hardening rates of different metals in polycrystalline form noted in section 5.1 reflect principally the differences between this stage in the different metals.   In Fig. 5.8, which shows stress-strain curves on polycrystals at different temperatures, the point A indicates when stage 3 commences in a single crystal; that is, the stress at A is that at which stage 3 starts in a single crystal of the same metal.   At most, with copper only the first few per cent of deformation are not in stage 3, and with aluminium practically the entire stress-strain curve lies in stage 3 at room temperature.   The engineering behaviour of pure metals is thus largely determined by the processes occurring in stage 3, that is, by the strain hardening due to multiple slip and by the cross slip which mitigates it in stage 3.   Strain-hardening mechanisms are discussed in section 5.10.   Here may be noted the connection discussed earlier between stacking fault energy, cross slip, and stage 3.   For example, if the stacking fault energy is taken to be twice the energy of a coherent twin boundary, the stacking fault energy in aluminium[16] is about 200 ergs/cm², in copper[17] 20 ergs/cm², and in silver still lower, to judge by the commonness of annealing twins in silver.   The ease of cross slip should decrease in the same order.   Stage 2 is therefore expected to increase in length, and the rate of strain hardening in stage 3 to decline less, at a given temperature, in the order aluminium, copper, silver.   These expectations are borne out by experiment.   This order is also that of increasing steepness of the polycrystalline stress-strain curves in Fig. 5.3. Evidently the steepness of the stress-strain curve of a polycrystal depends mainly on the steepness of stage 3 hardening but also to some extent on the length of stage 2, and both these depend on the stacking fault energy. In this way, the differences in strain hardening among the fcc metals noted in section 5.1 are ascribed to differences in the ease of cross slip.

There are not such extensive data for other lattices as for the fcc. However, in hexagonal metals which slip on more than one plane, the three stages can be distinguished.[18]   In stage 1 the rate of strain hardening

[16] R. L. Fullman, *Imperfections in Nearly Perfect Crystals*, John Wiley and Sons, New York, 1952, p. 336.

[17] M. C. Inman and A. R. Khan, *Phil. Mag.*, 1961, **6**, 937.

[18] G. A. Geach, R. A. Jeffery, and E. Smith, Associated Electrical Industries Report A.1096, 1960.

is weaker than with fcc metals, at least as far as those hexagonal metals that only slip on the basal plane at room temperature are concerned; for example, in magnesium it is only 0.4 kg/mm^2 per 100% shear. In stage 2 the rate of strain hardening is similar to that with fcc metals; for example, in rhenium, which slips on other planes besides the basal plane at room temperature, the coefficient in stage 2 at room temperature is about 0.004G as with fcc metals.[18] The hexagonal metals thus behave in much the same way as the fcc metals.

There is no good reason for doubting that a similar behaviour underlies the strain hardening of the bcc metals, but nevertheless the three-stage hardening curve has not been experimentally realised in these metals. A detailed study[19] of iron has revealed several complications which obscure or impede its full development. The most important of these complications is that cross slip occurs so readily in iron that stage 2 is nonexistent at room temperature. When this situation arises with an fcc metal, stage 2 can be made prominent by lowering the temperature (section 5.4), but this recourse is of no avail with iron. Lowering the temperature to $-80°C$ has no effect, and at lower temperatures twinning intervenes to prevent the study of strain hardening by slip per se. It is also interesting to note that raising the temperature to 400°C has no influence on the rate of strain hardening. Cross slip evidently occurs very readily over the whole range from $-80°C$ to 400°C. Another complication is that "pencil glide" occurs in iron: that is to say, glide occurs in the [111] direction but on numerous planes providing they contain a [111] direction. Pencil glide is discussed again in the next paragraph. The significant feature of it in the present connection is that it has the effect of preserving the original slip bands as bands in which glide is relatively easy. At the same time, these bands seriously hinder slip on other intersecting planes. Such a situation impedes the development of a stage 2 characterised by simultaneous slip on several systems.

Possibly as a result of pencil glide, a third complication arises. A crystal necessarily changes its orientation relative to the stress axis as it is deformed[20]; it "rotates." With iron single crystals there are ranges of initial orientation for which different parts of the crystal commence by slipping on different systems and rotate about different axes during straining, so that the crystal breaks up into roughly defined subgrains. The steepest strain hardening occurs for those initial orientations which result in this effect. The influence of orientation is therefore somewhat different from that with fcc metals, as intimated in connection with the curves for iron in Fig. 5.4. A similar kind of breaking up of a crystal is

[19] B. Jaoul and D. Gonzalez, *J. Mech. Phys. Solids*, 1961, **9**, 16.
[20] E. Schmidt and W. Boas, *Crystal Plasticity*, F. A. Hughes, London, 1950.

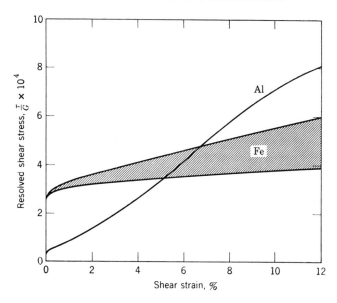

Fig. 5.5b. Stress-strain curves of Fe and Al single crystals at a temperature equal to 0.16 × melting temperature, that is, 25°C for Fe and −120°C for Al (Ref. 19).

also known in fcc metals,[21] but its effect there is overshadowed by that of multiple slip.

A crystal slips initially in the direction in which the resolved shear stress is largest, and of course rotates as it does so. Iron crystals continue rotating well past the point at which the resolved stress favours another direction without this direction coming into prominent operation[19]—a behaviour known as "overshooting." Pencil glide may favour over-shooting in the following way. During pencil glide dislocations travelling in opposite directions on different slip planes will intersect. They always make repulsive intersections, which are relatively weak (section 4.7). No attractive intersections of oppositely moving dislocations can occur when the dislocations must have Burgers vectors along the same direction. Consequently, intersection hardening is relatively weak along the existing slip bands. Slip on other systems crossing these bands can, however, make attractive junctions in them. They therefore hinder slip that tries to cross them, whereas the bands themselves remain relatively easy paths for slip.

The relatively weak strain hardening in bcc metals has already been discussed. Figure 5.5b shows stress-strain curves for iron and aluminium

[21] J. Sawkill and R. W. K. Honeycombe *Acta Met.*, 1954, **2**, 854.

at equal fractions of their melting temperatures and brings out the weakness of iron particularly clearly.   In this figure, the shaded band shown for iron indicates the influence of orientation, the upper edge of the band corresponding to the breaking up described earlier.   The strain-hardening rate varies from $G/1000$ at the bottom of the band to $G/400$ at the top, compared with about $G/250$ for fcc metals.   Three reasons can now be seen for the relatively weak strain hardening of iron: the ease of cross slip, the weakness of attractive junctions in the bcc metals, and the occurrence of pencil glide.   In addition, it may be that the contribution to hardening from point defect production differs as between bcc and fcc metals.

5.3   Comparison of Single and Polycrystals: Effect of Grain Size

Since plastic strains are so much larger than elastic ones, once plastic strain commences elastic anisotropy gradually ceases to be a significant cause of irregular stress from one grain to another.   New effects arise essentially due to plastic anisotropy, and cause grain boundaries to influence strain hardening in several ways.   They cause the steep initial barrier hardening described in section 4.1, which arises because slip cannot continue uninterruptedly across a grain boundary into the next grain. They also introduce a complexity effect, which has two aspects.   In the first place multiple slip has to take place in nearly every grain if each grain is to remain coherent with its neighbours.   To enable each grain to match the deformation of its neighbours along grain boundaries, slip on a minimum of five systems is necessary in theory,[22, 23] and six have been observed in practice.[24]   In addition, the individual grains of a polycrystal are stressed in a rather irregular way, unlike the carefully arranged uniform stressing applied to single crystals, for each grain is forced to deform unevenly owing to the fact that it is faced by a different grain across each boundary.   The resulting very heterogeneous deformation across each grain is attested by the varying local elongation found,[25, 26] and by the resistance to deformation sometimes seen near the boundaries of bicrystal.[27]   This influence of a grain boundary of enforcing complex slip takes longer to spread across large grains than across small ones.   In this way the complexity effect introduces a grain size dependence of strain hardening, which seems usually to be weaker than the grain size dependence arising from barrier hardening but extends to higher strains.   This

[22] R. von Mises, *Z. angew., Math. Mech.*, 1928, **8**, 161.

[23] G. I. Taylor, *J.I.M.*, 1938, **62**, 307.

[24] W. Boas and G. J. Ogilvie, *Acta Met.*, 1954, **2**, 655.

[25] W. Boas and M. E. Hargreaves, *P.R.S.*, 1948, **A193**, 89.

[26] V. M. Urie and H. L. Wain, *J.I.M.*, 1952, **81**, 153.

[27] H. C. H. Carpenter and C. F. Elam, *P.R.S.*, 1921, **100**, 329.

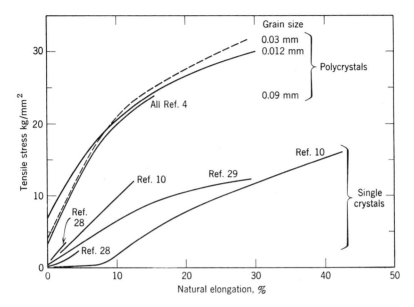

Fig. 5.6. Comparison between stress-strain curves of single crystals and of poly-crystals at room temperature. Cu (99.98–99.999% pure) tested at room tempera-ture.

probably explains why grain size may affect the rate of strain hardening up to several per cent elongation.

After several per cent of elongation, therefore, the stress-strain curves of single crystals in which multiple slip is occurring and of polycrystals should run parallel when stress and strain are expressed in comparable ways, although in practice the stress-strain curve of a polycrystal tends to be steeper than that of the corresponding single crystal, probably because the slip is more complicated in the polycrystal than in the single crystal. Typical comparisons between single and polycrystals are contained in Fig. 5.6 and 5.7 and show approximate parallelism; cases of strict paral-lelism have also been reported.[30] Consequently, past the region where grain size influences the rate of strain hardening, there is not much difference between these rates in single and polycrystals. Thus, just beyond this region the rate of strain hardening in fcc polycrystals is often about $G/40$,[30] or somewhat higher.[31] Allowing for the fact that the average resolved shear stress on a slip plane is rather less than half the

[28] F. D. Rosi, *T.A.I.M.E.*, 1954, **200**, 1009.

[29] T. H. Blewitt, R. R. Coltman and J. K. Redman, *J.A.P.*, 1957, **28**, 651.

[30] B. Jaoul, *J. Mech. Phys. of Solids*, 1957, **5**, 95.

[31] P. Feltham and J. D. Meakin, *Phil. Mag.*, 1957, **2**, 1237.

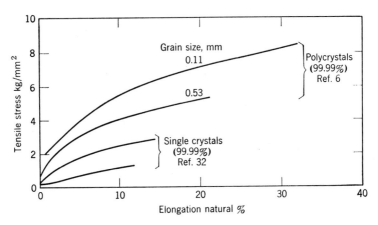

Fig. 5.7. Comparison between stress-strain curves of single crystals and of poly-crystals at room temperature. Al tested at room temperature.

applied tensile stress, and the average shear strain parallel to a slip plane is rather more than twice the tensile elongation, we see that this is equivalent to the rate of shear strain hardening ($0.004G$) found in stage 2 of fcc metals. In the hexagonal metal rhenium the rate of strain hardening is also approximately $G/40$[33] in a tensile test. Presumably something like this value is general for all fcc and hexagonal metals, with a rather lower value applying to bcc metals.[34]

A simple extension of these considerations makes understandable the fact that the stress-strain curve of a fine grained metal is steeper than that of coarse grained material at low strain, and parallel to the latter at high strain. Fine grain size also produces rather bigger reductions in area and UTS values; evidently fracture is easier in coarse grained metal. Table 5.1 illustrates these points.[35]

Table 5.1

Influence of Grain Size on Tensile Properties of Copper

Grain Size	0.5% Proof Stress kg/mm²	UTS kg/mm²	RA %
0.03 mm	10.4	24.8	77
0.15 mm	9.3	23.4	62

[32] K. Lücke and H. Lange, *Z. Metallk.*, 1952, **43**, 55.
[33] A. T. Churchman, *T.A.I.M.E.*, 1960, **218**, 262.
[34] B. Jaoul, *J. Mech. Phys. Solids*, 1961, **9**, 69.
[35] L. M. Clarebrough, M. E. Hargreaves, and M. H. Loretto, *Acta Met.*, 1958, **6**, 725.

5.4 Effect of Temperature

In fcc metals temperature has a big effect on strain hardening, even when the temperature is too low for thermal recovery to play a part. The stress-strain curves of polycrystalline specimens of copper and aluminium at different temperatures shown in Fig. 5.8 demonstrate this, for at $-253°C$ the stress-strain curves are appreciably steeper than at room temperature, and in these metals thermal recovery of mechanical properties does not occur at room temperature or below.   The effect of temperature varies among the fcc metals; for example, lowering the temperature from room temperature to $-253°C$ has the effect of raising the stress-strain curve of aluminium more than that of copper.   However, at $1.6°K$, strain hardening in aluminium polycrystals is effective enough to raise the true fracture stress to 160 kg/mm².[37]   On the other hand, at temperatures high enough for thermal recovery to occur during straining, the effective rate of strain hardening is much reduced; the curve in Fig. 5.8 for copper tested at 400°C illustrates this.

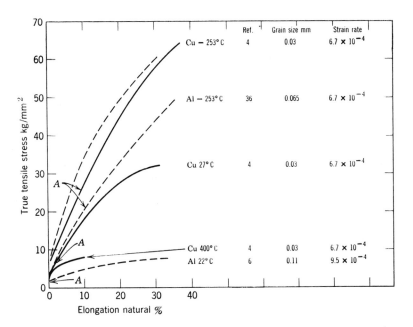

Fig. 5.8. Effect of temperature in tensile tests on Al and Cu. *A* marks the stress at which stage 3 starts in single crystals.   The top dashed curve is obtained from the curve for Al at $-253°C$ by multiplying the ordinate by G_{Cu}/G_{Al}.

[36] R. P. Carreker and W. R. Hibbard, *T.A.I.M.E.*, 1957, **209**, 1157.

[37] O. V. Klyavin and A. V. Stepanov, *Fiz. Metallov i Metallovdenie*, 1959, **8**, 274.

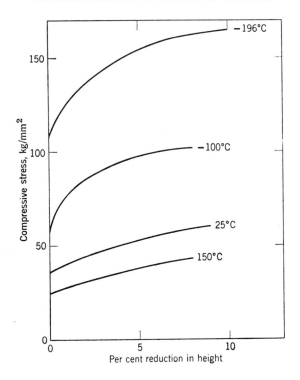

Fig. 5.9. Effect of temperature on stress-strain curve of Mo. Compression tests (Ref. 38).

For bcc metals temperature has a smaller effect on strain hardening,[19, 34] although comparison between different temperatures is not as complete as with fcc metals because the bcc metals generally deform only a small amount at low temperature before breaking, and also are liable to twin. However, the stress-strain curves of polycrystalline molybdenum in Fig. 5.9 show that with this metal the rate of strain hardening rises relatively slowly with decrease in temperature, particularly at the higher strains. As is characteristic of bcc metals, in Fig. 5.9 the strain hardening increment is superimposed on a large bodily lifting of the whole stress-strain curve by an amount equal to the increase in yield stress, which is further evidence for the large Peierls force in these metals (chapter 4). It might be added here that over a certain temperature range (100–300°C), strain hardening in iron *increases* with temperature[39] (e.g. see Fig. 5.11), but

[38] G. A. Alers, R. W. Armstrong, and J. H. Bechtold, *T.A.I.M.E.*, 1958, **212**, 523.
[39] A. W. Sleeswyk, *Acta Met.*, 1958, **6**, 598.

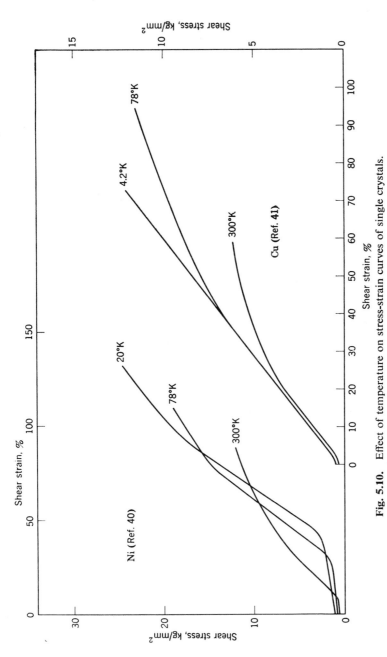

Fig. 5.10. Effect of temperature on stress-strain curves of single crystals.

[40] P. Haasen, *Phil. Mag.*, 1958, **3**, 284.
[41] T. H. Blewitt, R. R. Coltman, and J. K. Redman, Conference on Defects in Crystalline Solids. *Phys. Soc.*, 1955, p. 369.

this is believed to be connected with the "blue brittle" effect, and if so is not a feature of pure iron per se. A similar behaviour has been found in tantalum.[42]

In hexagonal metals like zinc, which at room temperature slips easily only on the basal plane, strain hardening is rapid in polycrystalline specimens in the region of room temperature and below because the "hard" nonbasal slip systems, and also twinning, are forced to operate to retain coherence along grain boundaries. At higher temperatures, where the nonbasal slip systems operate more easily (Fig. 4.10b), strain hardening is slower. Most of the effect of temperature on strain hardening is due to this effect, and it is not yet certain what the effect is of temperature on strain hardening by multiple glide per se. Titanium is a hexagonal metal which slips on more than one plane at room temperature, but twins fairly readily at low temperature, and this again complicates any attempt to determine the effect of temperature on the rate of strain hardening caused by multiple glide.

Experiments on single crystals of fcc metals explain the main effect of temperature in the fcc metals themselves very simply in terms of the three stage hardening curve of Fig. 5.5. The influence of temperature on the stress-strain curves of copper and nickel single crystals is shown in Fig. 5.10. The two main results are that as the temperature is lowered, stage 2 is prolonged to higher stresses and the average slope in stage 3 is increased, both of which are ascribable to the increasing difficulty of producing cross slip the lower the temperature. As these two results clearly account for the effect of temperature on the stress-strain curves of fcc polycrystals, they help to show that cross slip is the determining factor in the temperature dependence of strain hardening below temperatures at which thermal recovery occurs.

Probably the same considerations apply to hexagonal metals except that as already pointed out they are overlaid by other factors. It would be reasonable to expect them to apply also to bcc metals, but it is not yet certain that they do. The rather weak effect of temperature on strain hardening in molybdenum was mentioned earlier. In iron it seems to be still weaker.[43] This is illustrated by the stress-strain curves of single crystals of iron taken at different temperatures shown in Fig. 5.11. Below 0°C the rate of strain hardening actually declines, although temperature sensitivity in the yield-locking mechanism (chapter 6) might be responsible for the appearance of a decline by augmenting the yield stress. So far these results can fit the cross slip explanation which applies to the fcc

[42] J. H. Bechtold, *Acta Met.*, 1955, **3**, 249.

[43] W. P. Rees, B. E. Hopkins, and H. R. Tipler, *J.I.S.I.*, 1951, **169**, 157.

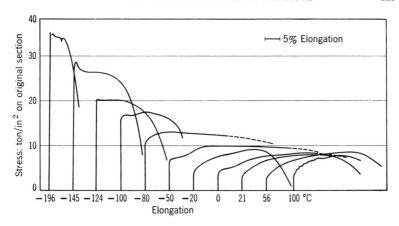

Fig. 5.11. Effect of temperature on stress-strain curves of Fe single crystals. The steeper strain hardening above 50°C is probably a strain-ageing effect connected with blue brittleness (N.P.L. Data).

metals, for the absence of a really marked effect of temperature on the strain hardening of bcc metals would of course result if cross slip occurs readily under all conditions. At the same time, a small difference between molybdenum and iron in their ability to cross slip could be held to account for the larger effect of temperature on molybdenum than on iron. Whether the relative difficulty of cross slip in iron and molybdenum actually fits this explanation is not known.

The effect of temperature on stage 1 hardening is worth noting. In Fig. 5.10, lowering the temperature lengthens stage 1, but the actual rate of strain hardening in this stage is rather insensitive to temperature, at least in nickel. A similar insensitivity also characterises basal glide in hexagonal close packed metals. The strain hardening of magnesium in basal glide is shown as a function of temperature in Fig. 5.12. Although the drop between 0 and 100°C is believed to be due to thermal recovery, the horizontal part below 0°C shows that, apart from this, temperature has a negligible effect on strain-hardening rate during easy glide. Cadmium[44] and zinc[45] give similar results. Probably, therefore, this insensitivity is a general characteristic of easy glide.

Stress-strain curves at different temperatures such as those in Fig. 5.8–5.11 involve two factors, namely the effect of temperature on the flow stress of a given strained structure, and the difference in structure produced at different temperatures by a given strain. To separate these effects,

[44] W. Boas and E. Schmid, *Z. Physik*, 1930, **61**, 767.
[45] W. Fahrenhorst and E. Schmid, *Z. Physik*, 1930, **64**, 845.

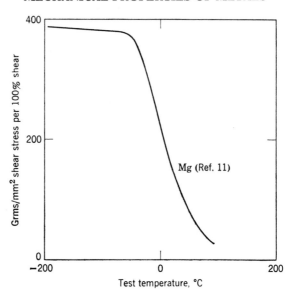

Fig. 5.12. Strain hardening in Mg. Specimen in the form of a single crystal oriented for basal slip.

specimens have been strained at one temperature, the temperature changed, and the flow stress redetermined by making a small strain at this temperature, the original temperature reapplied and the specimen restrained. The cycle is repeated several times up to quite a large strain. These experiments have been performed on fcc and bcc metals, with different results.

With the fcc metals the ratio of the flow stress at two temperatures is virtually constant over a wide range of strain after the first few per cent of deformation. In one investigation[46] it was found to settle down in the first 5% of elongation to a figure that remained practically constant up to the experimental limit of about 53% strain, the constant ratio therefore probably characterising mainly stage 3. This result is only true if the flow stress at each temperature is divided by the elastic modulus at that temperature; otherwise it would not be sensible. The ratio depends on the temperatures chosen and, since it is independent of the amount of strain above some minimum, it can be usefully plotted as in Fig. 5.13a and b. Here the modulus-corrected flow stress at temperature T divided by that at $0°K$ (Fig. 5.13a) or that at $4.2°K$ (Fig. 5.13b) is plotted against T. (The flow stress at $0°K$ was deduced by linear interpolation in Fig. 5.13a.) To give some indication of the breadth of test

[46] A. H. Cottrell and R. J. Stokes, *P.R.S.*, 1955, **A233**, 17.

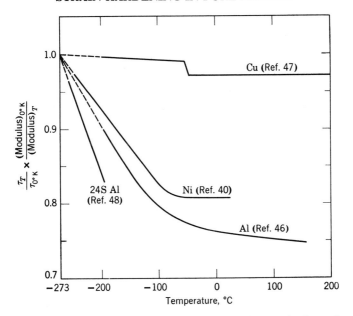

Fig. 5.13a. Effect of temperature on the flow stress of a given strained state for some fcc metals. Single crystals used except for 24S Al.

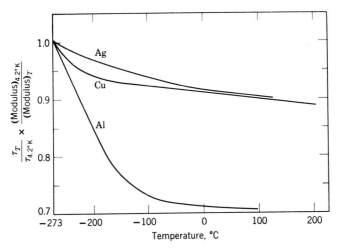

Fig. 5.13b. Effect of temperature on the flow stress of a given strained state for some fcc metals. Both single and polycrystals of Al were tested, and the results fell on the same curve. Only single crystals of Ag and Cu were tested (Ref. 49).

[47] M. J. Makin, *Phil. Mag.*, 1958, **3**, 287.
[48] Z. S. Basinski, *P.R.S.*, 1957, **A240**, 229.
[49] Z. S. Basinski, *Phil. Mag.*, 1959, **4**, 393.

conditions covered in these experiments, it might be mentioned that for the experiments of Fig. 5.13a the stresses applied ranged up to about 3 kg/mm² shear stress for copper, about 10 kg/mm² for nickel, about 2 kg/mm² for aluminium single crystals, and about 20 kg/mm² tensile for the commercial aluminium polycrystal.

Three conclusions to be drawn from these figures are:

1. For none of the metals tested is the true temperature variation of the flow stress very great. Other similar measurements on polycrystalline copper and nickel[50] give the same result. Consequently, nearly all the effect of temperature on the strain hardening curve of fcc metals arises because a different worked structure, for example, a different dislocation density, develops at different temperatures.

2. The flow stress varies less with temperature for copper than for the other metals shown.

3. The variation is roughly similar for pure aluminium single crystals and for commercial aluminium polycrystals (24 S aluminium) requiring stresses of the order of ten times greater, which suggests that grain boundaries and impurities do not alter the nature but only the intensity of the cold worked structure.

With bcc metals it is not the ratio of the flow stresses at different temperatures that is unaffected by the amount of strain, but the difference between these stresses, and this difference varies smoothly with temperature.[51, 52] These conclusions are illustrated in Fig. 5.14. Points are plotted for iron at three different strains, and all fall on the same curve. To show that the behaviour is a property of the pure iron itself, results are included for iron containing 0.0027%C and for the same iron after being decarburised in wet hydrogen; both sets fall practically on the same curve. According to Fig. 5.14, the flow stress of a bcc metal is much more sensitive to temperature than that of any of the fcc metals in Fig. 5.13. In Fig. 5.14 the temperature sensitivity is 30 kg/mm² per 100°C, or approximately 15 kg/mm² per 100°C in terms of shear stress. It can be deduced from Fig. 5.13a and 5.10 that the temperature sensitivity of the shear flow stress of nickel at large strain, where it is greatest, is only 3 kg/mm² per 100°C. The interpretation of Fig. 5.14 is of course that already foreshadowed by other results; namely that the yield stress rises steeply enough as the temperature is reduced to overshadow any effect of temperature on the already rather weak strain hardening. The experi-

[50] J. H. Frye, J. L. Scott, and J. W. Woods, *T.A.I.M.E.*, 1957, **209**, 708.
[51] Z. S. Basinski and J. W. Christian, *Australian J. Phys.*, 1960, **13**, 299.
[52] H. Conrad and G. Schoeck, *Acta Met.*, 1960, **8**, 791.

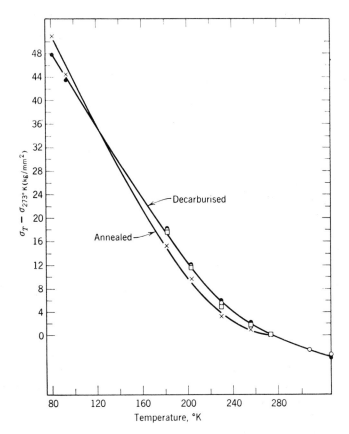

Fig. 5.14. Temperature dependence of flow stress of iron. ● represent points taken at 2% strain; ○ represent points taken at 10% strain; □ represent points taken at 20% strain (Ref. 51).

mental results[52] make it clear that the latter effect is not more than 10% of the change in yield stress between room temperature and 90°K.

Similar experiments have also been made on magnesium single crystals.[11] They behaved like the bcc metals in kind but not in degree. In the temperature range −105 to −70°C, where the strain hardening was constant (Fig. 5.12), the change in flow stress with temperature was equal to the change in the initial yield stress, but the magnitude of the change was much smaller than in Fig. 5.14.

5.5 Effect of Speed

As pointed out in connection with eq. 4.10c, there is a close connection between increasing the speed of straining and reducing the temperature,

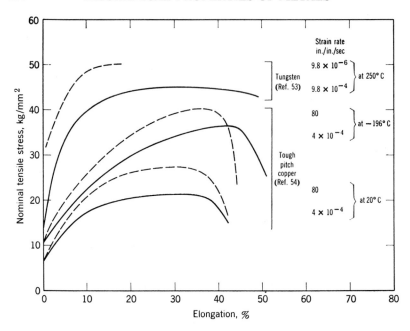

Fig. 5.15. Effect of strain rate on stress-strain curves. Polycrystalline specimens.

even at temperatures too low for thermal recovery to occur during straining, since the slip processes themselves are aided by thermal agitation. This connection is well borne out by experiment.

Figure 5.15 shows for copper and tungsten the general effect of straining at increasing rates. Whereas strain hardening is intensified in copper, with tungsten strain hardening itself is not much affected by speed at the temperature of these tests—250°C. The whole stress-strain curve of tungsten, however, is lifted by an amount roughly equal to the increase in the yield stress. Results with molybdenum are similar.[55] These results clearly parallel those for the effect of temperature. It again looks as though in the body centred cubic metals there is simply an increased frictional resistance to slip at high speeds. It is, therefore, to be expected that increasing the speed of straining will tend to increase the UTS and perhaps the elongation, especially in the case of fcc metals. Experiments on a variety of metals[56] (at straining speeds several times faster than the fastest in Fig. 5.15) bear out this expectation, showing that the

[53] J. H. Bechtold, *T.A.I.M.E.*, 1956, **206**, 142.
[54] H. G. Baron, *J.I.S.I.*, 1956, **182**, p. 354.
[55] R. P. Carreker and R. W. Guard, *T.A.I.M.E.*, 1956, **206**, 178.
[56] D. S. Clark and D. S. Wood, *A.S.M.*, 1950, **42**, 45.

UTS is usually increased by amounts ranging from a few per cent to 40%, and the elongation is also generally increased by amounts varying from 5% to 20%.

At still higher speeds, reaching to explosive loading, complications enter because plastic flow only occurs when the propagating elastic wave arrives and the deformed shape is not always that which would be produced by a similar static load but depends on the shape of the wave front.[57] A remarkable effect has been found to occur[58, 59] when a metal is explosively loaded with very high pressures. Without the dimensions being changed significantly, the hardness can be raised to a level equivalent to severe strain hardening. For example, in such experiments an explosive load of 4200 kg/mm² resulted in the hardness of annealed copper being raised from 54 to 132 units and an explosive load of 6000 kg/mm² resulted in the hardness of Armco iron being raised from 95 to 284. For comparison, 95% reduction by ordinary cold work raises the hardness to 129 and 259 respectively. Metallographic examination showed that twin-like markings were present in copper as well as in iron after explosive loading. An exceedingly high rate of strain therefore produces a situation inside the metal that is different from the ordinary one. This perhaps comes about because dislocations exhibit a relativistic effect whereby resistance to their movement rises without limit as their speed approaches a critical value near to that of sound in the metal. Consequently, beyond a certain point it is only possible to increase the strain rate by increasing the number of dislocations, and the ordinary forces due to stress fields, intersection etc. are relatively unimportant compared with the relativistic effect.

Adiabatic heating becomes significant at the fastest speeds (8000%/sec) used in Fig. 5.15. This effect is particularly marked beyond the UTS, because heating by straining is then concentrated in a small volume. In one experiment the temperature rise in the necked region was estimated to be 200°C. Such a temperature rise softens the material and causes the load-elongation curve to fall steeply. This effect should set in at slower speeds at very low temperature because the specific heat is small at very low temperature.

As it is with changing the temperature, so the effect on the flow stress of varying the speed is resolvable into two components, namely, the true effect for a given cold worked structure and the effect of the speed on the cold worked structure. Experiments have been made in which the true

[57] J. S. Rhinehart and J. Pearson, Behaviour of Metals under Impulsive loads, *A.S.M.*, 1954.

[58] C. S. Smith, *T.A.I.M.E.*, 1958, **212**, 574.

[59] A. S. Appleton, G. E. Dieter, and M. B. Bever, *T.A.I.M.E.*, 1961, **221**, 90.

effect has been separated out by suddenly altering the strain rate during the course of a test.   Figure 5.16 contains results for some fcc metals which were obtained in the same piece of work as the temperature sensitivities in Fig. 5.13*b*, and Fig. 5.17 contains results for iron which were obtained in the same piece of work as the temperature sensitivities in Fig. 5.14.   It will be seen that, as expected, the bcc metal iron has the bigger strain rate sensitivity.   The strain rate sensitivity of iron in Fig. 5.17, like the temperature sensitivity in Fig. 5.14, is not much affected by addition of carbon and nitrogen, again pointing to its being an inherent property of the iron lattice.   In Fig. 5.16, and in other similar work,[4, 5, 36] aluminium has a larger strain rate sensitivity at low temperatures than copper or silver, which is likewise to be expected from the relative temperature sensitivities in Fig. 5.13*b*.

According to eq. 4.10*c*, $[(T/\dot{\epsilon})(\partial\sigma/\partial T)_{\dot{\epsilon}}/(\partial\sigma/\partial\dot{\epsilon})_T]$ is equal to $\ln(\nu NxLb/\dot{\epsilon})$, which is not expected to vary much with temperature.   In Fig. 5.18 $(\partial\sigma/\partial T)_{\dot{\epsilon}}$ is plotted against $(\dot{\epsilon}/T)(\partial\sigma/\partial\dot{\epsilon})_T$ for iron from the data in Fig. 5.14 and 5.17, and follows a straight line to about the degree of accuracy expected for eq. 4.10*c*.   The data for fcc metals in Fig. 5.13*b* and 5.16 also follows a straight line to about the same accuracy.   These results

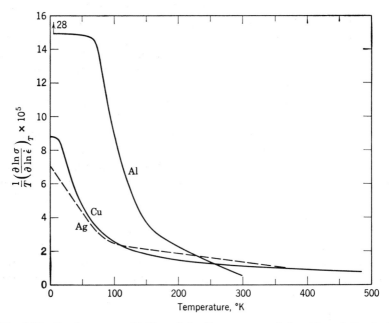

Fig. 5.16. Strain rate sensitivities of the flow stresses of Ag, Al, and Cu single crystals as a function of temperature (Ref. 49).

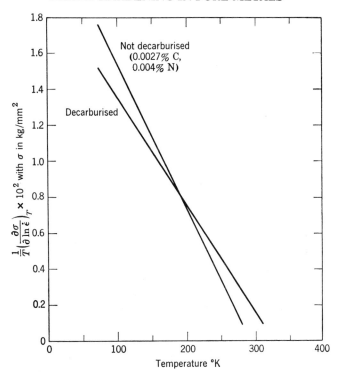

Fig. 5.17. Strain rate sensitivity of the flow stress of Fe polycrystals as a function of temperature (Ref. 51).

therefore provide experimental confirmation of eq. 4.10c. There is however, a difference here between iron and the fcc metals. For iron, the quantity $\ln (vNxLb/\dot\epsilon)$ is 28, whereas for the fcc metals it is only about 14. The mean value of $\dot\epsilon$ is about $10^{-3.5}$ fractional strain/sec in the experiments in question, whence $vNxLb$ is 1.6×10^8 for iron and 400 for an fcc metal.

These values have implications for the controlling deformation processes in the two cases in the following way. Consider iron first. The dislocation density after a few per cent strain will be about 5×10^9 cm/cc (Fig. 5.28). Suppose that the Peierls force in iron is overcome by the process described in section 4.7 of small loops jumping forward a distance b with the help of thermal agitation and dragging a long length of dislocation into the new position. A likely length for the loop is in the region of 10 atoms,[51] in which case there are a total of $5 \times 10^9/10b = 2.5 \times 10^{16}$ sites per cc at which slip can be nucleated; this is the value of N. Taking the vibration frequency v as 10^{10} and b as 2.5×10^{-8} cm, the length of

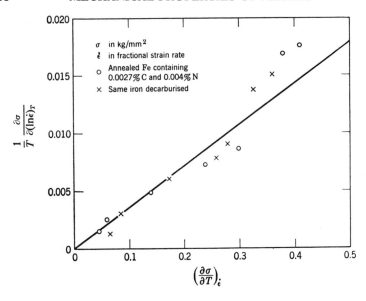

Fig. 5.18. Relation between temperature and strain rate sensitivities of the flow stress of Fe.

dislocation L which is dragged forward is 9.8×10^{-4} cm. This is of the same order as, but rather larger than, the cell diameter of a micron or two of the cold worked structure (section 5.9), and considerably larger than the mean spacing between junctions, which is close to 10^{-5} cm. In an fcc metal, suppose that a dislocation intersection process is the controlling one. Then L and x are both equal to the spacing between junctions. As junctions will be about 10^{-5} cm apart, $Lx = 10^{10}$. Putting the vibration frequency ν again equal to 10^{10}, we have $N = 1.6 \times 10^{10}$ per cc. The total number of junctions, however, is equal to (dislocation density)/(junction spacing), that is, 10^{15} per cc. Consequently, only one junction in $10^{15}/1.6 \times 10^{10} = 6 \times 10^4$ is active at any given moment.

5.6 Minor Yield Points

Two yield-point mechanisms connected with strain hardening and associated with low temperature deformation of face centred metals have been discovered. One, called "work softening,"[46] was found to occur when a specimen was strained at a low temperature and the straining was continued at a higher temperature. When aluminium single crystals were used, a small yield drop of about 50 grm/mm² occurred, but was followed by yielding at constant stress up to 10% elongation or more. Subsidiary experiments showed that the effect was not due to impurities.

Some measurements of stored energy seem to be connected with this phenomenon. In Fig. 5.21 an alloy cold worked 60% at −196°C contains the amount of energy corresponding to point A. After the alloy is warmed to room temperature, the energy stored drops to point B. The feature which seems connected with the yield point phenomenon is that, on then cold working the alloy at room temperature, the energy stored drops further to point C. A possible explanation of these results is that raising the temperature enables cross slip to occur; this leads to a reduction in dislocation density and further strain takes place to make good this loss.

A different yield-point mechanism has been observed in copper[60] and nickel[40] when a single crystal is strained, unloaded, and reloaded. The yield drop is again very small and in this case the yield elongation is also small. With copper, for example, the yield drop was only $\frac{1}{70}$ the applied stress (approximately 100 g/mm² after 50% shear at −196°C), and the original stress-strain curve was quickly rejoined. A similar effect occurs in polycrystalline samples of several nonferrous metals and alloys,[61] and its magnitude is proportionately similar. In alpha brass for example the flow stress increment (and the subsequent yield drop) was again about $\frac{1}{70}$ the applied stress, so that at an applied stress of 15 kg/mm² the effect amounted to 0.2 kg/mm². Allowance for these yield-point effects was made in Fig. 5.13a in the curves for copper and nickel.

At very low temperatures, a jerky extension causing the stress-strain curve to be serrated has been observed in fcc metals and resembles mechanical twinning in bcc metals. In copper[29] it has been observed at 4°K and at 77°K and is due at least partly to mechanical twinning. Twins were found to form when the stress was favourably oriented to tear apart the partial dislocations of each whole dislocation and so to widen the stacking fault between them. As the stacking fault has the same misfit as a twin boundary, its extension by a pole mechanism would produce a twin. The same process is believed to take place in nickel.[40] Similar discontinuities in the stress-strain curve have also been observed in aluminium,[48] but have been ascribed to an effect of local heat flashes produced when slip occurs, which are supposed to heat up and soften a slab containing the slip band, so that more slip can occur in the same place— that is, an adiabatic heating effect like that mentioned at the end of section 5.5.

5.7 The Bauschinger Effect

Suppose a metal is strained to the point A in Fig. 5.19 and is then unloaded. If it is restrained in the same direction, the new stress-strain

[60] M. J. Makin, *Phil. Mag.*, 1958, **3**, 287.
[61] G. F. Bolling, *Phil. Mag.*, 1959, **4**, 537.

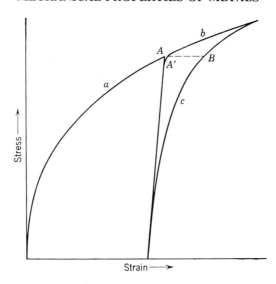

Fig. 5.19. To illustrate the Bauschinger effect. Curve *a*, original stress-strain curve, unloaded at *A*. Curve *b*, re-strained in same direction as *a*. Curve *c*, re-strained in reverse direction. *A'B* is the Bauschinger strain.

curve is curve *b*, which closely retraces the unloading line until a stress just below that at *A* is reached, then yields by the small amount *AA'* as the stress *A* is approached, and soon follows the extrapolation of the original curve *a*.   However, if the metal is strained in the opposite direction to the original, the new stress-strain curve is curve *c*, which departs from the unloading line at a relatively low stress and at the stress corresponding to *A* exhibits the "Bauschinger strain" *A'B*; curve *c* eventually joins curve *b*. This behaviour in reversed strain is known as the Bauschinger effect.

The Bauschinger effect occurs in single crystals as well as in poly-crystals.   Figure 5.20 for example shows results for single and polycrystals of aluminium.   In this figure the Bauschinger strain, that is, *A'B* in Fig. 5.19, is plotted against the amount of strain hardening, that is, the amount by which the stress at *A* in Fig. 5.19 exceeds the yield stress.   The effect here is larger in the single crystals than in the polycrystals.   The Bau-schinger effect therefore cannot be ascribed, as it once was, to the stresses built up at grain boundaries, although these doubtless play some part in polycrystals.   Indeed, quite apart from these stresses modern theory predicts some such effect, since equal hardening in both directions requires a special distribution of dislocations that is unlikely to be produced by a unidirectional strain.   The theories of strain hardening described in

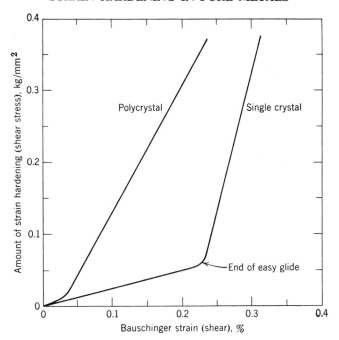

Fig. 5.20. Variation of Bauschinger strain with amount of strain hardening in polycrystals and single crystals of Al (99.996% pure; Ref. 62).

section 5.11 have the result that hardening should be greater in the forward than in the reverse direction, and thus predict a Bauschinger effect.

5.8 Energy Stored during Deformation

Many measurements have been made of the amount of the energy expended during deformation that is stored, as dislocations, point defects, etc. Probably all the measurements made so far relate to stage 3 of the generic stress-strain curve, and all show that somewhere in the region of 5% of the energy that is expended during deformation is stored; the remaining 95% or so is of course dissipated as heat.

The available measurements indicate how the stored energy varies in amount with the conditions of deformation. The results in Fig. 5.21 show that the amount is greater when the metal is deformed at low temperature than when it is deformed at room temperature. This is in agreement with the deduction made from the effect of temperature on the stress-strain curve to the effect that more dislocations persist during a given amount of deformation in stage 3 at low temperatures than at room temperature.

[62] S. N. Buckley and K. M. Entwistle, *Acta Met.*, 1956, **4**, 352.

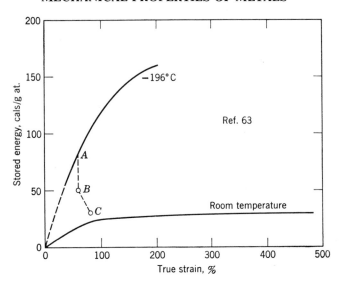

Fig. 5.21. Influence of temperature and amount of deformation (by wire drawing) on the stored energy. A polycrystalline alloy of 82.6% Au and 17.4% Ag was used. After cold working at $-196°C$ to point A, on warming to room temperature the stored energy dropped to D. It dropped further to C on straining at room temperature. The lower curve shows the result obtained when the straining was done throughout at room temperature.

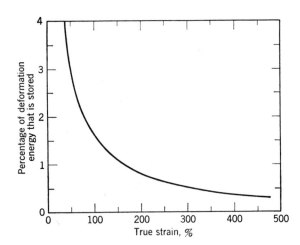

Fig. 5.22. Relation between the fraction of energy expended during deformation that is stored and the amount of deformation. Alloy of 82.6% Au and 17.4% Ag wire drawn at room temperature (Ref. 63).

[63] A. L. Tichener and M. B. Bever, *T.A.I.M.E.*, 1959, **215**, 326.

These results also show that the amount of energy stored rises with deformation more slowly the higher the deformation.

The results in Fig. 5.21 are replotted in Fig. 5.22 with the stored energy expressed as a percentage of the total energy used in the deformation. Figure 5.22 shows how this percentage decreases as the amount of deformation increases, bearing out the idea that annihilation of dislocations occurs more frequently the further the deformation is carried into stage 3. Similar data for copper are contained in Fig. 5.23; for silver in Table 5.2.

Table 5.2

Energy Stored in Silver during Deformation at Room Temperature[64]

Elongation %	Tensile Flow Stress, kg/mm²	Stored Energy, cal/g-at
11	13.3	2.7
21	17.8	5.1
32	21.3	7.75
43	23.2	7.27

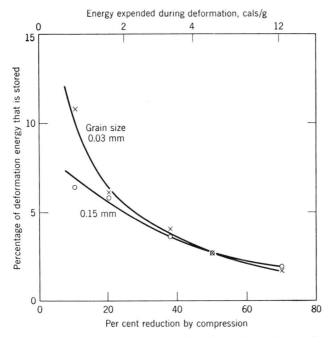

Fig. 5.23. Proportion of the energy expended during deformation that is stored in the metal as a function of strain and grain size.   Commercial Cu (99.98%) deformed at room temperature (Ref. 35).

[64] J. E. Bailey and P. B. Hirsch, *Phil. Mag.*, 1960, **5**, 485.

From the point of view of the theory of strain hardening discussed in section 5.11, the percentage of energy expended during deformation in stage 2 that is stored is particularly important, since the theories differ about its magnitude.   Insofar as extrapolation to small deformations in Fig. 5.23 is reliable, the results for the coarse-grained specimen in this figure indicate that the percentage would not be more than about 10%. The curve for the finer-grained specimen extrapolates to a considerably larger percentage, but this is to be expected from the large elastic stresses centred on the grain boundaries, for a group of dislocations which is pushed against an obstacle and which thereby creates a large elastic stress resembles a compressed spring, inasmuch as both store all the energy put into them.

5.9   Textures Produced by Cold Work

It is well known that the orientation of single crystals changes continuously with strain relative, say, to the axis of stress.   Since this is a result of slip, it also happens to the grains in a polycrystal.   The amount and direction of the change in orientation depend on the number and indices of the active slip planes, and therefore on the initial orientation. Hence different groups of grains, the grains in each group being separated in space but similar in initial orientation, may finish up in different orientations, although slip sometimes tends to align all grains.   The *preferred orientations* produced by different methods of working (e.g. rolling, wire drawing, tensile straining) have been discussed.[65]   An explanation of these which is simple in principle and has had a fair degree of success has been developed.[66-69]   This explanation supposes that the stress in each grain is equivalent to a tensile stress, the direction of which determines the operative slip planes in the usual way. Knowing which slip planes operate, we can predict the rotations.

5.10   Structure of Strained Pure Metal

The typical structure of a moderately- or well-worked metal is cellular, the cell walls consisting of relatively densely packed dislocations and the cell interior of a more open dislocation network.   Figure 5.24 shows an example of this structure.   A feature is that slip bands cannot usually be picked out.   The cell diameter is of the order of a micron or two and the

[65] C. S. Barrett, *The Structure of Metals*, 2nd edition, 1952, McGraw-Hill, New York.
[66] E. A. Calnan and C. J. B. Clews, *Phil. Mag.*, 1950, **41**, 1085.
[67] E. A. Calnan and C. J. B. Clews, *Phil. Mag.*, 1951, **42**, 616.
[68] E. A. Calnan and C. J. B. Clews, *Phil. Mag.*, 1951, **42**, 919.
[69] E. A. Calnan and C. J. B. Clews, *Phil. Mag.*, 1952, **43**, 93.

Fig. 5.24 Cell structure in Ag strained 25% in tension. × 33,000. (J. E. Bailey and P. B. Hirsch)

cell wall accounts for about one-fifth of this. The orientation change across a cell wall is about 1°. The dislocation density inside the cell is about one-fourth of that in the cell walls.[64, 70] It is probable that the cell structure characterises stage 3 of the generic stress-strain curve.

There are also other structures, particularly at small deformations, which are connected with the stacking fault energy of the metal. In a metal of high-stacking fault energy and easy cross slip, an irregular dislocation arrangement like an incipient cell structure has been found to develop early. Figure 5.25 shows an example. Although slip bands are difficult to detect by transmission microscopy after heavy cold work, after a small strain in stage 1 they stand out clearly, at least in a metal of low-stacking fault energy in which cross slip is therefore difficult. Figure 5.26 shows several rows of dislocations, each row clearly lying on a slip plane. The typical appearance of a stacking fault (the fringes joining the leading and trailing partial dislocations) in transmission electron micro-

[70] A. S. Keh, U.S.S. Report, No. 908.

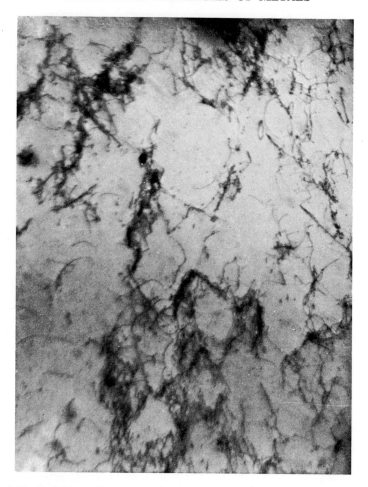

Fig. 5.25. Incipient cell structure in Fe cold worked 3%. ×15,000. (W. E. Carrington, K. F. Hale and D. McLean; Crown copyright reserved.)

scopy is also clearly evident. After somewhat larger deformations, believed to be in stage 2, it seems that groups of dislocations sometimes lie close together on neighbouring slip planes; Fig. 5.27 shows an example. One explanation of this structure is that dislocations on neighbouring slip planes are of opposite sign and form a stable dipole arrangement. A comparison between Fig. 5.25 and 5.27 suggests that the cell structure develops sooner the easier cross slip is, and the formation of the cell structure is discussed on this basis in section 5.11. But it is not certain whether the structure in Fig. 5.27 always characterises stage 2 in metals in

Fig. 5.26.   Slip bands in a Cu + 7 wt % Al alloy during stage 1 of work hardening.
× 60,000.   (A. Howie)

which cross slip is easy as well as in those in which it is difficult.   There
is in fact some evidence from slip line observations (see below) that the
structure in Fig. 5.27 may represent a stage 1 rather than a stage 2 structure.

The dislocation density in the cell structure has been determined as a
function of deformation.   Some results are shown in Fig. 5.28 and bear
out once again the importance of cross slip for strain hardening.   Thus,
in iron, in which cross slip is believed to be easy, the dislocation density
falls below a rate of increase that is linear with elongation after a few per
cent deformation, but in silver, in which cross slip is difficult, the rate of
increase is maintained up to ten times as large a deformation.   Moreover,
with iron, temperature over the range 250 to −70°C has no influence on

Fig. 5.27.   Dislocation pattern in Cu + 7 wt % Al alloy deformed into stage 2 of work hardening.   × 32,500.   (A. Howie)

the dislocation density, implying that cross slip occurs readily at least down to −70°C.   From the data here for silver, together with Table 5.2 and Fig. 5.21, an estimate of the dislocation density after extremely heavy cold work can be obtained.   In Table 5.2 and Fig. 5.21 (extrapolating to zero) the stored energy of silver and the gold-silver alloy increase with deformation at about the same rate.   Assuming that the dislocation density varies linearly with the stored energy, then after 500% deformation at room temperature silver would contain about four times the dislocation density it does after 20% deformation, that is, 2×10^{11} cm/cc of dislocation line.   After 200% deformation at −196°C, it would contain 2×10^{12} cm/cc of dislocation line.

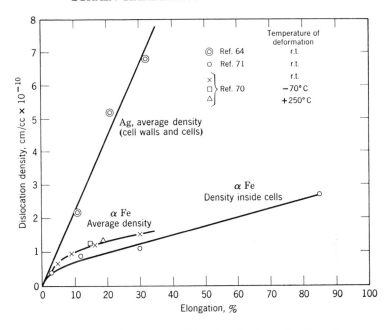

Fig. 5.28. Relation between dislocation density and deformation.

The dislocation density can also be expressed as a function of the flow stress. According to section 4.7, to obtain a linear relation the stress should be plotted against Gb/(dislocation spacing), that is, against $Gb\sqrt{}$(dislocation density). Such a plot is shown in Fig. 5.29 and yields a constant of proportionality between 0.4 and 0.5, which is similar to the values calculated in section 4.7. Apart from the slope, it will be noted that the results behave as might be expected in that the line for silver extrapolates back to a low stress at zero dislocation density, whereas the lines for both samples of iron extrapolate to positive friction stresses, that in the less pure sample being higher. The value yielded by the purer sample, namely $3\frac{1}{2}$ kg/mm², is the same as that previously deduced for the Peierls force in iron at room temperature.

The structures in Fig. 5.24–5.27 show the arrangements the dislocations take up but give no indication of how far they have travelled. Information on this point can be obtained from studies of slip lines. In some studies[72, 73] the surfaces of single crystals of copper and aluminium were repolished after each 2 to 5% strain in order to study the way slip changed

[71] W. E. Carrington, K. F. Hale, and D. McLean, *P.R.S.*, 1960, **A259**, 203.
[72] S. Mader, *Z. Physik*, 1957, **149**, 73.
[73] S. Sato and A. Kelly, *T.A.I.M.E.*, 1959, **215**, 413.

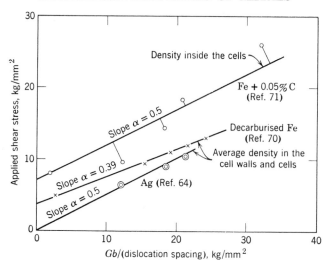

Fig. 5.29. Relation between flow stress and dislocation spacing.

with increasing strain. A clear correlation with the three stages of the stress-strain curve emerged. In stage 1 there was slip only on the system carrying the highest resolved shear stress, and the slip lines were long and weak. Dislocations evidently travelled out of the crystal or formed dipoles in which small groups of opposite sign lay close together on adjacent planes and largely compensated each other's stress fields. This makes an interesting contradiction with Fig. 5.27, where this structure is thought to characterise stage 2. In stage 2 the slip lines were short as well as weak, being only some tens of microns long and about 20 atoms high, and traces of slip on the system of next highest resolved shear stress appeared. Figure 5.30 shows an example of this stage. During this stage, dislocations evidently got stuck inside the crystal. The slip lines (for constant increments of strain) grew shorter as the strain grew larger, and in one of the theories of strain hardening described below the relation between them played an important part; it was

$$L = \frac{100\Lambda}{\epsilon - \epsilon^*} \tag{5.1}$$

where L is the mean slip line length, Λ is a constant equal to 4×10^{-4} cm for copper, ϵ is the shear strain in per cent, and ϵ^* is a constant equal to 8% for copper.[74] In stage 3 some of the short slip bands of stage 2 joined up by cross slip and evidently became somewhat stepped bands in

[74] A. Seeger, *Handbuch der Physik*, Springer, 1958, **2**, (Crystal Physics) p. 1.

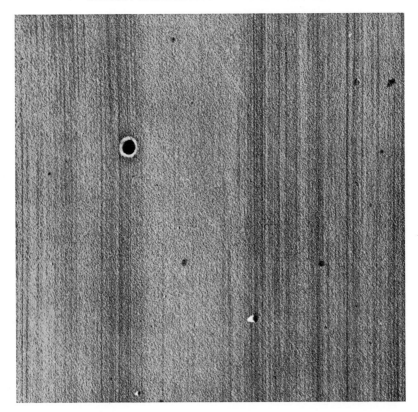

Fig. 5.30. The fine slip bands characterising stage 2; some slip on a second system can be seen.   Cu near the beginning of stage 2, × 12,500.   (S. Mader, Ref. 72)

which slip was relatively easy, for much slip obviously occurred in them; Fig. 5.31 shows an example of this stage.

The slip lines or bands are at all stages much larger than a cell diameter and give no hint of a cell structure.   The cell structure as seen by transmission electron microscopy on the other hand often gives no hint of slip bands.   These somewhat contradictory observations can be reconciled to some extent in the following way.

(*a*) Etch-pit patterns of slip bands (e.g. Fig. 4.3), probably relating to stage 3, reveal the slip bands as often being wider than a cell and as containing dislocations all along their length.   Evidently dislocations get stuck at all parts of a slip band and presumably new ones are formed to carry on the slip, by the process depicted in Fig. 4.16, for example.

(*b*) Dislocations travelling in the relatively wide slip bands do not

Fig. 5.31. The coarse slip bands characterising stage 3. Cu well inside stage 3.
× 3,700. (S. Mader, Ref. 72)

appear, at least in metals of high stacking fault energy to judge from structures like these in Fig. 5.24 and 5.25, to have long lengths lying in one plane. They seem to pay little regard to crystallographic directions either as a result of acquiring numerous jogs, of cross slip, or of the cutting intersection.

As already discussed in chapter 2, deformation produces vacancies and probably interstitials as well as dislocations. Although the vacancies and interstitials remaining account for a considerable part of the stored energy, there are not enough of them to have much influence on the flow stress.

5.11   Theories of Strain Hardening

The problem of strain hardening resolves itself into four separate problems, two of which have already been discussed. The first is the nature of the dislocations sources and how the dislocations multiply. This was discussed in section 4.6 and here it will only be added that in the cell interiors there is plenty of room for the processes of multiplication mentioned there to operate; for when the dimension of a cell is 1 to 2 microns the applied stress will be such that the diameter of a dislocation loop that can expand under the applied stress will be about one-tenth as big. The second is the initial hardening in polycrystals which has already been discussed in section 4.1. Problems 3 and 4 remain to be discussed. These are the problems of how the cold worked structures form and how the various causes of resistance to flow discussed in section 4.7 are to be adapted to these structures.

Only a limited amount can be said about how the cold-worked structure forms. It is easier to ask questions than to suggest answers. For example, why does slip occur in bands? Is it because of a limited number of large capacity sources, or because the bands are lamellae offering relatively weak resistance to shear? It would also be interesting to know how much of the deformation occurs in the bands and how much occurs as slip too fine to see on a previously polished surface. A key point seems to be to reconcile the prominence of slip bands on a polished surface, implying of necessity the presence of clusters of dislocations at the ends of the slip bands, with the difficulty of observing these clusters by transmission microscopy.

As to the way the cell structure in particular forms, there seem to be two directions which an explanation might take. One is that random distributions see to it that here and there small clusters of dislocations collect. Since these clusters are difficult to penetrate, they trap other dislocations and extend, eventually joining up and dividing the metal into separate cells. The other is that cross slip is essential to the cell structure. Thus, idealizing this structure so that the cell walls are two sets of orthogonal lines like the streets and avenues of New York, perhaps the streets are slip bands and dislocations cross slip down the avenues. This is simple, but requires dislocations always to move in places where the dislocation density is high.

Much more effort has been devoted to the last problem and the rest of this section will discuss this work. It will probably be clearest to discuss separately the connection between strain and the three causes of resistance to flow, namely, the internal stress, dislocation intersection, and defect production and then, in section 5.11d and e, we shall attempt to bring them together.

Stage 2 is the focal point. Given stage 2, stages 1 and 3 are easier to understand. In stage 1 the dislocations either escape from the specimen or form dipoles, and little hardening occurs. In stage 3 they cross slip to avoid each other and to annihilate dislocations of opposite Burgers vector, so the rate of strain hardening declines.

A full theory of strain hardening in stage 2 should explain several things. It should explain: (a) the relation between the amount of strain, the dislocation structure, the dislocation density, slip bands, and the flow stress; (b) why steep strain hardening is associated with multiple slip; (c) why fcc metals strain harden faster than bcc; (d) the Bauschinger effect; and (e) the temperature and strain rate dependence of the flow stress.

(a) *Flow Stress due to the Stress Field.* In its most recent form[74] the idea that strain hardening depends mainly on the stress field of all the dislocations makes use of the experimental observation of a connection between slip distances and amount of strain described in section 5.9. The basic idea is very similar to that of an earlier version.[75] It is that dislocations run out from a source, and the leading one forms a Lomer-Cottrell barrier against which the following ones pile up until the back stress stops the source. The model thus depends inherently on multiple slip since the large number of Lomer-Cottrell reactions needed requires a substantial amount of slip on other systems than the primary one. The theory predicts a value for the strain-hardening coefficient in the following way. Let L be the observed slip length, dN the surface density of active dislocation sources (i.e., the surface density of slip bands) during the extension $d\epsilon$, and n the average number of dislocations in each slip band. Then

$$dE = Lbnd\text{N}$$

Substituting for L from eq. 5.1 and integrating, we have

$$(\epsilon - \epsilon^*)^2 = 2\Lambda nb\text{N} \tag{5.2}$$

If each piled-up group is regarded as a single dislocation of Burgers vector nb, the stress between the piled-up groups, where a new slip band is supposed to form in this theory, is taken as

$$\tau = \frac{G}{2\pi} nb\sqrt{N} \tag{5.3}$$

τ is thus the stress needed to force a new slip band between two existing ones and is therefore the flow stress. Using eq. 5.3 to eliminate N from eq. 5.2 and differentiating, we get

$$\frac{\partial \tau}{\partial \epsilon} = \frac{G}{2\pi} \sqrt{nb/2\Lambda} \tag{5.4}$$

[75] N. F. Mott, *Phil. Mag.*, 1952, **43**, 1151.

Putting n and Λ equal to the experimental values of 20 and 4×10^{-4} respectively gives $\partial\tau/\partial\epsilon = G/250$, which is very close to the experimental value.

The theory relates the amount of strain, the flow stress, the strain-hardening coefficient and the observed slip lines. It also explains the Bauschinger effect, since on removing the applied stress, the dislocations in each piled-up group tend to run back to their source. To explain why only a few do so, it is thought that enough slip occurs on other systems to lock most of them. Since most of the energy expended during deformation is stored as elastic energy, the theory predicts that a large fraction of the deformation energy is stored during stage 2. The theory also helps to explain the influence of orientation on stage 2 hardening in fcc crystals, for analysis shows that the largest proportion of Lomer-Cottrell type intersections occur for those orientations which show the most rapid hardening, and the smallest proportion for those which show the weakest hardening. There are, however, some difficulties with the theory. It is not easy to reconcile the essential structural feature required by it, namely, piled-up groups of about twenty dislocations, with the structures observed, such as those shown in Fig. 5.24–5.26. To explain strain hardening in the bcc lattice, it must presumably be assumed that $\langle 100 \rangle$ dislocations formed by intersection of slip dislocations are effective barriers. However, both these and the Lomer-Cottrell dislocations can be broken from their ends in the way discussed in connection with intersection hardening in section 4.7b.

According to section 4.7c, if a uniform distribution of dislocations were assumed instead of starting from the idea of piled-up groups suggested by slip bands a flow stress of the form of eq. 4.3 would be arrived at. The distance x in eq. 4.3 can be put approximately equal to $\sqrt{\varrho}$, where ϱ is the dislocation density, and eq. 4.3 becomes

$$\tau = \alpha G b \sqrt{\varrho} \tag{5.5}$$

For a uniform distribution of dislocations, $\alpha \sim 0.1$.[76] It can also be shown that the distribution of dislocations suggested by the slip band observations discussed earlier likewise leads to eq. 5.5 with $\alpha \sim 0.2$.[77]

(b) *Flow Stress due to Intersection of Dislocations*. In the structures in Fig. 5.24 and 5.25, it seems impossible for a dislocation to move far without making many intersections. The flow stress caused thereby can be calculated from eq. 4.3 and also eq. 5.5 because there appears to be little or no tendency in these structures for neighbouring dislocations to be

[76] G. Saada, *Acta Met.*, 1960, **8**, 200.

[77] A. Seeger, *Dislocations and Mechanical Properties*, John Wiley and Sons, New York, 1956, p. 243.

parallel to each other, so that the distance x in eq. 4.3 can again be put equal to $\sqrt{\varrho}$. The calculated value of α is about $\frac{1}{3}$ (section 4.7b), although there is some ambiguity about whether the dislocation density inside the cells or in the cell walls should be taken (see section 5.11e). The dislocation density, the flow stress, and to some extent the structure are thus related. Intersection hardening helps to explain why bcc metals strain harden more slowly than fcc metals because the junctions formed in bcc metals are weaker than those formed in fcc and also because cutting intersections should be more frequent. It also helps to explain the influence of orientation on stage 2 hardening in fcc metals, for analysis shows that for those orientations which show the most rapid hardening the strongest junctions occur, and for those which show the weakest hardening the weakest junctions occur.[78]

(c) *Flow Stress due to Jogs.* Arguing again from the structures in Fig. 5.24 and 5.25 that there are numerous intersections, we expect that many jogs will be made. The flow stress these give rise to depends on the jog density along each dislocation. An estimate[79] of the resultant stress has been made following the idea discussed in section 4.7e that vacancy jogs cannot move sideways but that interstitial jogs can. During deformation, jogs of both sorts are made by intersection, but some are also eliminated, for example because interstitial jogs run along their dislocation and meet vacancy jogs. As a result of these two opposing processes, a density of vacancy jogs is set up which is estimated as being approximately equal to $\varrho^{-\frac{1}{2}}$, that is, the separation of jogs along each dislocation is $\varrho^{\frac{1}{2}}$. From eq. 4.8, with $Q_f = Gb^2$ and $y = b$, the flow stress is then again given by an equation like eq. 5.5 with $\alpha \sim 0.2$. From the net rate of production of jogs the distance a dislocation travels before it acquires so many jogs that it can move no further under the applied stress can be estimated, and turns out to be very similar to the observed length of slip bands in fcc metals (e.g., Fig. 5.30). In the same way the rate of strain hardening is also calculated to be about $G/200$, which is the value observed experimentally in stage 2.

(d) *Resultant Flow Stress.* Since all the forces discussed in section 4.7 may still operate when a metal has been strained and there are no new ones, eq. 4.15 or 4.16 must describe the flow stress of strained metal. The central problem of a theory of strain hardening of pure metals is to decide in each particular case the relative magnitude of the contribution from each of the three causes of resistance to flow that grow with deformation, namely, the stress field S, intersection $I + J$, and defect production D.

The internal stress term may be the important one for the structure

[78] J. D. Baird and B. Gale, to be published.
[79] N. F. Mott, *T.A.I.M.E.*, 1960, **218**, 962.

shown in Fig. 5.27, in which intersection does not seem prominent, although its dependence on dislocation density is uncertain for this kind of structure. Intersection seems unavoidable in the structure shown in Fig. 5.24 and 5.25, and all three causes of resistance may be expected to contribute. A difficulty is that the actual structures do not correspond to either of the assumptions made, namely, simple piled-up groups or a uniform distribution of dislocations. For the cell structure of Fig. 5.24, a simplifying approximation is to consider the cell walls and interiors separately and to use the appropriate dislocation density accordingly; the question of whether the cell wall or interior offers the bigger resistance to a dislocation will be discussed in section 5.11e. With the adoption of this simplification, all three causes of resistance contribute a term of the form of eq. 5.5. Consequently, if the Peierls force, which should not alter with strain, and the contribution to the stress field arising from grain boundaries are neglected, the flow stress can be expressed as

$$\tau = \alpha' G b / x = \alpha' G b \varrho^{\frac{1}{2}} \qquad (5.6)$$

which fits Fig. 5.29. The problem is to decide how much each process contributes to α'. The estimates in section 4.7 of the value of α for the various processes suggest that $I + J$ and $S + D$ each contribute about half. A similar division is suggested by Fig. 5.29, in which the slope for iron is less than that for silver. According to section 4.7, this is because I is smaller in a bcc metal than in an fcc, given equal dislocation densities. Comparing the estimates given there of α for intersection hardening in the two lattices with the slopes in Fig. 5.29 again suggests a similar division of the flow stress between the different processes. Recovery experiments (chapter 8) suggest the further tentative conclusion that D is usually small. A useful improvement in the accuracy of apportioning the estimate of the share of the stress field in strain hardening would come from a better knowledge of the amount of deformation energy that is stored during stage 2, since a large stress field arising from piled-up groups of dislocations would be associated with a large stored energy during stage 2.

One uncertainty is the way temperature sensitivity of the flow stress shown in Fig. 5.13 should be explained. Qualitatively, the greater variation with aluminium, which has unextended dislocations, than with copper or silver, which have extended dislocations, is consistent with the temperature sensitivity being due to the jogs produced during intersection. However, it is doubtful whether the results in Fig. 5.13 with nickel fit this scheme, and in any case the size of the effect is too large. This is the difficulty mentioned in section 4.7f. In Fig. 5.13, both aluminium and nickel have flow stresses one-fourth to one-third higher at absolute zero than at room temperature. Although, according to the estimate in section

4.7*b*, the full resistance from the jogs would amount to about one-third of that from junction formation, this is reduced by a factor of $\frac{1}{2}$ because of the symmetry effect and by another factor of $\frac{1}{2}$ again because jogs are significant at only half the junctions. The result is that the jog force can only be expected to be about one-twelfth of the junction force. However, an alternative source of temperature sensitivity is provided by the production of interstitials, given that the jogs producing them experience difficulty in moving sideways at low temperature.

Partial answers, at least, can thus be seen to several of the questions raised at the beginning of this section. It is clear why steep strain hardening requires multiple slip, and there are several reasons why fcc metals should strain harden faster than bcc metals. The Bauschinger effect arises from the stress field because, for example, intersection which takes place where the internal stress opposes an applied stress in the forward direction finds that the internal stress assists a reversed applied stress. The dependence of the flow stress on temperature at low temperatures may be due to interstitial jogs.

Some estimates can be made about the physical processes that occur during strain hardening. According to eq. 5.6, strain hardening depends fundamentally on increasing the total length of dislocation line. Using the experimental value of the strain-hardening coefficient, we can estimate the rate of increase of line length, and hence we can deduce the amount of energy stored in the form of dislocations. The rate of increase in line length is estimated in the following way. Suppose the movement of unit length of dislocation across a mesh, that is, through a distance $x = \varrho^{\frac{1}{2}}$, is accompanied on average by an increase in line length of amount f, for example by the processes described in section 4.6*a*. Then $d\varrho = \varrho f$ for a strain increment $d\epsilon = \varrho^{\frac{1}{2}}$, from which $d\varrho/d\epsilon = \varrho^{\frac{1}{2}}f/b$. From eq. 5.6, $d\tau/d\varrho = \frac{1}{2}\alpha'Gb\varrho^{-\frac{1}{2}}$. Consequently the strain-hardening coefficient is

$$\frac{d\tau}{d\epsilon} = \frac{d\tau}{d\varrho}\frac{d\varrho}{d\epsilon} = \frac{1}{2}\alpha'fG \tag{5.7}$$

The experimental value of the strain-hardening coefficient in fcc metals is about $G/200$ when there is no cross slip. Putting $\alpha' = 0.4$ gives $f = \frac{1}{25}$. According to this, the dislocations on average increase their length by one-twenty-fifth as they cross a mesh. Twenty-five junctions are therefore made and broken while a length of dislocation equal to $\varrho^{-\frac{1}{2}}$ is being made. As each junction is made, an energy that on average is equal approximately to that of $\frac{1}{2}\varrho^{-\frac{1}{2}}$ of dislocation line is dissipated as heat, and is provided again by the stress as the junction is broken. As the estimated values of α for stress field hardening and interstitial hardening are roughly similar, suppose that an equal amount of energy is dissipated against the

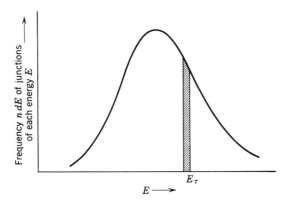

Fig. 5.32.

internal stress field. Then the ratio of energy stored in the form of dis-locations to energy used is $\frac{1}{25}$. This is about half the value which the curve in Fig. 5.23 for coarse-grained copper indicates if extrapolated backwards to elongations small enough to be in stage 2, which agrees well with the estimate at the end of chapter 2 that about half the stored energy exists as dislocations.

The fraction of active loops can also be calculated to compare with the fraction estimated in section 5.5 from the sensitivity of the flow stress to temperature and speed. It is good enough and simplest to make the estimate assuming only intersection hardening. Figure 5.32 shows diagrammatically a plot of junction frequency against E, the energy saved when the junction is formed. As mentioned earlier, this energy is approxi-mately that of $\frac{1}{2}\varrho^{-\frac{1}{2}}$ of dislocation line on average. At the flow stress τ, all the junctions represented by the dashed line in Fig. 5.32 are supposed to be used up. The active ones are those contained in the shaded band, of width approximately kT, whereas all junctions will now be contained within the energy band stretching from zero to the energy E corresponding to the flow stress τ. The proportion of active junctions is therefore $kT/\frac{1}{2}\varrho^{-\frac{1}{2}}W$ where W is the energy of unit length of dislocation line, and the variation of junction frequency with energy is neglected. At a flow stress of $G/1000$, $^{-\frac{1}{2}}\varrho$ is $1000b/3$. Taking the dislocation energy as 4 ev per atom length then gives the proportion of active junctions at 100°K as 1.3×10^{-5}, or 1 in 7.7×10^4, which is to be compared with the propor-tion estimated in section 5.5 of 1 in 6×10^4.

(e) *Movement of Dislocations: Crossing a Cell Wall.* It is possible to think of the movement of dislocations through the work-hardened struc-ture in a general way that evades the formidable problem presented by the actual dislocation pattern.   A moving dislocation moves against a very variable opposing force.   It travels through a stress field whose magnitude and direction change in space and also in time as the other dislocations producing this field also move.   It intersects dislocations, and the strength of the junctions formed is affected by several factors such as the distance along each dislocation to the next junction and the angle at which the dislocations intersect.   It experiences a drag from the defects it produces as it moves, and this varies, for example, with the number of jog-producing intersections made and with the amount of annihilation of jogs.   In this complicated situation, certain points can be picked out.   One is that the local contributions from the stress field, intersection and defect production may vary.   Another point is that, although τ must, by definition at least, equal the yield stress everywhere, it may be exceeded at many points. This is the situation depicted in Fig. 5.32, which can be regarded as applying to all the causes of resistance separately and to their sum.   In annealed metal, ordinary heterogeneity, for example, uneven distribution of dislocations, will ensure that τ varies from place to place, giving rise to the gradual yield behaviour observed when there is not a large Peierls force.   In cold worked metal a small stress increment is expected to start movement at a few points where dislocations can run down from stress peaks, break junctions, or defect-jogs can annihilate at the stress applied. In the diagram of Fig. 5.32, these points lie in the shaded band.   The stress on adjoining lengths is thereby increased, these move, and so on.

Although, in the cell structure of Fig. 5.24, the dislocation density in the cell walls is higher than in the cell interiors, it does not automatically follow that the cell walls predominantly determine the flow stress.   There are two alternative possibilities.   The analogy with grain boundaries may be valid and a dislocation may enter the wall from one side and attract another into the wall from the neighbouring cell, just as slip "crosses" a grain boundary.   The cell interior will then be important just as a grain interior is.   But since the lattice is continuous through a cell wall, there is the alternative that it is physically possible for a dislocation to travel right across.   Even then, the cell interior can hardly be unimportant, however. A simple argument leading to this conclusion is that a dislocation will do whichever of these two things is the easier, and if the cell interior provides an important source of resistance in the first alternative, it must provide a relatively larger part in the second alternative when this is easier than the first.   A similar conclusion is arrived at from the assumption that a piled-up group, whose length is equal to a cell diameter, tries to spear its way through a cell wall, and is retarded by the wall itself at its head and by the dislocations in the cell interior acting as a friction resistance.   Equation 4.7 then applies, with τ_f given by eq. 5.6 and with ϱ equal to the dislocation density ϱ_i in the cell interior, τ_s given by the same equation but with ϱ equal to the dislocation density ϱ_w in the cell wall, l equal to $\varrho_w^{-\frac{1}{2}}$ and L equal to the cell diameter. If we put $L = 1$ micron, $\varrho_i = 10^{10}$ cms of dislocation per cc, and $\varrho_w = 4 \times 10^{10}$ cms of dislocation per cc, it transpires that the friction resistance of the cell interior is twice as large as the resistance of the cell wall.

Application of eq. 4.7 in this way produces another result. A further straining which produces smaller values of cell diameter L doubtless also produces larger values of ϱ_i and therefore of τ_f in eq. 4.7. It can then be seen that, if the flow stress τ is plotted against the cell diameter as in Fig. 4.7, a line could be produced which extrapolates to cut the stress axis at a negative value. This is the situation in Fig. 4.7 and seems otherwise difficult to explain.

6

Alloy Hardening

6.1 General Survey

The main effect of alloys is to raise the yield stress and to intensify or prolong strain hardening. Of course, there may also be special embrittling effects, which are discussed in Chapter 7. Leaving these aside, in all metals except perhaps those alloyed to high strength, there is probably not much effect on the true fracture strength. It is not possible to be sure of this since the true fracture strength of many pure metals is uncertain, owing to their habit of pulling down to a fine point whose cross-sectional area is too small to measure accurately. However, no such effect need be assumed to rationalise the effect of alloys, namely: in weakly or moderately alloyed metals strain hardening is prolonged so that a higher UTS and uniform elongation is attained; in strongly alloyed metals yield stress and initial strain-hardening rate are raised but strain hardening soon declines, and a high UTS is reached at a smaller uniform elongation.

The effect of an alloying element may depend on the form in which it is present. In general, it has the least effect in the form of coarse, well-separated particles of precipitates, the greatest effect when present as a finely dispersed precipitate with a spacing of the order of 100 A, and an intermediate effect when present in solid solution. This general tendency is illustrated in Fig. 6.1, which shows stress-strain curves of Al-Cu alloys, taken at $-196°C$ to avoid the complicating effects of strain ageing that would otherwise occur in this alloy. The metal has its lowest yield stress when overaged (curve 1) and its highest when aged to contain very small

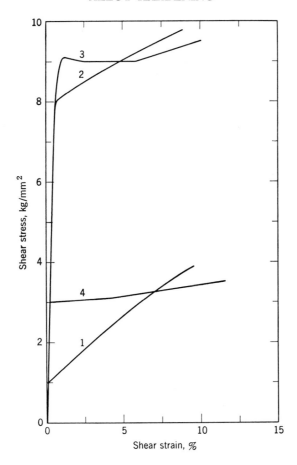

Fig. 6.1. Stress-strain curves of single crystals of Al−2 at % Cu, oriented to favour single slip and tested at −196°C. Curve 1, aged 2 days at 350°C; alloy contains non-coherent particles of CuAl₂ about 25,000 A apart. Curve 2, aged 27½ hours at 190°C; alloy contains noncoherent particles about 400 A apart. Curve 3, aged 2 days at 130°C; alloy contains GP [1] zones, that is, platelets of Cu atoms 100 A in diameter and 1 atom thick about 150 A apart. Curve 4, as quenched; alloy is a solid solution (Ref. 1).

and closely spaced particles of precipitate (curves 2 and 3). When the copper is in solution the yield stress lies between these extremes (curve 4). The influence of the form of the alloying element on strain hardening in Fig. 6.1 is different from this influence on yield stress. Steep strain

¹ G. Greetham and R. W. K. Honeycombe, *J.I.M.*, 1960–61, **89**, 13.

hardening here apparently requires that particles larger than some minimum size be present (curves 1 and 2); otherwise little strain hardening takes place. The reason for this is that these crystals were oriented to favour easy glide, which evidently occurred unless sizeable precipitate particles were present. In polycrystals or in single crystals oriented to favour multiple glide, the difference in strain hardening rates would be less apparent.

Yield stress comparisons like that in Fig. 6.1 between the effect of the alloying element when present as a precipitate and when in solution are somewhat misleading, because the volume fraction of alloying agent is not equal in the two conditions. In the condition represented by curve 2, for example, there is about three times as large a volume fraction of precipitate as there is of copper in the condition represented by curve 4, so that the copper is about equally as effective as the precipitate when compared on the basis of equal volume fractions. In fact, it seems generally true that badly misfitting solutes (as copper is in aluminium) have a similar effect on the yield stress to that of the same concentration of an efficiently hardening precipitate. Another example of this is that an aged-hardened copper-beryllium alloy containing the equivalent of 30 at % of precipitate has a yield stress 80 kg/mm² higher than that of pure copper, whereas particularly effective solid solution hardening of copper (e.g. by tin, Fig. 6.4) may amount to 60 kg/mm² for 30 at %. In practice, of course, precipitates are more useful strengthening agents than soluble elements because more can be introduced than of a badly misfitting solute.

Alloying elements may influence the temperature sensitivity of the strength properties. Figure 6.2 gives an idea of the range of temperature sensitivity of yield (or proof) stress encountered in practice. The general rule seems to be that the temperature sensitivity of this property can be highest for solid solutions in polycrystalline form and lowest for precipitation hardened alloys.

From the point of view of strength, not all metals appear to have been equally exploited. Table 6.1 lists some of the highest UTS values achieved with different base metals. Taking the ratio of UTS to shear modulus given in the second row as the significant comparative figure, copper is the best exploited base metal and magnesium and nickel the worst. A 100-ton steel is quite poor compared with the copper figure. Although we might reasonably expect some base metals to offer greater potentialities than others under given conditions, nevertheless the relatively high ratio for the copper alloy, and even more the figures for copper and iron whiskers, suggest that with several metals there is scope for alloying to considerably higher strengths by finding more suitable alloying elements and treatments.

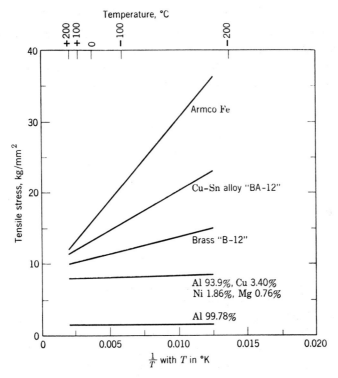

Fig. 6.2. Effect of temperature on yield stress (Ref. 2).

Table 6.1
Strengths of Strongest Alloys on Different Base Metals; Tests at Room Temperature

Base Metal	UTS kg/mm²	UTS/Shear Modulus	Ref.
Al	66	0.025	3, p. 718
Cu	135	0.043	3, p. 727
Cu whisker	300	0.081*	4
Mg	36	0.021	3, p. 748
Fe, 100-ton steel	158	0.020	
Fe, 180-ton steel	280	0.036	
Fe whisker	1340	0.22*	4
Ni	126	0.016	3, p. 754
Ti	118	0.028	3, p. 759

* Using the shear moduli reported for the whiskers of Table 4.3; Cu 3700 kg/mm²; Fe 6100 kg/mm².

[2] P. S. Pashkov, *Fiz. Metal. Metalloved*, 1956, **3**, 565.
[3] C. Smithells, *Metals Reference Book*, Butterworth, London, 1955.
[4] Table 4.3.

The effect of alloys may be useful in manufacture as well as in service. For example, zinc added to copper does not raise the proof stress as much as many other alloying elements, but it prolongs strain hardening so that necking is postponed. Typical figures are given in Table 6.2.

Table 6.2

	0.1% Proof Stress kg/mm²	UTS kg/mm²	E% on 2"
Copper	3.0	15	40
70/30 brass	5.5	21	65
90 Cu 10 Sn	21	46	65
	(0.5% proof stress)		

This effect of zinc is helpful in manufacturing operations involving tensile stresses, for example, in deep drawing.

It is probable that alloying elements alter the density of dislocations in a metal. Quite a large part of the effect of solutes on yield stress could be due to this, since the increase in yield stress is generally equivalent to only a small strain of the pure metal, although the change in dislocation density could hardly be big enough to affect the later stages of the stress-strain curve. Since little is yet known about the structural changes associated with alloying, they will not be discussed further. In comparisons of alloys and pure metals, it might be expected that any disparities of this sort would be mitigated by heat treatments which give the same grain size in the pure metal and the alloy.

6.2   Effect of Solutes on Yield Stress

This section discusses alloy systems where no significant ferrous type yield point occurs. Such systems will be discussed in section 6.7.

No cases are known where the addition of a solute lowers the yield stress of a pure metal; invariably, the yield stress is raised. Figure 6.3 illustrates this point. It shows the way the yield stress varies over the entire composition range of the completely miscible system silver–gold. The yield stress rises at both ends to a peak at approximately the mid-composition point. The rise at each end is approximately linear and also quite slow, as might be expected in a system with such a small lattice perturbation that there is complete miscibility. Less soluble solutes, which distort the parent lattice more, also show an approximately linear effect

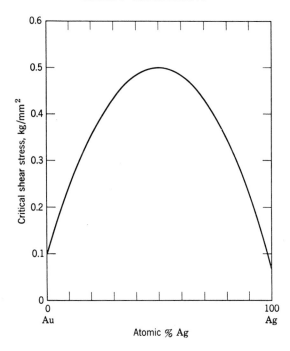

Fig. 6.3. Variation with composition of resolved shear stress of Au–Ag single crystals. There is complete solubility over the whole range of composition (Ref. 5).

for small percentages, but it is much steeper. Some results for such solutes in copper single crystals are shown in Fig. 6.4a; the slopes are six to a hundred times steeper.

Some of the same alloys as those in Fig. 6.4a have been studied in poly-crystalline form. The variation with composition of the 1.0% proof stress of the polycrystalline alloys is also approximately linear and is shown in Fig. 6.4b. The scales in Fig. 6.4a and 6.4b are adjusted so that lines of equal slope are parallel when both are calculated in tensile stress. It is significant that although the whole stress level is higher for the poly-crystalline specimens—the ordinate intercept is twenty-five times higher in Fig. 6.4b than in Fig. 6.4a—the slopes for the same alloys do not differ by more than a factor of 2. This is one of several pieces of evidence mentioned in this chapter that a large part of the hardening effect of soluble alloying elements, perhaps especially those of limited solubility, can be regarded as a frictional force that adds on to any other hardening effect present.

[5] G. Sachs and J. Weerts, *Z. Physik*, 1930, **62**, 473.

Measurements of the variation with temperature of the yield stress of alloys which do not have a sharp ferrous type yield point show that solutes can raise the temperature sensitivity. The results of some such measurements on alloy single crystals that do not have this kind of yield are shown in Fig. 6.5. Among these, the yield stress rises with decrease in temperature more steeply in the alloys than in pure copper, and more steeply with 0.2% silver than with 0.1%.

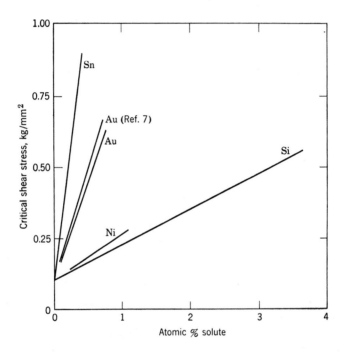

Fig. 6.4a. Effect of soluble alloying elements on the critical shear stress of Cu single crystals (Ref. 6).

In ternary systems, the yield stresses are sometimes fairly accurately additive from those of the binary alloys, for example, in Al–Mg–Zn alloys.[8] Other examples of such additive effects will be mentioned later in this chapter.

[6] J. O. Linde and S. Edwards, *Arkiv Fysik*, 1954, **8**, 511.

[7] J. Garstone and R. W. K. Honeycombe, *Dislocations and Mechanical Properties of Crystals*, John Wiley and Sons, New York, 1957, p. 391.

[8] E. Schmid and W. Boas, *Plasticity of Crystals*, English ed. F. A. Hughes & Co., 1950, London, p. 144.

6.3 Effect of Solutes on Strain Hardening

Figure 6.6 illustrates what appears to be the typical effect on the early part of the stress-strain curve of solid solution alloying in fcc single crystals oriented for easy glide; the yield stress is raised, easy glide is made more extensive, and stage 2, to use the terminology of the previous chapter, starts at a higher stress. The difference between an ordered and a dis-

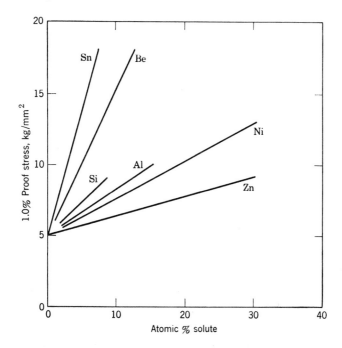

Fig. 6.4b. Effect of soluble alloying elements on the 1.0% proof stress of Cu poly-crystals at room temperature (Ref. 9).

ordered alloy is similar to this difference between a pure metal and an alloy,[8] and single crystals of brass compared with those of copper are well known to show just the same effect (e.g., ref. 10). The effect is similar to that in Fig. 5.10 of lowering the temperature of test of a nickel single crystal oriented for easy glide. The simple explanation,[7] starting from the premise that easy glide ends when the stress concentration around clusters of dislocations on the primary slip plane are sufficiently large to initiate slip on another plane, is that these clusters need bigger stress fields,

[9] R. S. French and W. R. Hibbard, *T.A.I.M.E.*, 1950, **188**, 53.
[10] A. Seeger, *Dislocations and Mechanical Properties of Crystals*, John Wiley and Sons, New York, 1957, p. 243.

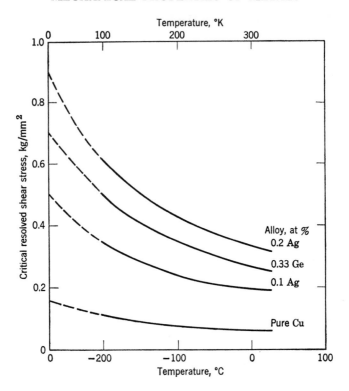

Fig. 6.5. Effect of temperature on critical resolved shear stress of Cu and Cu alloy single crystals (Ref. 7).

and easy glide must therefore be more extensive to move these secondary dislocations when their yield stress is raised.

When easy glide is particularly extensive "overshooting" occurs; that is, the yield stress of inactive slip planes becomes higher than that of the active one. The best-known instance occurs in 70/30 brass. The reason[11] for this behaviour is that the primary slip planes act as a barrier to slip on intersecting planes and that no equivalent barrier hinders primary slip.

A more important effect of alloys than either of these two is that they prolong stage 2 and cause steeper strain hardening in stage 3. The evidence for this in single crystals[12] is not yet extensive but is confirmed by their effects in polycrystals. A typical set of stress-strain curves on

[11] G. R. Piercy, R. W. Cahn, and A. H. Cottrell, *Acta Met.*, 1955, **3**, 331.
[12] E. E. Underwood and L. L. Marsh, *T.A.I.M.E.*, 1956, **206**, 477.

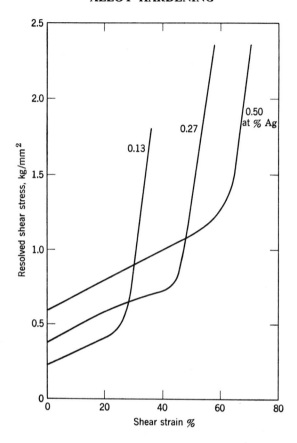

Fig. 6.6. Stress-strain curves of Cu–Ag single crystals at 17°C (Ref. 7).

polycrystalline specimens illustrating the effect of alloying is shown in Fig. 6.7. Here, alloy additions to copper shift the whole stress-strain curve upward, tilt it somewhat more steeply, and delay the eventual decline in the rate of strain hardening. In alpha iron, substitutional solutes have a similar effect[13] (these iron alloys were annealed in wet hydrogen to eliminate possible complications by interstitial elements) as they do in aluminium.[14] Since most of a polycrystalline stress-strain curve relates to stage 3, the simple interpretation of this behaviour is that the alloying elements introduce a frictional force that raises the whole stress-strain curve uniformly and hinders the cross slip and recovery that characterises

[13] C. E. Lacy and M. Gensamer, *A.S.M.*, 1944, **32**, 88.
[14] J. E. Dorn, P. Pietrokowsky, and T. E. Tietz, *T.A.I.M.E.*, 1950, **188**, 933.

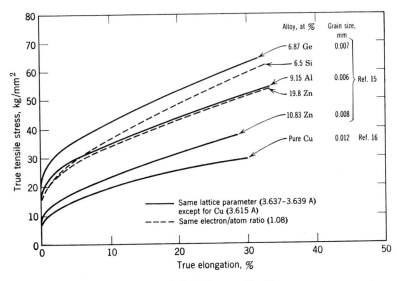

Fig. 6.7.   Stress-strain curves of Cu and some Cu alloys at room temperature.

stage 3.   Moreover, different solutes have been found to alter the shape of stress-strain curves in the same way.   Thus, identical stress-strain curves can be obtained with many aluminium base binary alloys[14] although a different concentration of each alloy element is necessary, and iron base binary alloys behave in the same way.[13]   Moreover, with the iron base alloys it was also found that the stress-strain curves of ternary and quaternary alloys could be deduced with quite good accuracy from those of the simple binary alloys by simple addition—an additive effect which is in marked contrast to the complicated way ternary alloys behave in regard to some other properties.   The replaceability of one solute by another which these experiments demonstrate indicates that the frictional force and the hindrance to cross slip are both connected in the same way with the lattice disturbance on which the effect of solutes must depend.

The stress-strain curves of some copper-base alloys in polycrystalline form are distinctly flatter than that of copper itself for the first few per cent of elongation.[15, 17]   Alpha brass is one of these metals, and of course, in single crystal form has a rather high yield stress and a long easy glide region.   In addition to introducing a frictional force, these alloying elements are believed to introduce one of the forms of hardening

[15] W. R. Hibbard, *T.A.I.M.E.*, 1958, **212**, 1.
[16] R. P. Carreker and W. R. Hibbard, *Acta Met.*, 1953, **1**, 654.
[17] P. Feltham and G. J. Copley, *Acta Met.*, 1960, **8**, 542.

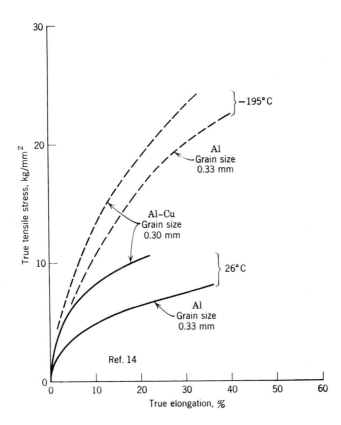

Fig. 6.8. Stress-strain curves of Al (99.98%) and Al−0.23 at % Cu at two temperatures.

that disappears during straining (section 6.4), and this accounts for the flat initial part of the stress-strain curve.

Lowering the temperature has qualitatively much the same effect on strain hardening as in pure metals, but the effect is weaker in solid solutions. In Fig. 6.8 for instance, lowering the temperature has more effect on aluminium than on the aluminium-copper alloy, as though there were more scope for preventing dynamical recovery in the aluminium than in the alloy. Some other results on aluminium alloys are shown in Fig. 6.9 and indicate the same tendency; this figure shows that the flow stress after 15% strain rises less rapidly with decrease in temperature in the alloys than in the pure metal. It contrasts with Fig. 6.5, which shows that for the yield stress the reverse behaviour obtains. Evidently, if the alloying

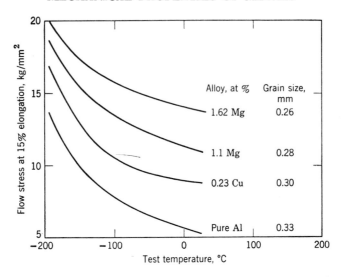

Fig. 6.9. Flow stress of Al and some alloys after 15% true elongation in tests at different temperatures (Ref. 14).

element restricts cross slip there is less scope for further restriction by lowering the temperature.

Since soluble alloys must owe their effect to some kind of lattice disturbance, it has been variously suggested that the appropriate measure of this is (*a*) effect on lattice parameter (or difference in atomic size between solvent and solute), and (*b*) effect on electron-atom ratio. There is certainly a rough correlation with (*a*) when the strengthening by solutes of a wide range of atomic sizes is plotted, but in detail the correlation is poor. The results in Fig. 6.7 are from experiments designed to test the two hypotheses. With the particular alloys chosen, (*a*) fails more obviously than (*b*). Examples of almost perfect agreement with (*b*) have found in copper base alloys[18] and a combination of (*a*) and (*b*) has been used to rationalise results on aluminium alloys.[14]

A special strain-hardening effect occurs in stainless steel. It has long been known that stainless steels of some compositions become ferromagnetic during cold working and, because the rate of strain hardening is rather steep, the belief has arisen that martensite is formed during cold working. Examination with the electron microscope has shown that this is so.[19]

[18] N. P. Allen, T. H. Schofield, and A. E. L. Tate, *Nature*, 1951, **168**, 378.

[19] J. A. Venables, Conference on Electron Microscopy, de Nederlandse Vereniging Voor Electronenmicroscopie, Delft, 1961, 443.

6.4 Theory of Solute Hardening

A number of mechanisms are believed to be understood in principle whereby solutes raise the yield stress, introduce a friction stress, or have the effect of intensifying strain hardening, but so far little progress has been made in understanding which are the important mechanisms in particular cases. It is not yet possible to do much more than describe the properties expected from each mechanism.

Leaving aside dislocation locking mechanisms, which are discussed later, there is one other source of hardening which is effaced by strain. This is

1. Order or Fisher hardening,[20] and is believed to occur in alloys which are partly ordered on a local scale, as presumably most alloys are since a solute-solvent bond energy is unlikely to be exactly half way between that of a solvent-solvent and a solute-solute. If, in equilibrium, an alloy has some local order, the passage of a dislocation must diminish the degree of order, which raises the energy, and this is reflected in a higher yield stress. The increase in yield stress produced by the order hardening mechanism is $\tau = \gamma/b$, where γ is the disordering energy per unit area of slip plane and b as usual is the Burgers vector. This result is obtained by equating the work done, τb, when one dislocation moves across unit area of slip plane, with the disordering energy γ, and amounts to assuming that the passage of one dislocation completely destroys the partial order. A value for γ can be deduced from thermodynamical considerations. For 70/30 brass, in which the flat yield referred to earlier is supposed to be due to order hardening, the value 10 ergs/cm^2, or 0.004 ev per atom has been deduced,[20] giving $\tau = 4$ kg/mm^2. As the yield stress of 70/30 brass crystals is 1.5 kg/mm^2 at room temperature it appears that a significant fraction of the yield strength of brass is caused by short-range ordering.

There are four possible "frictional" mechanisms whereby a solute introduces a resistance to the movement of a dislocation that is unaffected by strain and can thus be regarded as a constant frictional force which simply leads to an additional term in eq. 4.15 and 4.16 and does not alter the terms already present.

2. Mott-Nabarro hardening.[21, 22]

3. Electrical interaction between dislocations and solute ions.[23]

[20] J. Fisher, *Acta Met.*, 1954, **2**, 9.

[21] N. F. Mott and F. R. N. Nabarro, Conference on Strength of Solids, *Phys. Soc.*, 1948, p. 1.

[22] N. F. Mott, *Imperfections in Nearly Perfect Crystals*, John Wiley and Sons, New York, 1952, p. 173.

[23] A. H. Cottrell, S. C. Hunter, and F. R. N. Nabarro, *Phil. Mag.*, 1953, **44**, 1064.

4. Effect of solute on the Peierls force.
5. The Snoek effect.[24]

The idea underlying (2) is that solute atoms strain the lattice around them and an extra force is needed to push the dislocations past these strained regions. A contribution from the electrical strains is represented by (3). It is comparable with the interaction in ionic crystals between dislocations and (electrically charged) vacancies,[25] and in theory can be distinguished from the elastic strains, since the elastic strain around and the electric charge on the solute ions are more or less independent. (2) and (3) then give a frictional force which corresponds exactly with the frictional force that solutes have been inferred to introduce. As regards (4), the possibility must also exist that the Peierls force is altered by a large amount of solute. Such an effect might reasonably be ignored in fcc solid solutions since the Peierls force is very small in such metals, but might be important in bcc. The Snoek effect, (5), is discussed below after (2) and (3).

Theoretical calculations have been given for both (2) and (3). Calculation of (2) starts from the knowledge that a dislocation cannot be on the "uphill" stress side of every solute atom when for example the atoms are only 4–5 atomic diameters apart (i.e., a 1% solution) because the stresses required by eq. 2.7 to bend the dislocation as sharply as would be necessary are too large. Consequently the resistance to the motion of a dislocation is equal to the statistical sum of the stresses, positive and negative, around the solute atoms near the dislocation. The number of such solute atoms per length L of dislocation is proportional to L, so that the statistical result is proportional to $L^{1/2}$. The force on the length L due to an applied stress, however, is $\tau b L$. The flow stress τ is therefore determined by the equation

$$\tau b L = \text{constant} \times L^{1/2}$$

or
$$\tau = \text{constant}/L^{1/2} \qquad (6.1)$$

and to evaluate τ, some choice of L must be made. Two different calculations have been made, the essential difference between them residing in the criterion used for choosing L. The first calculation (a)[21] takes a large value for L; it assumes that L is equal to the radius of the arcs into which the average internal stress bends the dislocations. The second, (b)[22] takes what is probably the minimum value for L; it assumes that L is of such length that, given the same curvature as in (a), its centre part moves forward a distance equal to the mean separation of solute atoms,

[24] G. Schoeck and A. Seeger, *Acta Met.*, 1959, **7**, 469.
[25] P. L. Pratt, "Point Defects in Metals," *Inst. Metals*, 1958, p. 99.

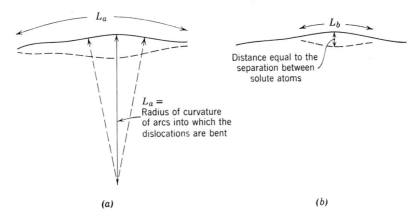

Distance equal to the
separation between
solute atoms

$L_a =$
Radius of curvature
of arcs into which the
dislocations are bent

(a)   (b)

Fig. 6.10. Dislocation movements envisaged in theories of solute hardening.

when the loop is assumed to find a new position of equilibrium. Figures 6.10a and b illustrate these two criteria. The lengths derived are

$$L_a = \frac{G^2 p^2}{\tau_i^2 d}, \qquad L_b = \frac{(pG)^{2/3} d^{1/3}}{\tau_i^{2/3}}$$

where G is the shear modulus, p the solvent atom diameter, τ_i the internal stress due to each solute atom, and d the spacing between solute atoms. By substituting [21] $\tau_i = Gqc$ where q is taken as the (extrapolated) fractional change in lattice parameter per 100% solute, c is the fractional atomic concentration and $d = pc^{-1/3}$, we have

$$\frac{L_a}{L_b} = \frac{1}{q^{4/3} c^{1/2}}$$

so that L_b, the independently moving length according to (b), is the smaller by a considerable amount. The constant in eq. 6.1 is easily seen to be $\tau_i d^{1/2}$; by substituting in eq. 6.1 for this and for L, we have

$$\tau_a \sim Gq^2 c \qquad (6.2)$$

$$\tau_b \sim Gq^{4/3} c \qquad (6.3)$$

Both these equations predict the linear dependence on concentration which is found experimentally and hence explain the additive nature of the frictional force in ternary alloys. As to magnitude, since L_a and L_b are upper and lower limits respectively and τ is proportional to $L^{-1/2}$, τ_b and τ_a should be upper and lower limits respectively of the contribution to the flow stress from (2). Table 6.4 shows that in fact both are on the high side compared with the measured flow stress at room temperature for fcc alloys, but that τ_b has the right magnitude for iron base alloys.

Table 6.4

Experimental and Theoretical Values of Frictional Force (Extrapolated Linearly to 100% solute)*

	Cu base[9]				Al base[14]		Fe base[26]			
Solute	Al	Be	Sn	Zn	Cu	Mg	Si	Mn	Ni	Mo
Experimental †	17	48	88	8.5	80	25	118	127	157	177
Theoretical										
Eq. 6.2	26	68	477	22	68	36	4.6	8.0	3.0	10.9
Eq. 6.3	132	245	910	114	220	150	55	93	41	480

* Units, shear stress in kg/mm².

† Experimental values refer to polycrystals.

To judge from Fig. 6.9 the discrepancy in the case of fcc alloys would not be removed by doing experiments at absolute zero.

Electrical binding, although somewhat analogous to dislocation locking, should produce a steady frictional force because the electrons can readjust themselves fast enough as the dislocations move to maintain the dipole distribution described earlier. One calculation has been made of the electrical interaction between edge dislocations and solutes.[23] The changes in interatomic spacing around an edge dislocation have the effect that the electrons concentrate in the expanded side of an edge dislocation and leave the compressed side, so that the dislocation becomes a line dipole, negatively charged on the expanded side. By calculating the strength of this effect and taking a value for the charge on the solute atom, the electrical binding energy was deduced; for solutions of Zn, Ga, Ge, and As in copper it was estimated to be $\frac{1}{8}$ to $\frac{1}{4}$ ev. In experiments on the plastic flow of these alloys[18] electrical interaction appeared to be the important factor, since the same stress-strain curves were obtained at equal electron-atom ratios. However, this is perhaps more likely to be due to the influence of solute on stacking fault energy discussed below.

The Snoek effect (5) is believed to apply to carbon and nitrogen dissolved in alpha iron. Carbon atoms dissolved in alpha iron are known to lie with their centres at [½00] positions, and to produce both shear and dilational distortion. The three different sorts of site, along the three different crystallographic axes, become distinguishable when a stress is applied since the unit cube becomes elongated in one direction, and the carbon atoms will prefer those sites at which the stress already produces

[26] W. P. Rees, B. E. Hopkins, and H. R. Tipler, *J.I.S.I.*, 1954, **177**, 93.

the distortion their presence involves. Consequently, near a dislocation carbon atoms are not randomly distributed on the Ox, Oy, and Oz axes, but prefer certain positions; for example, if we could walk round a screw dislocation, we should find positions along Ox, Oy, and Oz successively preferred over angular intervals of $2\pi/3$. Similarly, at an edge dislocation there is ordering of this nature, but calculation shows the gain in energy to be smaller.[27] It is believed that nitrogen atoms behave in iron in the same way as carbon atoms. The Snoek effect produces a frictional force on dislocations because, as a moving dislocation passes near carbon or nitrogen atoms, the latter tend to jump into the now favoured positions. This ordering dissipates energy and the dislocation finds itself in an energy well. The degree to which the ordering can approach the equilibrium degree obviously depends on how slowly the dislocation moves. For a slowly moving dislocation the force is calculated to be 45 kg/mm² per at % of carbon and to a first approximation is independent of temperature; for comparison, according to Fig. 6.31, the experimental value for the frictional force exerted by carbon is 32.5 kg/mm² shear stress per at %. This agreement is probably not as good as it seems, however, since it is not certain how much of the carbon and nitrogen was in solution during the experiments leading to Fig. 6.31.

The other problem with solutes is to explain why the rate of strain hardening does not fall off as soon as with pure metals. The obvious explanation is that cross slip is impeded, and this result can be produced by solute elements in two ways.

6. As a consequence of the frictional force.[10]
7. By decreasing the stacking fault energy.

The explanation of the first of these is that dislocations can only cross slip when they are in pure screw orientation. The elastic and electrical strains around solute atoms must tend to make dislocations wavy, and so hinder cross slip. In the alloys mentioned earlier, in which the effect of one solute on the stress-strain curve can be duplicated with a different solute, both frictional resistance and hindrance to cross slip presumably arise from the same cause, which implies that as far as cross slip is concerned (6) is the important factor in these alloys. As regards (7), besides the effect of segregation of solute to stacking faults, the stacking fault energy must depend on the atomic binding forces. An alteration in stacking fault width with composition has been seen in the electron microscope,[28] and

---

[27] A. W. Cochardt, G. Schoek, and H. Wiedersisch, *Acta Met.*, 1955, **3**, 533.
[28] A. Howie, Conference on Electron Microscopy, de Nederlandse Vereniging Voor Electronenmicroscopie, Delft, 1961, 383.

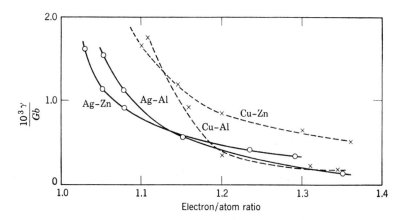

Fig. 6.11. Influence of solid solution alloying on stacking fault energy γ, measured in units of Gb. For pure Cu, unity on the ordinate scale equals 10.5 ergs/cm^2 and for pure Ag it equals 7.1 ergs/cm^2. (A. Howie)

X-ray observation has shown that alloying may increase the amount of stacking fault detected after cold work.[29, 30] Examples of the influence of solutes on the stacking fault energy of copper are shown in Fig. 6.11. Judging from the steeper strain hardening of the copper-silicon alloy in Fig. 6.7 compared with the copper-zinc alloy, silicon has a bigger effect on the stacking fault energy of copper than has zinc. The influence of a solute on stacking fault energy is probably electrical in origin, since atomic size difference is unlikely to be important at a stacking fault where the misfit between nearest neighbours is zero to a first approximation. Unlike the frictional forces discussed earlier, effects (6) and (7) do not add new terms to eq. 4.15–4.17 so much as alter the terms already present which depend on dislocation density.

Two other possible ways in which solutes may harden are:

8. Cluster hardening.[31] In this, aggregates of solute atoms are expected to impede slip like a precipitate. It can thus be regarded as a kind of precipitation hardening, probably less effective than ordinary precipitation hardening since it should normally be easier for slip to pierce the clusters than a particle of precipitate.

[29] R. Thomson, *Acta Met.*, 1958, **6**, 23.

[30] C. S. Barrett, *Imperfections in Nearly Perfect Crystals*, John Wiley and Sons, New York, 1952.

[31] E. R. Parker and T. H. Hazlitt, "Relation of properties to Microstructure," *A.S.M.*, 1954, p. 30.

9. By causing phase changes to take place during cold work as in stainless steel.

6.5 Effect of Precipitates

Precipitates not only raise the yield stress substantially but also raise the rate of strain hardening, and in single crystals stage 1 is suppressed.[32, 33] In fact a single crystal of Al-1.5 at % Cu aged to near peak hardness evidently gives a stress-strain curve very similar to that of a polycrystalline specimen of the same alloy. The stress-strain curve shown in Fig. 6.12

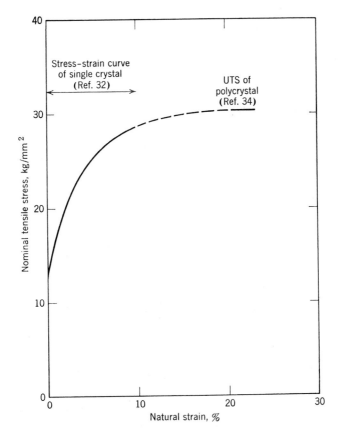

Fig. 6.12. Stress-strain data of Al−1.5 at % Cu alloy at room temperature after ageing to peak hardness.

[32] K. M. Carlsen and R. W. K. Honeycombe, *J.I.M.*, 1954–5, **83**, 449.
[33] F. Haessner and D. Schreiber, *Z. Metallk.*, 1957, **48**, 263.
[34] D. Hanson and M. L. Gayler, *J.I.M.*, 1923, **29**, 492.

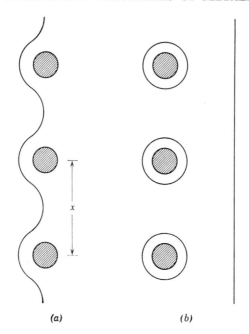

(a)   *(b)*

Fig. 6.13. A dislocation bulges between particles (*a*). If the particles are widely enough spaced, the bulges spread around the particles and join up, leaving a ring of dislocation around each particle, and the dislocation moves on (*b*).

was determined on a single crystal of such an alloy and extrapolates smoothly to the UTS point shown, which was determined on a poly-crystalline specimen. This is understandable since the grain boundaries provide infrequent barriers compared with the numerous particles of precipitate. In general, the rate of strain hardening in alloys containing finely dispersed precipitate is initially very steep but soon falls off, and a high UTS is reached after a relatively short uniform elongation.

First consider the yielding process. When the precipitates are suffi-ciently far apart, slip evidently proceeds by the dislocations looping between them, as illustrated in Fig. 6.13. The minimum radius of curvature into which a dislocation must bend is between $x/4$ and $x/2$, where x is the spacing between the particles, whence, from eq. 2.7 which relates stress and curvature, the stress required to push a dislocation between the particles is

$$\tau \sim 2Gb/x \qquad (6.4)$$

Experimentation gives quite close agreement with eq. 6.4. In Cu-Al alloys heat treated to give spacings of 16,000–60,000 A (shear stress 0.6 to 1.8 kg/mm²), the constant of proportionality was found to be 3½ instead of 2,[35] and in Nimonic alloys tested under creep conditions, which probably resulted in the proportionality constant being underestimated, it was found to be unity.[36] The precipitate spacings in the latter tests ranged from 800 to 20,000 A (shear stress 2–20 kg/mm²) so that eq. 6.4 is approximately confirmed by experiment over a range of particle spacings of 70-fold. The general trend indicated by eq. 6.4 is of course well supported by general experience, for example in steels,[37] in Cu-Cr alloys,[38] as well as in Al–Cu alloys.[39] Figure 6.1 shows how the strength properties change as the spacing of the precipitate particles is altered. In this figure, curve 1 relates to an alloy containing well-spaced precipitate particles. As the particle spacing is reduced, the stress needed to make the dislocations bend between them increases, and the yield stress rises (curves 2 and 3).

Eventually, as the spacing between the particles continues to be reduced, a point is reached where it is easier for the dislocation to cut through the particles. Examination with the electron microscope confirms that very closely spaced particles are cut through by slip.[40] There may be a range of spacings in which cross slip over the particles can help to avoid cutting through them. It is believed that the small particles present in precipitation-hardened metal contain no dislocations,[41] and observation supports this.[42] They should, therefore, have their full theoretical strength, although this is probably irrelevant except for large particles. In any event there seem to be four distinct reasons why they act as barriers to dislocations.

1. Since the slip distance inside the particle will rarely match exactly that in the matrix, after a dislocation has cut through there will be atomic misfit across the slip plane inside the particle, and the corresponding energy must be provided by the applied stress. An estimate of the stress τ arising from this effect can easily be made.[43] Suppose that a dislocation cutting through a precipitate causes a derangement energy of ΔE per

[35] D. Dew-Hughes and W. D. Robertson, *Acta Met.*, 1960, **8**, 147.

[36] J. R. Moon and D. McLean (unpublished).

[37] M. Gensamer, E. B. Pearsall, W. S. Pellini, and J. R. Low, *T.A.S.M.*, 1942, **30**, 983.

[38] W. R. Hibbard and E. W. Hart, *T.A.I.M.E.*, 1955, **203**, 200.

[39] R. B. Shaw, L. A. Shepard, C. D. Starr, and J. E. Dorn, *A.S.M.*, 1953, **45**, 249.

[40] R. B. Nicholson, G. Thomas, and J. Nutting, *Acta Met.*, 1960, **8**, 172.

[41] J. C. Fisher, "Impurities and Imperfections," *A.S.M.*, 1955, p. 28.

[42] D. McLean and K. Hale, *Acta Met.*, 1959, **7**, 438.

[43] A. Kelly and M. E. Fine, *Acta Met.*, 1957, **5**, 365.

atomic area traversed, and that a fraction f of the dislocation line is occupied by precipitate. Then,

$$\tau b^3/f = \Delta E$$

or

$$\tau = \frac{f\Delta E}{b^3} \qquad (6.5)$$

Equation 6.5 has been applied to Al–Cu and Al–Ag alloys. In an alloy of aluminium containing 2 at % copper, quenched and aged to maximum hardness, the "precipitate" consists of discs of copper atoms, one atom thick, about 100 A in diameter, and 150 A apart; an average value for f is roughly $\frac{1}{6}$. E is obtained from the heat of reversion, this being the energy required to redissolve the zones, and is 0.077 ev per copper atom. Equation 6.5 then gives $\tau = 13.7$ kg/mm² shear stress. This is smaller than the flow stress given by eq. 6.4, which is 25 kg/mm², and compares with the actual flow stress of a polycrystalline specimen of about 7 kg/mm² shear stress. In an alloy of aluminium containing 13 at % silver, quenched and aged to maximum hardness, about half the silver is present in the form of clusters about 100 A apart, each of which contains about 50% silver so that an average value for f is probably 0.13. The value of ΔE obtained from reversion data is 0.047 ev. Using this, we see that eq. 6.5 and 6.4 give $\tau = 6.5$ kg/mm² and 35 kg/mm² shear stress respectively, compared with the actual flow stress of a polycrystalline specimen of 20 kg/mm² shear stress. In both these alloys in the condition of maximum hardness these estimates indicate that slip prefers to cut through the particles rather than loop around them if effect (1) provides the main barrier.

Another way of looking at the effect (1) is suggested by the Nimonic and Inconel alloys. The precipitate particles in these are mostly Ni_3Al, are isomorphous with the matrix, and differ in lattice parameter from the matrix by not more than 1%. They therefore have the same orientation as the matrix so that slip planes pass uninterruptedly through them, but the Burgers vector changes by perhaps 1%. After the passage of a dislocation there will be a disregistry of about 1% across the slip plane inside and around a particle. The corresponding shear stress is $G/100$, or about 50 kg/mm², which must impede slip.

2. As illustrated in Fig. 6.14, slip passing through a particle creates new particle-matrix interface at AA' and BB', and energy may be needed for this.[43]

3. Any elastic strain around the particles will impede dislocations.[21] Elastic strains may be present initially either because of a difference in density between precipitate and matrix when the precipitates are formed at the temperature at which the metal is to be used, and also because of a

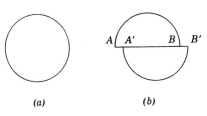

(a)   (b)

Fig. 6.14.   Shearing of a particle by slip creates new interface AA' and BB'.

difference in thermal contraction when the particles are formed at a high temperature and the metal is cooled.   The elastic strains increase the effective volume of a particle.   The so-called coherency strains arising from the pulling into register of atoms on either side of the interface when these nearly match are probably a less important source of hardening than the two mentioned, since they are likely to be confined to a rather narrow shell around each particle.

4. The final factor is the shape of the particles.   There are two effects here.   One is that the number of slip planes pierced by a given volume fraction of precipitate depends on the shape of the particles, being least for spherical particles, more for discs, and still more for rods.   It is perhaps significant that particularly hard vanadium steel contains rod-shaped particles of vanadium carbide.[44, 45]   The other effect is that the temperature sensitivity of the yield stress is influenced by the thickness of the particles.

The alloy hardening produced by a precipitate should not usually be sensitive to temperature.   The reason for this can be seen in the following way.   Suppose the yield stress is 50 kg/mm^2, that the particles of precipitate are 100 A apart, and that they are 100 A in diameter.   Then the work done as a dislocation cuts through the particles is $5 \times 10^9 \times 10^{-6} \times 100 \times 10^{-8} \times b$ per particle, where b is the Burgers vector; this is 75 ev, so that thermal agitation can scarcely assist, at least at ordinary temperatures.   The temperature sensitivity of an Al–Ag alloy treated to contain particles 100 A in diameter is illustrated in Fig. 6.15; the flow stress of this alloy is unaffected by temperature.   This circumstance is probably partly responsible for the fact that the stress-strain curves of precipitation-hardened alloys tend to be less affected by temperature than do those of pure metals, as is indicated by the UTS ratios in Table 6.5.   But if the particles are very thin, a temperature dependence can be expected.   The Al–Cu system provides an example of this.   In this system

[44] K. Kuo, *J.I.S.I.*, 1956, **184**, 258.
[45] A. K. Seal and R. W. K. Honeycombe, *J.I.S.I.*, 1958, **188**, 9.

Table 6.5

Effect of Temperature on the Mechanical Properties of Different Metals*

Metal	Description	Temperature of Test, °C	UTS kg/mm²	Uniform E%	RA%
Al	Annealed single phase	r.t.	6.9	36	90
		−180	14.6	44	87
		Ratio 2.2			
Duralumin	Precipitate present	r.t.	40.5	27	27
		−183	50.5	28	29
		Ratio 1.25			
Cu	Annealed single phase	r.t.	22.0	48	77
		−180	35.5	58	77
		Ratio 1.6			
70/30 brass	Annealed solid solution	r.t.	35.7	49	77
		−180	51.5	75	73
		Ratio 1.44			
Cu-2.56% Be	Precipitate present	r.t.	130	2.6	5
		−180	150	3.0	6
		Ratio 1.15			
Ni	Annealed single phase	r.t.	46.0	42	78
		−180	68	53	75
		Ratio 1.48			
80/20 Ni/Cr	Probably annealed solid solution	r.t.	93	28	52
		−253	132	35	50
		Ratio 1.42			

* Data taken from Ref. 46.

the first formed particles consist of platelets of copper one atom thick. (Curve 3 in Fig. 6.1 represents this condition.) Here that part of the barrier effect arising from (2) is a short-range force which temperature can help to overcome. The temperature sensitivity of an Al–Cu alloy aged to this condition is also illustrated in Fig. 6.15; the flow stress commences to rise below about −100°C. Above this temperature, strengthening is probably due to effect (3).

Turning now to strain hardening, when the particles are far enough apart for the dislocations to bulge between them, strain hardening is steeper than in the pure metal; for example, compare curve 1 in Fig. 6.1 with Fig. 5.7, remembering that shear stress is plotted against shear strain in Fig. 6.1 and tensile stress against tensile strain in Fig. 5.7. Presumably,

[46] P. L. Teed, *Properties of Metallic Materials at Low Temperature*, Chapman & Hall, London, 1950.

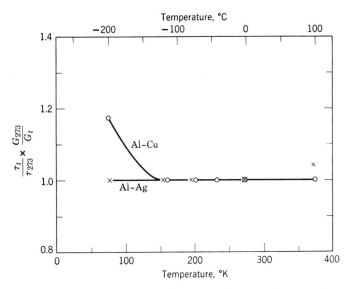

Fig. 6.15. Temperature dependance of flow stress of two Al alloys. Al–Cu, ref. 43; Al–Ag, ref. 47.

clusters of dislocations are formed around each particle—one ring is left each time a dislocation loops between according to Fig. 6.13—and the stresses from these oppose further slip,[48] and the clusters themselves form a penumbra that is difficult to penetrate, so that the effective diameter of the particles increases. Microscopic examination reveals much cross slip.[1, 47] But when the precipitates are very close together and small, strain hardening is weak in single crystals (curve 3 in Fig. 6.1). The dislocations cut through the precipitates and there is no intensified strain hardening. Slip lines are then long and straight, with negligible cross slip.[1] Probably cross slip is difficult because dislocations cannot easily form straight lengths in pure screw orientation on account of the irregular internal stress.

The strongest metals are produced, however, not merely by treating to form a precipitate, but by plastically deforming the metal before this treatment. Good examples of the results that can be obtained are provided by the 200-ton steels[49] and the Cu–Be alloys.[50] Some stress-strain curves of the latter alloys are illustrated in Fig. 6.16, and show how the strength is increased by precipitating copper–beryllium compound, and

[48] J. C. Fisher, E. W. Hart, and R. H. Pry, *Acta Met.*, 1953, **1**, 336.

[47] A. Kelly, A. Lassila, and S. Sato, *Phil. Mag.*, 1959, **4**, 1260.

[49] D. J. Schmatz and V. F. Zackay, *A.S.M.*, 1959, **51**, 476.

[50] C. S. Smith and C. van Wagner, *A.S.T.M.*, 1941, **41**, 825.

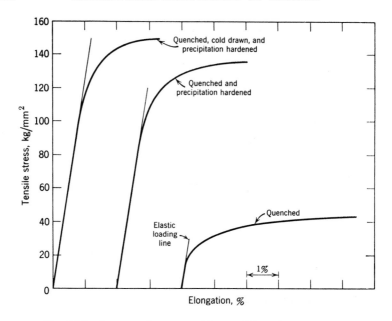

Fig. 6.16.   Stress-strain curves of $Cu - 2.2\%$ Be alloys (Ref. 50).

that it is increased still further if the alloy is cold drawn before this.   In the former condition, no plastic strain was observed with a sensitivity of detection of 0.0001% up to 35 kg/mm² tensile stress.   In the latter condition, none was observed up to 70 kg/mm², and no permanent set after unloading up to 112 kg/mm², so that up to this stress there was no unrecoverable looping between or cutting through particles.   The enhanced strength when plastic deformation precedes the precipitation treatment suggests that precipitation occurs on the dislocations and is possibly nucleated at more centres, and so is more closely spaced.   In addition, perhaps, if the straining produces a cell structure, the precipitate is concentrated in the cell walls and is still more closely spaced for this reason. If so, such a metal is an example of a desirable degree of nonuniformity.

When precipitation hardening is important, eq. 4.15–4.17 lose their significance.   At yield, precipitation hardening evidently swamps the other terms.   The steep strain hardening which follows yield in these alloys implies that the various terms, or some of them, then grow rapidly.

6.6   Dislocation Locking

A solute atom which is larger than the space in which it fits in the perfect lattice is attracted to the underneath, or expanded, side of an edge dis-

Fig. 6.17.   Release of a dislocation from a row of anchoring atoms.

location, and a solute atom which produces only shear distortion in the lattice around it is attracted to the side of an edge dislocation, that is, tends to lie in the slip plane, and is also attracted to screw dislocations, being evenly distributed around such dislocations. There is thus a binding energy between solutes and dislocations which anchors dislocations at temperatures too low for atomic diffusion.[51] Shear distortion as well as dilational distortion is certainly substantial around carbon and nitrogen atoms in alpha iron, so that locking of screw as well as of edge dislocations can be expected here. Shear distortion around substitutional solutes in fcc metals is probably small. However, the dislocations in these metals are split into partials, which cannot both be pure screw simultaneously, so that at least one partial can always be anchored. The two partials are connected together by a stacking fault which in many pure metals provides quite a strong tie. For example, in copper the stacking fault has an energy of about 20 ergs/cm^2, so that to separate the partials indefinitely requires a resolved shear stress of 8 kg/mm^2. Thus, in fcc metals, pure dilational distortion around solute atoms should often anchor dislocations effectively.

Estimates have been made of the force required to release a dislocation from its anchoring atoms. One estimate[52] assumes that when there is strong locking the locking atoms can be thought of as a line of atoms along the line of the dislocation, as illustrated in Fig. 6.17. The anchoring force is overcome when the applied stress and thermal agitation succeed in pushing forward a loop x that is now partly free from the anchoring atoms and is long enough to be extended indefinitely by the applied stress. For the case of carbon in alpha iron, such a loop is one a few atoms long. Assuming that the extra dislocation line energy of the loop is small, on the grounds that the change in the dislocation's stress field is localised[53] (section 2.1e), the energy of the loop is mainly the binding energy of the carbon atoms from which it is partially freed, and is about 1 ev. Consequently, the anchoring stress is sensitive to temperature; as the temperature is reduced more of this energy has to be supplied by the stress which must therefore rise.

[51] A. H. Cottrell, Report on Strength of Solids, *Phys. Soc.*, 1948, p. 30.
[52] A. H. Cottrell and B. A. Bilby, *P.P.S.*, 1949, **A.62**, 49.
[53] A. H. Cottrell, "Conference on High Rates of Strain," *Inst. Mech. Engrs. London*, 1957, p. 1.

However, a detailed estimate of the distribution of solute atoms around a dislocation has been made for the case of carbon in alpha iron,[27] and throws doubt on the idea of a single line distribution. The shear distortion around the carbon atoms was taken into account. The estimate leads to these conclusions.

1. The atmosphere is extensive, is distributed with $\pi/3$ symmetry around a $\frac{1}{2}\langle 111 \rangle$ screw dislocation, and at an edge dislocation is concentrated in the slip plane and in the space below the dislocation:

2. One atomic distance from the dislocation line the carbon concentration is about 6%, approximately independently of whether the dislocation is edge or screw, so that the total carbon content at this distance is less than one carbon atom per atomic length of dislocation.

3. The binding energy exceeds kT at room temperature up to a distance of 30 atomic diameters from the dislocation line, and within this distance there are 15 carbon atoms per atomic length of dislocation. If the larger entropy of the dilute matrix is taken into account, the atmosphere would not extend as far as this. Nevertheless, it would seem that to release the dislocation from such an atmosphere the front of the loop must be thrown much further forward than if there were only a single line of atoms, and the loop's energy may be so big that thermal agitation cannot give much help in forming it. To the extent that this is so, the effective anchoring stress would be independent of temperature.

When dislocations are preferred nucleation sites for precipitation, the precipitates should be more closely spaced along a dislocation than elsewhere. It should then be more difficult to start yield than to continue it. In this way precipitate locking is expected to arise. As already pointed out, precipitates are not likely to produce a force that is very sensitive to temperature. The locking force in steel seems rather insensitive to temperature (section 6.7), and of course the equilibrium solubility of the usual locking elements, carbon and nitrogen, is very small. Dislocation locking is possibly due to precipitates of carbide or nitride in steel. Precipitates are unlikely to produce a locking force as uniform from dislocation to dislocation as solute segregation, since the precise site of a precipitate is probably determined by some accidental feature like the presence of a jog, with the result that the precipitate spacing and the locking force vary from place to place. In such a situation, observed yield stresses presumably correspond to the weakest locking.

6.7 The Sharp Yield

Sudden yielding accompanied by a drop in load is a behaviour best known in mild steel. It brings advantages and disadvantages to engineering applications. The fact that the stress for yield in mild steel is high is a big advantage, but the usual concomitant large elongation at yield (Lüders strain) is undesirable since it gives rise to "stretcher strains" in deep drawing and the associated strain ageing can cause embrittlement. Stretcher strains may also occur with aluminium–magnesium alloys, which likewise exhibit a marked yield point. Although the ultimate purpose of studying the sharp yield is to retain the high strength but to avoid the disadvantageous features, the procedure followed here is to review systematically the various effects associated with the sharp yield. This is done in some detail because so much of the metal that is made is mild steel.

Although the sharp yield is most important commercially in the two metals mentioned, it is by no means confined to them. Prominent yield point effects have also been detected in polycrystalline specimens of the fcc alloys of copper–zinc and copper–tin,[54] nickel–manganese, copper–beryllium and standard silver,[55] and copper–antimony,[56] and are to be found in the bcc metals molybdenum, niobium, and tantalum[57] of normal purity. At the same time, weak but definite yield points have been found in single crystals of zinc[58, 59] and cadmium containing nitrogen,[60] and in single crystals of fcc and bcc copper–zinc alloys.[61] The sharp yield point thus occurs in all three main crystal lattices.

In these metals the sharp yield is ascribed to locking of dislocations by the impurities present; in iron and steel it is associated with small quantities of carbon or nitrogen. A sharp yield drop and a yield elongation of some degree associated with a Lüders band will of course occur whenever the initiation of slip is more difficult than its continuation. Besides impurity locking, four other processes are known which produce a sharp yield point in this way; yield in whiskers (section 4.3), locking of dislocations by point defects, and two processes that occur in strain-hardened materials described in section 5.6. Mechanical twinning is also similar in principle but deformation by twinning does not seem able to spread along a specimen as continuously as deformation by slip can. In what follows, the yield point resulting from impurity locking is described.

(a) *Sequence of Events.* As the upper yield stress (uys) is approached a

[54] M. Kuroda, *Sci. Papers Inst. Phys. Chem. Research, Tokyo*, 1938, **34**, 1528.
[55] C. A. Edwards, D. L. Phillips, and Y. H. Liu, *J.I.S.I.*, 1943, **147**, 145.
[56] L. M. T. Hopkin, *J.I.M.*, 1955–6, **84**, 102.
[57] E. T. Wessel, *T.A.I.M.E.*, 1957, **209**, 930.
[58] E. Orowan, *Z. Physik*, 1934, **89**, 614.
[59] H. L. Wain and A. H. Cottrell, *P.P.S.*, 1950, **B.63**, 339.
[60] C. L. Smith, *Nature*, 1947, **160**, 466.
[61] G. W Ardley and A. H. Cottrell, *P.R.S.*, 1953, **A.219**, 328.

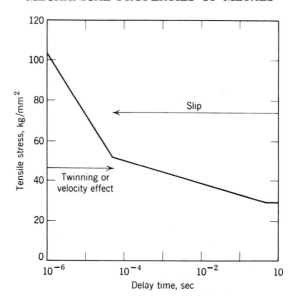

Fig. 6.18a. Delay time for yield of mild steel as a function of stress.   Test temperature 23°C (Ref. 62).

small plastic strain occurs.   Yield then occurs sharply at the uys, and the stress drops suddenly to the lower yield stress (lys).   A "Lüders band" of deformation (see section 6.7d) propagates across the specimen so rapidly that it cannot be stopped by unloading, which means that it propagates at a relatively low stress.   The band then gradually extends along the specimen at the lys.   The strain in the Lüders band, or Lüders strain, is the strain needed to work harden the metal sufficiently to bear the lys once the locking forces have been overcome.   In ordinary testing, Lüders bands usually start at more places than one and spread until they meet.   When the whole specimen is covered and every portion is strained by the amount of the Lüders strain, normal work hardening begins.

(b) *Delay Time; Pre-yield Strain.*   Even with stresses greater than the static yield stress as determined in a conventional test yield is not instantaneous.   There is a "delay time" which decreases as the stress is increased in the way illustrated in Fig. 6.18a for steel and in Fig. 6.18b for beta brass.   Of course, a delay time is not peculiar to metals exhibiting a sharp yield point.   It arises with any process of yield in which thermal activation assists the stress.   Thus eq. 4.12 can be rewritten as:

[62] J. M. Krafft, *A.S.M.*, 1956, **48**, 249, in discussion.

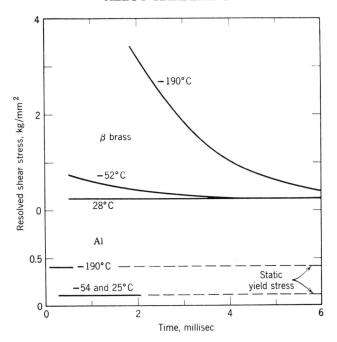

Fig. 6.18b. Delay time for yield of β brass as a function of temperature. Absence of delay time for yield in Al (Ref. 63). Compare Fig. 4.11.

$$\tau = \frac{kT}{xbd}\left[-\ln \delta t - \ln \frac{\nu N x L b}{\delta \epsilon}\right] + \frac{W}{xbd}$$

to connect the stress τ with the delay time δt required to produce an extension $\delta \epsilon$, and some time effect is to be expected with all metals. It will be clear from the discussion in section 4.7e, however, that with the "unlocking" yield process depicted in Fig. 6.17 in which x and d are small, an effect is to be expected at relatively large values of δt. Comparison of Fig. 6.18a with the data for aluminium and copper in Figs. 6.18b and 4.10c confirms that the effect does set in at larger values of δt with steel than with aluminium or copper. Nevertheless, this is not a proof that an impurity-controlled process like that depicted in Fig. 6.17 is responsible, since the Peierls force itself will produce a similar time effect at large values of δt, as the discussion in section 4.10c makes clear. In view of the relative insensitivity to temperature of the locking mechanism in steel (section 6.7g), it is likely that the locking mechanism does not make a large contribution in Fig. 6.18a.

[63] I. R. Kramer and R. Maddin, *T.A.I.M.E.*, 1952, **190**, 197.

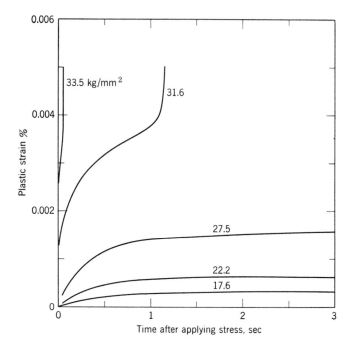

Fig. 6.19. Relation between plastic strain (i.e., additional to elastic) and time when the stress was applied very rapidly and then held constant. Low-carbon steel (Ref. 67).

A "pre-yield strain" is also observed, that is to say, some plastic strain precedes the drop in load and the Lüders extension. The reported magnitude of the pre-yield strain varies from 0.003%[64] to 0.5%[65] in mild steel alone, larger strains being found at low temperature so long as the tough-brittle transition is not overstepped. Figure 6.29a shows how the pre-yield strain varies with temperature. There are also "artificial" pre-yield strains when local Lüders bands are formed at obvious stress raisers such as pop-marks.[66] The way the pre-yield strain varies with stress below the uys is shown in Fig. 6.19. As might be expected from the delay time curves in Fig. 6.18a, the time scale for the events shown in Fig. 6.19 increases rapidly as the stress is reduced below the nominal uys.[65, 68] The small pre-yield strains shown in Fig. 6.19 are presumably

[64] T. Vreeland, D. S. Wood, and D. S. Clark, *A.S.M.*, 1953, **45**, 620.
[65] W. S. Owen, M. Cohen, and B. L. Averbach, *A.S.M.*, 1958, **50**, 517.
[66] V. A. Phillips, A. J. Swain, and R. Eborall, *J.I.M.*, 1953, **81**, 625.
[67] T. Vreeland, D. S. Wood, and D. S. Clark, *Acta Met.*, 1953, **1**, 414.
[68] E. T. Wessel, Discussion to ref. 65.

associated with grain-boundary hardening in the way discussed in section 4.1, since the hardening rates in the two cases are rather similar. For example, in Fig. 6.19, which shows results for steel, a 0.001% strain requires a tensile stress increment of 10 kg/mm^2, or a shear stress increment of 6.4×10^{-4} G. In copper, the same strain requires a tensile stress increment of 1 kg/mm^2 when the grain size is 0.025 mm, or a shear stress increment of 10^{-4} G. Therefore, in the iron, slip probably occurs during this small strain in a smaller proportion of the grains than in copper.

Recovery occurs after the pre-yield strain and is referred to in section (f).

(c) *Upper Yield Stress and Experimental Technique.* It is difficult to measure the uys reproducibly because the plastic strain before yield is usually so small that heterogeneous stress distribution is not smoothed out. A large-scale heterogeneity arises principally from nonaxial loading, and there is a smaller source in the stress concentration at the specimen shoulders.[69] With a round specimen, the ratio of peak to mean stress arising from nonaxial loading is $(1 + 8t/d)$, where d is the diameter of the specimen and t the distance between the stress axis and the specimen axis. With normal machines and normal care in preparation, a ratio of 2:1 might be reached. With conventional specimens, the stress at the shoulders is about 5% higher than elsewhere.

There have been two ways of meeting the axiality difficulty. In one method, (a), nonaxialty is allowed for[69] by putting three extensometers on the specimen 120° apart from each other and computing the peak stress from the three readings. In one set of experiments using this method, uys values reproducible to within 1.3% were obtained for specimens of differing size, whether tested in tension or compression. A modification of this method is to adjust the loading arrangement until the elastic strains measured at different places around the specimen (or on opposite sides of a flat specimen) are equal to within a specified amount.[70, 71] In the other method, (b), long wire specimens are used, and either a thick soft deposit is formed on the ends[72] to absorb bending, or long end pieces are arranged to be hard[73] so that they act as flexible elastic links. Some results obtained with these methods are given in Table 6.6.

The ratios of uys/lys are much higher than the ratio usually obtained of, say, less than 1.1:1. Besides the macro stress concentrations arising from

[69] J. L. M. Morrison, *Inst. Mech. Engrs. London*, 1939, **142**, 15.
[70] A. N. Holden and J. H. Holloman, *T.A.I.M.E.*, 1949, **185**, 179.
[71] H. Schwartzbart and J. R. Low, *T.A.I.M.E.*, 1949, **185**, 637.
[72] W. Sylwestrowicz and E. O. Hall, *P.P.S.*, 1951, **64B**, 495.
[73] N. M. Hutchison, *J.I.S.I.*, 1957, **186**, 431.

Table 6.6

Upper and Lower Yield Stress of Mild Steel Tensile Stresses in kg/mm^2

Method	(a)	(b) (Armco)	(b)	(b)
C%	0.21	0.02	0.045	0.03
Grain size, mm	—	0.0075	0.0075	0.0022
uys	36	33.8	42.8	51.4
lys	—	26.5	27.4	26.1
uys/lys	—	1.28	1.56	1.97
Ref.	69	72		73

experimental inadequacy there are also micro stress concentrations arising from elastic anisotropy. The effect of elastic anisotropy on the uys has not been investigated but should be large when the pre-yield strain is small. In iron, for example, the modulus varies with crystal orientation by more than 2:1 (chapter 1) so that with a random orientation the stress carried by different grains will vary by this amount. As between a specimen with randomly orientated grains and one with the grains orientated so that the maximum modulus is parallel to the stress direction, a difference in uys of about 2:1 therefore seems possible.

The yield strain itself is so large that conventional techniques give reproducible results for the lys. A consequence is that most of the systematic yield stress data relates to the lys.

(d) *The Lüders Yield.* The suddenness with which a Lüders band is initiated indicates that it starts at one small region, since it is unlikely that this very critical condition is reached at the same moment at several regions in the band-to-be but nowhere else. Some calculations support this interpretation. By computing the shear stress on the slip planes of a random polycrystalline aggregate it has been shown[74] that the ratio of the shear yield stress in torsion to the tensile yield stress is 0.57 for a bcc and 0.58 for an fcc lattice if the condition for yield is that in all grains across the section the yield stress must be reached on the most favourably oriented slip plane. On the other hand, the ratio is 0.5 if yield starts in a single grain. Experiment supports the latter conception because the measured ratio tends to be 0.5 for large specimens.[69] We therefore suppose that the pre-yield strain develops stress concentrations which in one grain are large enough to initiate the Lüders band.

A detailed study[66] of the Lüders band made on aluminium–magnesium

[74] H. L. Cox and D. G. Sopwith, *P.P.S.*, 1937, **49**, 134.

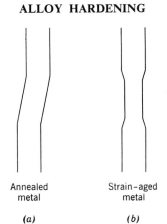

Annealed   Strain-aged
metal   metal

(a)   (b)

Fig. 6.20.   Forms of Lüders bands.

alloy showed that in annealed material it consisted primarily of a homogeneous shear as in Fig. 6.20a along the plane of maximum shear stress,
and in strain aged material of a simple thinning as in Fig. 6.20b. With a
polished specimen the tilted band of Fig. 6.20a is clearly visible. In one
experiment on annealed material, the total Lüders strain was 1.4%, of
which 0.8% was due to the homogeneous shear. This homogeneous shear
signifies that over the whole cross section of the specimen a corresponding
amount of directed slip took place. In the experiment just mentioned,
the remaining 0.6% extension was due to a uniform thinning of the
specimen which must have been caused by a corresponding amount of slip
in random directions. In strain-aged specimens all the slip was therefore
of this sort. Thus, in annealed material a large part of the Lüders strain
involved slip that was coordinated across the whole section, but in strain-
aged material all the slip was uncoordinated.

To spread the band, stress concentrations are available at the band
edges both on the macroscopic scale from the kink (Fig. 6.20) and on the
microscopic scale from the pressure of the loose dislocations in the band.
The latter seems usually to be the important factor. Thus in single
crystals narrow Lüders bands have been seen[75] which did not spread, presumably because the dislocations all ran out of the crystal; and there is
other evidence (section e on ageing effects) which also shows that the
pressure of loose dislocations is usually the important thing. It is necessary to assume, however, that there is a delay before the next region
yields, as otherwise the band would spread far more rapidly than it does.
This delay is presumably equivalent to that observed before the Lüders

[75] H. W. Paxton and I. J. Bear, *T.A.I.M.E.*, 1955, **203**, 989.

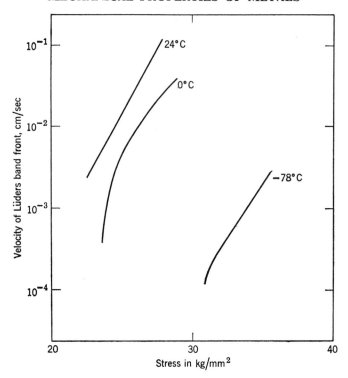

Fig. 6.21. Velocity of Lüders band front; influence of stress and temperature. SAE 1010 steel (Ref. 76).

band formed. The situation just ahead of the band can be described by saying that outside the Lüders band the events that occur during this delay time and precipitate yield have not yet taken place (otherwise a Lüders band would have formed there) and must now be completed under a stress equal to the lys × the stress concentration factor.

This conception of the spreading of the band was stimulated by measurements of band velocity in long steel wires. In these measurements the velocity was deduced from measurements of elongation and counts of the numbers of Lüders bands.[76] Some results are illustrated in Fig. 6.21 and show that the band velocity increases with applied stress and temperature. Bearing in mind that the metal just ahead of the Lüders band re-enacts the events which precede the Lüders yield, the effects in Fig. 6.21 can be ascribed to the influence stress and temperature have on the delay time in Fig. 6.18 and 6.18b.

[76] J. C. Fisher and H. C. Rogers, *Acta Met.*, 1956, **4**, 180.

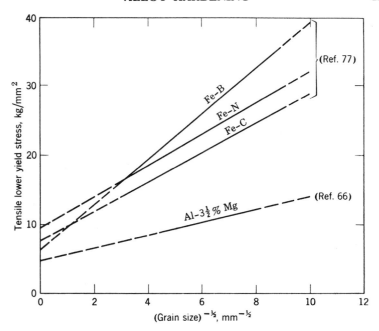

Fig. 6.22. Influence of grain size on lower yield stress. Tensile tests at room temperature.

Two modes of spreading of Lüders bands have been observed. The more usual is that in which the band front or fronts appear to travel steadily along the specimen, although the movement probably occurs in little jumps of a grain diameter at a time. The other mode is for the first band to be reflected at the edge of the specimen[65]; this second band is reflected again at the opposite side of the specimen, and so on. The delay period before each reflected band appears is evident to observation.

(*e*) *Lower Yield Stress and the Effect of Grain Size.* The lower yield stress rises with decreasing grain size according to an equation like eq. 4.7

$$\tau = \tau_f{}' + \tau_s{}'\left(\frac{l'}{L'^{1/2}}\right)^{1/2} \tag{6.6}$$

where the terms are marked with primes to distinguish them from those in eq. 4.7. Some results conforming to this relation are shown in Fig. 6.22. Such a relation immediately suggests an interpretation like that given in section 4.7 and this is discussed in detail in section 6.7*h*. The essential idea, however, is that the Lüders band is spread by the stress

[77] I. Codd and N. J. Petch, *Phil. Mag.*, 1960, **5**, 30.

concentration at the heads of slip bands held up by grain boundaries at the front of the Lüders band. According to this interpretation, τ_s' in eq. 6.6 is here the stress needed to move a dislocation just ahead of the Lüders band and near one of these slip bands; it measures the strength with which the dislocation is locked in position. Since the lys varies with grain size considerably more sharply than do the proof stresses (of pure metals) discussed in chapter 4, the quantity $\tau_s'l'^{1/2}$ must be considerably larger for the lys than the corresponding term in eq. 4.7. Since there is no particular reason why l' should be large, the conclusion is that τ_s' is large, which of course fits the basic idea that a yield drop occurs when dislocations are well anchored. τ_f' is a friction stress due mainly to alloy elements and to lattice friction.

Graphical plots like Fig. 6.22 have been used to determine τ_f' and $\tau_s'l'^{1/2}$ for different alloys. According to Fig. 6.22, for example, dislocations in steel are anchored by carbon, nitrogen, and boron with increasing firmness in that order. Some values of friction stress and locking stress for different metals are collected in Table 6.7. From these values it can be

Table 6.7

Locking Stresses and Friction Stresses*

System	Temperature °C	$\tau_s'l'^{1/2}$	τ_f'	$\dfrac{\tau_s'l'^{1/2}}{G} \times 10^4$	$\dfrac{\tau_f'}{G} \times 10^3$	Ref.
Al-3½% Mg	r.t.	0.15	2.3	0.6	0.9	66
Fe-C	r.t.	0.32	3.7	0.41	0.47 ⎫	77
	−196	0.50	22.2	0.65	2.8 ⎬	
Fe-N	r.t.	0.37	3.55	0.47	0.45 ⎫	77
	−196	0.80	22.2	1.02	2.8 ⎬	
Fe-B	r.t.	0.51	3.2	0.65	0.41 ⎫	77
	−196	0.97	20.0	1.24	2.6 ⎬	
Mo	r.t.	0.85	5.5	0.85	0.55	78
Nb	r.t.	Zero to 0.05	7 to 9	Zero to 0.13	1.9 to 2.3	79, 80

* The values quoted are for equivalent shear stresses $= \frac{1}{2} \times$ tensile stress. The units are kg/mm² for stress and cms for l.

seen that if l', the distance between the head of a slip band and the nearest source of dislocations, is taken as 10^{-4} cm, the ratio τ_s'/G is close to 10^{-2}. The friction stress is one-tenth of this at room temperature, and so satisfies the condition that it should be smaller than the locking stress.

From plots like these in Fig. 6.22, many other deductions are also

[78] A. A. Johnson, *Phil. Mag.*, 1959, **4**, 194.
[79] M. A. Adams, A. C. Roberts, and R. E. Smallman, *Acta Met.*, 1960, **8**, 328.
[80] A. T. Churchman, *J.I.M.*, 1959–60, **88**, 221.

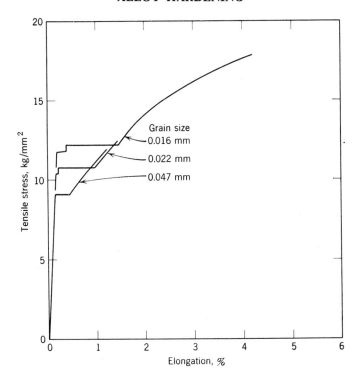

Fig. 6.23. Influence of grain size on yield of an Al$-3\frac{1}{2}$% Mg commercial alloy (Ref. 66).

drawn, some of which will be mentioned in other sections.   It is therefore worth emphasising that literal deductions from such a plot involve certain assumptions discussed in section 6.7*h*.   However, the broad picture is not likely to change as these assumptions are investigated, because measurements of the temperature sensitivity of the lys (section 6.7*g*) support eq. 6.6 and because the values obtained for τ_s' from plots like those in Fig. 6.22 can be approximately confirmed in other ways.   Thus, using values of $\tau_s'\left(\dfrac{l'}{L'}\right)^{\frac{1}{2}}$ obtained from a grain-size analysis, eq. 6.11 is satisfied within a factor of about two, the left-hand side tending to be smaller than the right.[81]

As eq. 6.11 implies, the Lüders yield increases as the grain size decreases. The general relation,[66, 82] between these two quantities is illustrated in Fig. 6.23.   It is approximately that which would result if there were a

[81] A. H. Cottrell, *T.A.I.M.E.*, 1958, **212**, 192.

[82] D. V. Wilson and B. Russell, *Acta Met.*, 1960, **8**, 36.

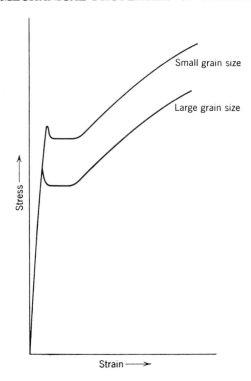

Fig. 6.24. Another influence of grain size on yield to compare with Fig. 6.23.

basic work hardening curve, the same for all grain sizes; the yield elongation for a particular grain size is approximately the strain abscissa at a
stress equal to the lys for this grain size. Exceptions to this normal
behaviour have been found, however,[83] and present a difficulty. The
exceptional behaviour is illustrated diagrammatically in Fig. 6.24, in which
the flow stress beyond the Lüders yield depends on grain size as much as the
lys itself does. Yet in this condition the strong locking, from which
the steep grain size dependence of the lys is supposed to arise, has disappeared. There should only remain the relatively weak grain size effect
discussed in chapter 4 and which is evidently present in Fig. 6.26 (curve 2).
    The yield point effects in single crystals are much weaker than in poly-
crystals. This is shown by the first four rows in Table 6.8, these tests
being made at room temperature. At room temperature in fact, the yield
point is not always observed.[70] At lower temperatures, however, the

[83] H. Conrad and G. Schoeck, *Acta Met.*, 1960, **8**, 791.

effects become much more marked[84, 85, 86] as shown by the data in the last two rows of Table 6.8.   As regards the application of eq. 6.6 to single crystals, the value of L' is presumably somewhat indeterminate but usually large, except when slip right across the crystal is favoured.   The lower yield stresses of single crystals should therefore be close to the value obtained for τ_f' from plots like Fig. 6.22, as in fact they appear to be.

Table 6.8

Yield Point Data on Single and Polycrystals of Iron*

	uys	lys	Yield Strain, %	Ref.
Pure iron, carburised				
Polycrystals	32	21.5	3	
Single crystals	8.4	8.1	0.1	
Pure iron, nitrided				71
Polycrystals	24.5	19.7	2	
Single crystals	8.5	8.4	0.8	
Pure iron single crystals, carburised				
Room temperature	4.9	4.9	0.3	
$-77°C$	12.7	10.5	1.5	84
$-196°C$	> 35			

* Stress in kg/mm^2.

(*f*) *Ageing Effects*.   There are several ageing effects which occur in connection with the sharp yield point.

1. The most important is strain ageing, which is the process whereby, when the metal is strained and then aged, the sharp yield and the yield elongation gradually return.   With them return the troubles in deep drawing operations connected with stretcher-strain markings, and ductility may be dangerously reduced.

There have been many studies of strain ageing, particularly in steel and

[84] A. T. Churchman and A. H. Cottrell, *Nature*, 1951, **167**, 943.
[85] H. W. Paxton and A. T. Churchman, *Acta Met.*, 1953, **1**, 473.
[86] N. P. Allen, B. E. Hopkins, and J. E. McLennan, *P.R.S.*, 1956, **A.234**, 221.

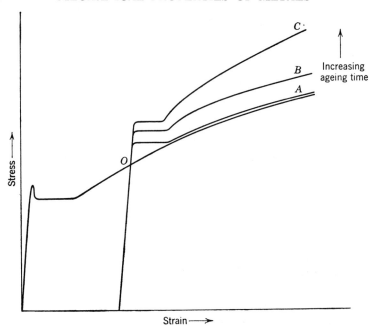

Fig. 6.25. Effect of strain ageing on the yield stress of steel containing 0.004% N in solution (after Ref. 82).

aluminium–magnesium alloy.[66, 82, 87, 88, 89, 90] The course of events observed in steel is illustrated in Fig. 6.25. The bottom curve is the original stress-strain curve. Other specimens were stopped after 4% elongation at point O, and aged at 60°C; raising the ageing temperature simply accelerates the ageing process. Up to an ageing time of $\frac{1}{2}$ hour the lys and the yield elongation increased but immediately beyond the yield elongation the original stress-strain curve was rejoined; curve A illustrates this stage. For ageing times of $\frac{1}{2}$ to $2\frac{1}{2}$ hours, the whole curve was raised, as illustrated by curve B; the Lüders strain did not change. During ageing beyond $2\frac{1}{2}$ hours, the lys rose very slowly, but the strain-hardening coefficient now began to increase, as illustrated by curve C; the UTS also rose. For ageing times of more than 150 hours the lys, strain-hardening coefficient, and UTS all decreased very slowly, indicating that overageing had begun. By performing similar tests on metal

[87] E. S. Davenport and E. C. Bain, *A.S.M.*, 1935, **23**, 1047.
[88] A. H. Cottrell and G. M. Leak, *J.I.S.I.*, 1952, **172**, 301.
[89] D. V. Wilson and B. Russell, *Acta Met.*, 1960, **8**, 468.
[90] D. V. Wilson and B. Russell, *Acta Met.*, 1959, **7**, 628.

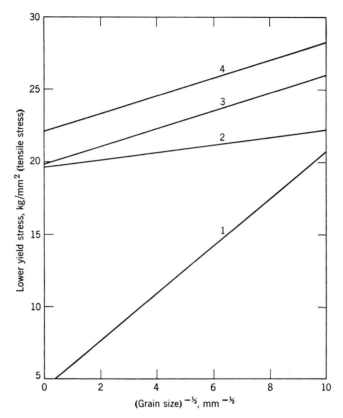

Fig. 6.26. Influence of grain size on lower yield stress at various stages during strain ageing (Ref. 82).

of various grain sizes the results illustrated in Fig. 6.26 were obtained. Here, curve 1 is for the original annealed material and curve 2 represents the situation immediately after straining 4%. The flow stress is then not very sensitive to grain size, and is another way of describing the weak influence of grain size on the flow stress mentioned at the end of the previous section. Although locking is now weak, the friction stress has of course been raised considerably by work hardening. Curve 3 represents the same situation as curve A in Fig. 6.25. Locking is restored, but the slope is less than for curve 1 because l' is smaller since there is now a higher dislocation density. Curve 4 represents the same situation as curve C in Fig. 6.25, and shows that continued ageing raises the friction stress.

The interpretation of these results is as follows. During the first half hour of ageing at 60°C, nitrogen segregates to the dislocations and locks them. Calculation indicates that at this time about one atom of nitrogen per atomic length of dislocation would have been able to segregate. Moreover, in separate tests[82, 89] in which the concentration of carbon and nitrogen were progressively reduced, the full yield elongation persisted until the combined carbon and nitrogen concentrations were reduced below that equivalent to one atom for each atomic length of dislocation (0.0005 at %); the lys had, however, begun to fall before this. Further ageing results in the formation of aggregates of some kind containing nitrogen, which raise the lys further and which also raise the stress-strain curve. Presumably some change in the character of these accounts for the increase in strain-hardening rate occurring between curves B and C, for the results of experiments in which specimens were subjected to two successive strain ageings indicated that the aggregates became more stable beyond the stage represented by B; prolonging the first ageing beyond that stage decreased the rise in lys during the second ageing, but when the first ageing was stopped before that stage it had no influence on this rise. Evidently the aggregates became too stable after the stage represented by curve B to redissolve and supply fresh nitrogen to relock dislocations. Possibly up to the stage represented by B the nitrogen atmosphere simply fills up to saturation, whatever this may mean, and thereafter true precipitation occurs.

At the beginning of the first stage there is an extremely rapid rise in lys. It is too rapid at room temperature to follow in detail and can only be seen in Fig. 6.27 as the positive value of the ordinate at which ageing apparently begins. It is some thousands of times faster than the main ageing process in the first stage; it is for example half complete at -12°C in 5 seconds; and its magnitude increases linearly with dissolved carbon or nitrogen content, amounting to 1 kg/mm^2 per 0.1% solute. The remainder of the rise in lys in the first stage is independent of solute content provided this is greater than about 0.001%, that is, sufficient to saturate the dislocations. The only explanation of the rapid rise seems to be the Snoek effect: the cargon and nitrogen atoms already close to the dislocations jump into those adjacent sites which are made the most favoured by the stress field of the nearby dislocation.

As might be expected from this account, the maximum effect of strain ageing takes as long to reach as does that of quench ageing. Quench ageing is the term used to describe ageing after quenching mild steel from the region of 700°C, and is believed to be a precipitation-hardening process which depends primarily on precipitation of iron carbide, since more of this dissolves than of iron nitride (see Fig. 6.28). According to hard-

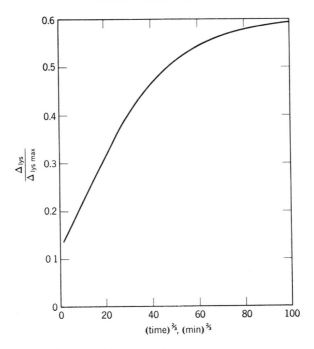

Fig. 6.27. Increase in lower yield stress with time during strain ageing. Δ_{lys} is the increase in lys after the given time, $\Delta_{lys\ max}$ the maximum increase after a very long time. Mild steel containing 0.01% C and 0.0044% N, quenched from 600°C and strained 4% before ageing at room temperature (Ref. 90).

ness measurements, both effects take several hundred hours at room temperature to reach full hardening.[87]   But the first sign of hardening during strain ageing is seen in about 10 min, and during quench ageing only after an hour or two.   Presumably the diffusion distances are smaller for strain ageing because the straining produces many dislocations, which act as nuclei for segregation and precipitation.

Although in principle any segregating element, particularly carbon and nitrogen in steel, can cause strain ageing, in practice strain ageing in steel is believed to be due primarily to nitrogen.   The solubility curves of carbon and nitrogen in iron are shown in Fig. 6.28; from these it is clear that there should be little carbon left in solution at room temperature but appreciable nitrogen.   This fact, and the fact that strain ageing is usually undesirable, are largely responsible for the considerable efforts that are being made to reduce the nitrogen content of commercial steel.

2. Ageing of mild steel specimens which have been strained so that a Lüders band has spread part way along the specimen may so lock the

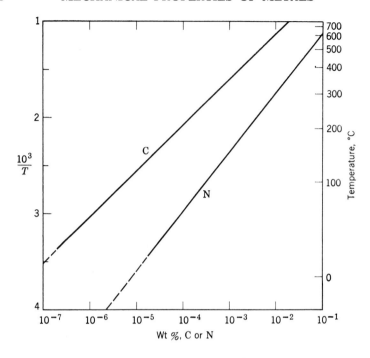

Fig. 6.28. Solubility of C and N in α Fe lattice. The total solubility, including solute segregated to dislocations and grain boundaries, will be considerably larger at the lower temperatures.

band front that the front does not spread until a new Lüders band is initiated. In one experiment[72] the original uys and lys were 28 and 20 kg/mm² respectively. After the steel was aged for 1½ hours at 200°C, a new uys of 37 kg/mm² was found. At this stress a new Lüders band was initiated near the grip, which was also the starting point of the first Lüders band. It spread through the first Lüders band at a stress of 29 kg/mm², and after reaching the front of the first band it continued to spread through the underformed region at a stress close to the original lys of 20 kg/mm². One conclusion from this experiment is that ageing had locked the dislocations at the Lüders band front, so preventing them from propagating the strain. Another is that the true uys of the undeformed material is at least 37 kg/mm², giving an uys/lys ratio of at least 1.85.

3. In some experiments[76] the rate of spread of the Lüders bands slowed down progressively at 24°C but stayed constant at 0°C. This could mean either that the material ahead of the band aged at 24°C as a result of the pre-yield strain and became harder, or that, as in 2, the Lüders band itself

aged, so that successive portions would become less and less effective at spreading the band.

4. Recovery takes place after the pre-yield strain alone. In some experiments[64] a 0.12% C steel was found to yield in 0.05 sec when a stress of 31.5 kg/mm^2 was applied. It yielded on the second pulse when two successive stress pulses of 31.5 kg/mm^2 lasting 0.04 sec each were applied. The damaging effect of the first pulse could be removed by a fairly substantial ageing treatment (e.g. 10 min at 93°C), for when such an ageing treatment was given after each pulse the cumulative delay time rose sharply, although neither uys nor lys nor the yield strain was altered. This experiment indicates that the delay time is not merely the time required for thermal agitation to initiate yield under the applied stress, but that during this time the state of the metal somehow changes; part at least of the pre-yield strain is presumably connected with the change. Two possible explanations of the recovery are that ageing permitted dislocations bowed out by the stress to regain their original positions, and that a few dislocations are set free during the delay time and strain ageing of these occurs.

5. Iron and mild steel, when aged under stress after straining, develop a uys 10–30% higher than the original one,[91, 92] and a sharp yield returns sooner the higher is the stress maintained during the ageing.[93, 94]   A suggested explanation is that the dislocations become locked by carbon in the bowed-out position, from which a higher stress is needed to release them.   Elimination of stress heterogeneity is an alternative explanation.

6. Yield-point effects in single crystals are made more marked by strain ageing.   In polycrystals, on the other hand, they are less marked than at the original yield; the uys may be raised, but the yield drop and yield extension are reduced.[71]   Perhaps the result with single crystals is because strain ageing increases the tolerance for plastic deformation, so that a yield point effect becomes experimentally easier to observe.

(g) *Temperature and Speed Effects.*   As the temperature is decreased the pre-yield plastic strain, the uys, the lys, and the Lüders strain all increase in the bcc metals iron, molybdenum niobium, and tantalum.[57] Figure 6.29 shows results for molybdenum illustrating some of these points.   In this figure the values of these properties increase until a temperature of 0°C is reached, at which point there is a sudden break in the curves.   This is typical of the bcc metals; the break occurs at the

[91] A. N. Holden and F. W. Kunz, *J.A.P.*, 1952, **23**, 799.
[92] M. M. Hutchison and N. Louat, *Acta Met.*, 1958, **6**, 8.
[93] T. Mura and J. O. Brittain, *Acta Met.*, 1960, **8**, 767.
[94] J. O. Brittain and S. E. Bronisz, *T.A.I.M.E.*, 1960, **218**, 289.

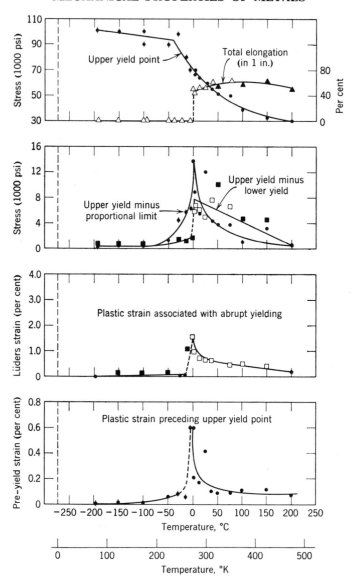

Fig. 6.29. Influence of temperature on yielding behaviour. Recrystallised Mo strained at a rate of $1.8 \times 10^{-2}\%$ per sec (Ref. 57. By courtesy of TAIME).

tough-brittle transition discussed in chapter 7. The way the lys of iron single crystals varies with temperature is illustrated in Fig. 6.30. Above room temperature, it remains constant at about $3\frac{1}{2}$ kg/mm², but below

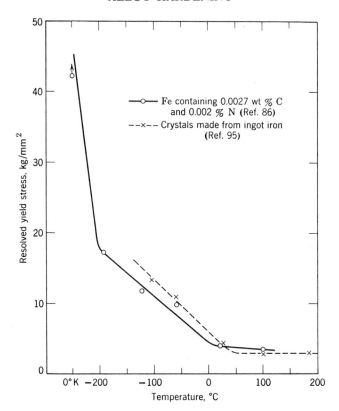

Fig. 6.30. Influence of temperature on the lower yield stress of Fe single crystals.

room temperature it rises rapidly, and below $-200°C$ rises still more rapidly. This branched curve is reminiscent of Fig. 4.8a, and implies that different mechanisms control the yield stress of iron in different temperature ranges.

It is interesting to know how much of the effects of temperature is due to changes in locking stress and how much to changes in friction stress. For the lys of steel this question can be answered by the grain size analysis in Fig. 6.31. From this figure it will be seen that most of the rise in lys as the temperature is decreased is due to a rise in friction stress; the locking stress also begins to rise below $-160°C$, but does not contribute much to the temperature effect down to $-196°C$. The same conclusion is to be drawn from the results for tests at room temperature and $-196°C$ quoted

[95] F. L. Vogel and R. M. Brick, *T.A.I.M.E.*, 1953, **197**, 700.

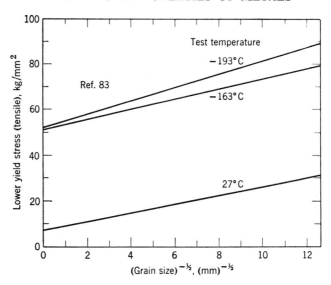

Fig. 6.31. Influence of temperature on the relation between lower yield stress and grain size. Fe containing 0.014% C and 0.003% N.

in Table 6.7. The values there for carbon-in-iron are very similar to those obtained from Fig. 6.30, namely, using the same units as in Table 6.7, 0.36 and 3.5 at room temperature and 0.48 and 26 at $-196°C$ for $\tau_s'l'^{\frac{1}{2}}$ and τ_f' respectively. The deduction from this kind of analysis that the influence of temperature on the friction stress τ_f' is the more important factor is of course confirmed by the fact, referred to in section 5.4, that the temperature dependence of the lys is virtually the same as that of the flow stress determined after the locking stress is eliminated by straining through the Lüders yield. This agreement is confirmation of the broad validity of the grain size analysis. Unfortunately, grain size analyses have not yet been carried to temperatures below $-196°C$, so that it is not possible to say whether the steeper rise in yield stress below this temperature in Fig. 6.30 is connected with friction or with locking stress.

By varying the carbon and nitrogen contents, it is possible to ascertain whether these elements contribute to the temperature sensitivity of τ_f' in steel. The results of such experiments are shown in Fig. 6.32, and point to the conclusion that the influence of the carbon and nitrogen hardly depends on temperature; practically the entire effect of temperature over the range room temperature to $-196°C$ apparently arises from the inherent lattice friction, or Peierls force. With a base metal having a small Peierls force, the lys should therefore be independent of temperature.

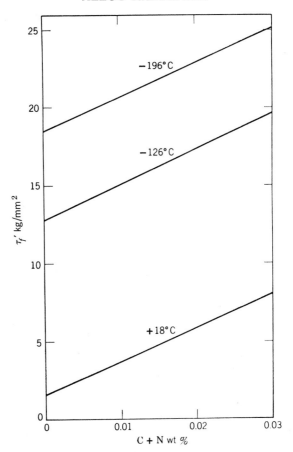

Fig. 6.32. Effect of temperature and solute concentration on the friction stress τ_f' in Fe (Ref. 96).

This condition is satisfied by the alloy Al–$3\frac{1}{2}$% Mg and experiments over the range from room temperature to $-76°$C have indeed shown its lys to be independent of temperature.[66]

Because of the connection between temperature and speed effects, it is expected that increasing the speed of straining should have the same effect as decreasing the temperature. Experiments on steel[97] show that this is so, and some results of a grain size analysis are given in Table 6.9. Increasing the speed from 10^{-3} to 2600 in/in/sec did not alter the value found

[96] J. Heslop and N. J. Petch, *Phil. Mag.*, 1956, **1**, 866.
[97] J. D. Campbell and J. Harding, Conference on Response of Metals to High Velocity Deformation, A.I.M.E. Interscience Publishers, New York, 1961, p. 51.

for locking stress, but increased the value found for the friction stress ten to twenty times.

Table 6.9

Influence of Strain Rate on Locking Stress and Friction Stress[97] *

Metal	Pure Fe			0.21% C steel		
Strain rate, fractional strain/sec.	0.001	960	2600	0.001	960	2600
$\tau_s' l'^{\frac{1}{2}}$	0.41	0.42	0.41	0.29	0.27	0.26
τ_f'	1.05	17.5	20	1.75	23	26

* The values quoted are for equivalent shear stresses $= \frac{1}{2} \times$ tensile stress. The units are kg/mm^2 for stress and cm for l.

It is interesting to note that these results lead to the conclusion that the dislocation sweeps through a very small area during the thermal activation responsible for the dependence of stress on strain rate. This conclusion is arrived at by applying eq. 4.11a, according to which $d\tau/dln\dot\epsilon = kT/xbd$, where x is the length of dislocation which moves during the activation and d is the distance it moves. From the data in Table 6.9, $d\tau/dln\dot\epsilon = 3.5 \times 10^{-9}$ for the pure iron and 2.8×10^{-9} for the steel, in units of (dynes/cm^2)$^{-1}$. Application of these values gives $xd = 9b^2$ for the pure iron and $7b^2$ for the steel. Such small "activation areas" are scarcely feasible for any other frictional force other than that involved in overcoming the Peierls resistance. Even if an activation area of this size could be accepted for the process of moving past an impurity atom, it would hardly be so similar, and yield a friction stress of similar magnitude, in two metals of such widely differing purities.

Another effect of lowering the temperature is to make it experimentally easier to obtain an uys, as with single crystals (Table 6.8) at least partly because more pre-yield plastic strain can be tolerated as the temperature is reduced. A probably related phenomenon is that in iron single crystals Lüders bands have been observed to propagate across a crystal and then fail to widen at $-68°C$, but not at room temperature.

(h) *Theory of the Lower Yield Stress.* A specimen along which a Lüders band is spreading is customarily thought of as divided into two regions, one in front and one behind the moving boundary. It seems closer to reality, however, to divide the specimen as follows into the four regions illustrated in Fig. 6.33.

1. Region 1 is well ahead of the Lüders band. There are no stress concentrations here. The applied stress is τ, which is much less than the

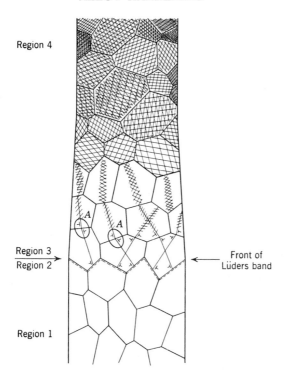

Region 4

Region 3
Region 2

Region 1

Front of
Lüders band

Fig. 6.33. Diagrammatic representation of the situation near the front of a Lüders band.

stress τ_s' needed to move a locked dislocation. Consequently nothing happens here.

2. Region 2 is that just ahead of the Lüders band and is just about to yield. The region is conceived to be a thin layer in the grains bordering the Lüders band, the advancing front of which is idealised as a continuous surface through the grain boundaries. Elastic anisotropy presumably causes certain grains along the Lüders front to yield before others, but is neglected in this account. As the region 2 is about to yield the stress in it must be τ_s', the stress required to move a locked dislocation. This stress is supplied partly by the applied stress, the lys τ, acting directly on this region, and partly through the stress concentration at the heads of slip bands in region 3. This concentrated stress is $(\tau - \tau_f')\left(\dfrac{L'}{l'}\right)^{1/2}$, where L' is the slip band length, l' is the distance from its head to the dislocation source that is going to yield, and τ_f' is the friction stress due to impurities

and the Peierls force. The square root relation for the stress concentration is an approximate one which is probably particularly in error close to the head of a slip band as it predicts a stress rising to infinity there, and must be considered only to apply outside this region. With this proviso,

$$\tau_s' = \tau + (\tau - \tau_f') \left(\frac{L'}{l'}\right)^{\frac{1}{2}} \tag{6.7}$$

3. Region 3 is at the advancing edge of the Lüders band. According to the usually accepted idea, slip has occurred in the grains at the advancing edge of the Lüders band to produce the stress concentration in eq. 6.7. No other slip has occurred, so that these grains are hardened only by the stress field centred on the ends of the slip bands. Thus the applied stress is τ in eq. 6.7, which, rearranged, becomes

$$\tau = \frac{\tau_f' + \tau_s'(l'/L')^{\frac{1}{2}}}{1 + (l'/L')^{\frac{1}{2}}} \tag{6.8}$$

Usually l' is believed to be much smaller than L'. The denominator in eq. 6.8 is then close to unity and this equation is the same as eq. 6.6.

4. Region 4 is well behind the Lüders front. Further in the yielded region, the situation changes because stress field hardening arising from the barrier effect of locked dislocations vanishes when these are unlocked. It is replaced by the weaker stress field hardening that occurs in polycrystals due to the difficulty of exactly matching slip on opposite sides of a grain boundary (chapter 4), for example, at places such as those marked A in Fig. 6.33. Following eq. 4.7, call this contribution to the flow stress $\tau_s \left(\frac{l}{L}\right)^{\frac{1}{2}}$. To replace the lost back stress hardening, that is, $\tau_s' \left(\frac{l'}{L'}\right)^{\frac{1}{2}} - \tau_s \left(\frac{l}{L}\right)^{\frac{1}{2}}$, the metal deforms until the grain interiors are strain hardened by the appropriate amount. Call this contribution to the flow stress τ_h. Then in region 4,

$$\tau = \tau_f' + \tau_h + \tau_s \left(\frac{l}{L}\right)^{\frac{1}{2}} \tag{6.9}$$

The transition from region 3 to region 4 merits further consideration as some significant points will come to light. The simplest way of considering it is to follow the sequence of events as the Lüders front advances from the position it occupied just before the stage shown in Fig. 6.33, that is, when it passed through the places marked A and eq. 6.6 (or 6.8) applied to the upper grains at A. The front then advances to the position shown in Fig. 6.33 as the lower grains at A yield. Equation 6.6 now applies to the lower grains at A. In applying equation 6.6, the tacit assumption is made that no strain hardening has occurred other than the stress field hardening $\tau_s'(l'/L')^{1/2}$. If it had, there should be a contribution from τ_h in the numerator on the RHS of eq. 6.6 which the customary grain size analysis (e.g., Fig. 6.22) would include with τ_f'. According to this idea, for eq. 6.6 to be reliable there must be negligible slip other than that producing the stress field hardening. This condition is probably usually quite well fulfilled since the amount of slip required to produce the stress field hardening is very small, and should produce little hardening in other ways. In an exceptional case, however, eq. 6.6 would be seriously in error. As the lower grains at A yield, the stress in the upper grains rising from the heads of the slip bands at A is partly nullified because dislocations of opposite sign arrive at these places on the lower side of the grain boundary, so more slip can occur in the upper grain parallel to the original slip direction. There are two factors, however, that encourage slip in directions other than the original one. First there is the grain coherency condition which requires several slip systems to operate if the specimen is not to split along grain boundaries. Second there is the possibility that moving dislocations liberate anchored ones in the way explained later. Both these factors become more important the more slip there is. Since this slip strain hardens the grain interiors and is responsible for the contribution τ_h, it has to be assumed that there is little of it in the grains just behind the Lüders front (region 3), but that there is more of it at positions further behind the front, and sufficiently far behind enough for eq. 6.9 to apply. It is impossible to predict the size of the transition zone theoretically, but experiment indicates that it is a few grain diameters, since the kink at the front of a Lüders band has been observed to extend over 5 grain diameters.[66] This circumstance affects the effective length L' of slip band in eq. 6.6, 6.7, and 6.8, perhaps especially in metals like iron that exhibit pencil glide, for although one end rests on the grain boundaries at the Lüders front, the band can be regarded as continuing through several grains with its other end resting on a cushion of work-hardened material. In the case just mentioned, L' is perhaps 4 to 5 grain diameters. If, as is usual, L' is taken as equal to the grain diameter L, eq. 6.6 should be rewritten as

$$\tau = \tau_f' + \alpha\tau_s'\left(\frac{l'}{L}\right)^{1/2} \tag{6.10}$$

where α in this case is about $\frac{1}{2}$ but presumably can vary. In the interpretation of experimental plots of yield stress versus grain size there are therefore two complicating factors, namely, the size of the inevitable small contribution from τ_h in eq. 6.9, and the effective length of the slip bands in region 3.

There are two other factors which also complicate the use of eq. 6.6. To use such an equation, a range of grain sizes L is produced by varying the heat treatment given to the specimen. The precise course of events during yielding is important at this point. The quantity l' in eq. 6.6 is the distance from the head of the slip band to the dislocation source that is going to be activated. If this source lies in the adjacent grain boundary or at the nearest particle of inclusion or precipitate, l' probably does not alter appreciably with heat treatment. But if the source is a part of the three-dimensional dislocation network, l' will be altered by a change in heat treatment. If it happens, for example, to be altered in the same ratio as L', then $(l'/L')^{1/2}$ is unaffected by heat treatment and the usual plot of lys against (grain diameter)$^{-1/2}$ yields a horizontal line. As already mentioned, this is approximately the result found with niobium. In addition, it is always possible that the alterations in heat treatment that produce different grain sizes also change τ_f' by causing changes in the distribution of impurity atoms.

In view of these complications it is fortunate that the two terms in eq. 6.6 can be determined in other ways. τ_f' can be determined from a plot like Fig. 5.29 of flow stress against (dislocation density)$^{1/2}$. From Fig. 5.29 the value of τ_f' for iron containing 0.05% carbon is 7 kg/mm^2, whereas from Fig. 6.32, based on eq. 6.6, the value is 12 kg/mm^2. From Fig. 5.29 the value for a decarburised iron is $3\frac{1}{2}$ kg/mm^2, whereas from Fig. 6.32 0.01 wt % (C + N) is needed to produce such a value. The locking stress term $\tau_s'(l'/L')^{1/2}$ can be determined by equating the RHS's of eq. 6.6 and 6.9. In eq. 6.9, the term $\tau_s(l/L)^{1/2}$ will develop almost completely during the first 0.2% extension or so, as it does in other metals. The term τ_h, however, should develop at much the same rate during and after the Lüders extension, this being the normal behaviour of metals. Consequently, if the strain-hardening coefficient determined just beyond the Lüders extension ϵ is h, $\tau_h = h\epsilon$. Neglect of $\tau_s(l/L)^{1/2}$ then gives the approximate relation, by equating eq. 6.9 to eq. 6.6,

$$h\epsilon = \tau_s' \left(\frac{l'}{L'}\right)^{1/2} \tag{6.11}$$

Comparison of the locking stress term determined from eq. 6.11 and eq. 6.6 shows that in several cases there is agreement within a factor of two as already mentioned. For niobium, eq. 6.7 yields a value of the normal magnitude,[98] suggesting that here the errors with eq. 6.6 are particularly important.

The different methods therefore usually agree to within a factor of two

[98] D. Hull, Conference on Nuclear Materials, Central Electricity Generating Board (London), 1961.

times or better which indicates that the model on which eq. 6.6 is based is correct in essentials. However, eq. 6.6 contains approximations which may occasionally lead to large errors, as evidently happens with niobium.

The grain size dependence of the flow stress beyond the Lüders yield arises through the grain size term in eq. 6.9 as with a metal exhibiting a rounded yield. In metals like iron, steel, and Al–Mg alloys, in which cross slip is easy, this term should be small (chapter 4). It has already been mentioned that only a small grain size dependence is usually found beyond the yield. The exceptional case referred to earlier where the grain size dependence after yield was as large as at the lys itself requires that

$$\tau_s l^{1/2} = \alpha \tau_s' l'^{1/2}$$

Since l and l' are expected to be similar in magnitude, even though α is somewhat less than unity, this requires a surprisingly large value for τ_s.

There are, however, two points at which it is difficult to reconcile the theoretical ideas with the experimental data. Both are concerned with the fact that the temperature dependence of the yield stress rises almost entirely from the temperature dependence of the friction stress τ_f', the locking stress contribution not being much affected by temperature.

One consequence of this is that the gap between locking stress and friction stress, on which the existence of a sharp yield is supposed to depend, may increase as the temperature is raised, and certainly should not decrease. A reasonable conclusion is that the sharp yield should remain marked as the temperature is raised and conversely should tend to disappear as the temperature is decreased. The opposite appears to happen, for in iron and steel the sharp yield behaviour disappears if the temperature is raised much above room temperature, and general experience is that it becomes more marked as the temperature is lowered below room temperature.

There is a pronounced Lüders yield in steel when the carbon and nitrogen contents are equivalent to one solute atom per atomic length of dislocation, according to the strain-ageing experiments referred to. This suggests that in these experiments the dislocation to which τ_s' in eq. 6.6 and 6.8 applies were not released from grain boundaries but already exist as such in the grains. If the solute is uniformly distributed along the dislocations as a single line of atoms, the locking stress should be sensitive to temperature at this solute concentration. The experiments which have shown the locking stress in steel to be independent of temperature have all been made on material containing a carbon or nitrogen concentration many times higher. Either, therefore, the temperature sensitivity of the locking stress in steel is high when the carbon and nitrogen concentrations are very small and decreases as these concentrations

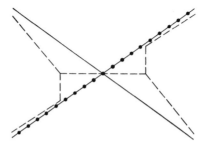

Fig. 6.34. Intersection of an unlocked $\frac{1}{2}\langle 111 \rangle$ dislocation and a locked one. The dashed lines show the final equilibrium arrangement.

are raised—without, as the experiments show, the room temperature value of the lys changing much—or the carbon and nitrogen atoms segregated at the dislocations collect into sufficiently large clusters even in very dilute solutions to give a locking stress that is insensitive to temperature. This probably means that the clusters are more stable than the condition in which the carbon and nitrogen are uniformly distributed along the dislocations which, in view of the very small lattice solubility of these elements in iron at room temperature, is perhaps not unlikely.

The locking stress in steel does apparently begin to rise below $-100°C$. It may not, however, be the locking stress itself which changes. From the derivation in section 4.7 of eq. 6.6 it is clear that the locking stress τ_s in eq. 6.6 includes any continuous force like the Peierls force, and it is possible that this becomes large enough in the region of $-100°C$ to manifest itself.

Two other points may be made:

1. A feature which may help to precipitate the Lüders yield is that once a dislocation starts to move through the crystal it should be a liberator of other dislocations by forming junctions with them. For since, in iron, about 2 ev is gained for each atom length of $\langle 100 \rangle$ dislocation formed from two $\frac{1}{2}\langle 111 \rangle$ dislocations, and the binding energy between a carbon atom and a $\frac{1}{2}\langle 111 \rangle$ dislocation is thought to be about $\frac{1}{2}$ ev, when the moving $\frac{1}{2}\langle 111 \rangle$ dislocation intersects a locked one it will combine with the latter as in Fig. 6.34 if geometry permits. Two freed lengths of $\frac{1}{2}\langle 111 \rangle$ dislocation now exist, and when their Burgers vectors are suitable they will be able to move under the applied stress, detaching the remaining anchored pieces.

2. It is striking how sensitive the uys is to bending caused by misalignment, and how relatively insensitive it is to local stress concentrations such

as scratches or indentations. It is clear that, if stress concentrations are present, the initial yielding which triggers off a Lüders band is most likely to occur in one that acts parallel to the applied shear stress. Bending due to misalignment is important perhaps because it has this property, and also because it extends over the whole length of the specimen. Other more obvious stress raisers such as gauge marks do not have these properties. They therefore initiate small Lüders bands which, however, do not spread far.

6.8 Portevin-Le Chatelier Effect

Some alloys, when strained at room or elevated temperature, extend jerkily and the stress-strain curve is saw-toothed, usually on a fine scale. This is frequently called the Portevin-Le Chatelier effect. The explanation is based on strain ageing[99]: individual dislocations are not believed to move smoothly through the lattice but from time to time are thought to be held up for a while, for example, at intersections or internal stress peaks. When a dislocation is held up, solute atoms have an opportunity to diffuse to it and lock it, so that the stress must be raised to move it again. Thus the process of strain ageing is suggested to occur during the straining. To explain why it occurs at room temperature in, for example, aluminium–magnesium alloys, at which temperature magnesium would normally diffuse too slowly, it is argued that vacancies are generated during deformation and will increase the speed of diffusion very greatly. Some measurements of the activation energy for strain ageing in these alloys are reasonably consistent with this explanation[100] provided the idea is accepted that the vacancies produced by the straining persist for a long time, presumably because they are captured by magnesium atoms. However, although some workers[66] find the effect is independent of grain size as would be expected from this explanation, others[101] find grain size to affect it. The general situation in this regard is unclear.

6.9 Structural Requirements of Strong Alloys

The strongest alloys all contain a finely dispersed second phase, so this must be the principal structural feature required for strength. The connection between fineness of distribution and strength seems satisfactorily understood, but not much is known for certain about the properties required in the precipitate itself and in the relation between the precipitate and matrix, although some ideas about this are discussed in this chapter.

[99] A. H. Cottrell, *Phil. Mag.*, 1953, **44**, 829.
[100] A. R. C. Westwood and T. Broom, *Acta Met.*, 1957, **5**, 249.
[101] A. Berghezan, Doctorate Thesis, University of Paris, 1952, p. 12.

The fact that solutes can only oppose dislocations with their statistically averaged stress fields should mean that for equal volume fractions, solutes cannot achieve as high a yield stress as precipitates, yet experimentally there seems little difference in the two effects.   In practice, precipitates are used because much larger amounts can be put into a metal than of a solute which strengthens efficiently.   Except in certain metals like sintered alumina powder, some solutes have to be present to saturate and produce or control the precipitate, but the amounts of solute present probably do not usually contribute substantially to the strength.   The most efficient method of producing a high yield stress, in the sense of requiring the smallest amount of alloy element, is dislocation locking, but it may also be the most dangerous since there is a close association between dislocation locking and brittleness.   Indeed, the difficult problem to solve in producing a strong alloy is not simply that of producing great resistance to flow, which is usually relatively easy, but that of combining great resistance to flow with great resistance to fracture.

7

Fracture

7.1 Introduction

The highest "true" breaking stresses of metals are about one-fifth to one-tenth of the theoretical breaking stress of approximately $E/10$, where E is Young's modulus. Thus, piano wire may have a tensile strength of 280 kg/mm², which is equal to $E/70$. For comparison, the strongest substance so far reported is probably silica fibre with a tensile strength up to 2500 kg/mm²,[1] or $E/2$, rather above the theoretical limit, and a figure which perhaps suggests that it is possible to achieve higher breaking stresses with metals than have yet been realised. The failure to reach the theoretical limit with metals is due to their structural heterogeneity, which has the result that fracture does not start everywhere simultaneously. Going to the other extreme, there are instances of exceedingly brittle metals; for example, alloys of iron and nitrogen can be heat treated to give tensile strengths as low as $\frac{1}{2}$ kg/mm² ($E/40,000$).[2] Such very low strengths are presumably due to some kind of flaw. The large part that flaws can play in fracture is illustrated by ordinary glass, which normally has a strength of about 5 kg/mm². If, however, an experimental arrangement is used whereby the stress is focused on the interior, the strength exceeds 700 kg/mm²,[3] proving that the weakness of ordinary glass is due to

[1] F. O. Anderegg, *Ind. Eng. Chem.*, 1939, **31**, 290.
[2] B. E. Hopkins and H. R. Tipler, *J.I.S.I.*, 1954, **177**, 110.
[3] K. Kolsky, *Conference on Fracture*, Wiley—M.I.T., 1959, p. 281.

serious surface flaws.   One object of studying fracture is therefore to improve the best existing strengths, although success in this direction will probably be limited.   Another is to better understand these rather rare instances of extremely severe embrittlement.   But the main object is undoubtedly to understand fracture in order to combine high fracture strength with ductility and high resistance to shear, and to avoid the common type of brittle behaviour described in this chapter.

From the point of view of the nature of the processes involved there are five different kinds of fracture which occur in metals: ductile, brittle, adiabatic shear, creep, and fatigue fracture.   This chapter is concerned with the first three; the other two are discussed in the chapters on creep and fatigue.   The classification of fractures into ductile and brittle according to the processes involved does not coincide with the classification an engineer would make, based on the amount of ductility displayed, because it is possible for fracture to take place by a ductile mechanism and yet involve so little general deformation that an engineer would classify such a material as brittle.   The special circumstances giving rise to this kind of behaviour are discussed in section 7.14.   This apart, fracture is discussed here as ductile or brittle according to the processes involved.

Most of what definite knowledge there is about fracture processes is drawn from experiments on fairly simple metals.   On the other hand, the fracture processes in strong, complex alloys need to be understood if the theory is to help in producing stronger metals.   At present it is only possible to make the plausible assumption that the process of fracture of most strong alloys resembles that described here as ductile even though their elongations are small.   This field of study is at present one of the weakest in metallurgy.

PART A.   DUCTILE FRACTURE

7.2   The Process of Ductile Fracture

A ductile fracture under tensile stress involves three successive events. First the specimen necks, cavities form in the necked region, and join together.   Second, a cavity eventually becomes large enough to spread fairly rapidly in the transverse direction.   Finally this crack, as it can now be called, spreads to the surface following a direction inclined at about 45° to the tensile axis.   The result is the "cup and cone" fracture illustrated in Fig. 7.1.

The first stage is not only the most important part since the second and third stages cannot take place until some cavities have formed, but is also by far the longest as a rule.   This is demonstrated by the data in Table 7.1,

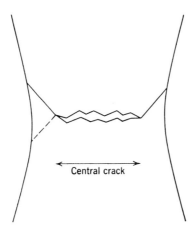

Fig. 7.1. Diagrammatic section through "cup and cone" ductile fraction. Part of the cone may follow the dashed line.

which show that the crack is only large enough to be readily detected just before fracture. Curves of true stress against true strain illustrate the same point when they are continued right up to fracture. The upper line in Fig. 7.2 is such a curve, and is practically linear right up to fracture, as has been observed in other cases.[4, 5] Apparently a definite crack forms

Table 7.1

Stage at Which Central Crack Forms

Metal	Al			Cu		Brass
Method of detecting crack*	a	b	b	a	b	b
Result	Crack present			No crack detected		
RA% at which observation made	80	76.5	78.2	—	51.7	41.9
RA% at fracture	—	80	81	—	53.7	47.4
Ref.	6	5		7, p. 82		5

* a, by sectioning; b, by radiography.

[4] J. Stead, *J.I.S.I.*, 1923, **107**, 377.
[5] C. W. MacGregor, *T.A.I.M.E.*, 1937, **124**, 208.
[6] P. Ludwik, *Z. Ver. deut. Ingr.*, 1927, **71**, 1532.
[7] A. Nadai, *Theory of Flow and Fracture of Solids*, Vol. 1, 2nd ed., McGraw-Hill, New York, 1950.

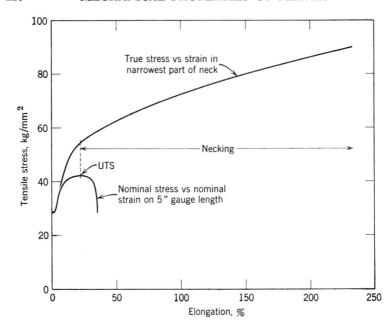

Fig. 7.2. Different ways of plotting tensile test results. Mild steel (Ref. 8).

too late in these cases to be registered on the curve, since linearity would hardly be expected after a definite crack had formed. Sometimes a drop in stress is detected before fracture which it is reasonable to identify with the appearance of a central crack, but when this happens, it does so very near the final rupture point. The last two stages of fracture, namely, the formation of a definite crack, and the separation of the two parts of the specimen along the "cone," therefore occur a long way beyond the UTS point in a ductile metal. This is emphasised in Fig. 7.2 by the difference between the lower curve—with nominal stress plotted against nominal strain—and the upper one.

   The process of ductile fracture has been studied in some detail in copper.[9, 10] Figure 7.3 shows the condition of a developing ductile fracture in copper when caught at a late stage. There is a small central crack surrounded' by numerous small cavities that had all formed at inclusions in this metal (tough pitch copper, which contains many inclusions) either by the metal drawing away from an inclusion or by an inclusion breaking

[8] H. W. Swift, *J.I.S.I.*, 1939, **140**, 181.

[9] K. E. Puttick, *Phil. Mag.*, 1959, **4**, 964.

[10] H. C. Rogers, *T.A.I.M.E.*, 1960, **218**, 498.

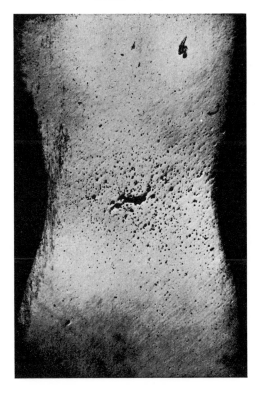

Fig. 7.3. Incipient ductile fracture. Longitudinal section through necked part of a tensile specimen of tough-pitch copper (K. Puttick, Ref. 9).

in two. The cavities are unusually evident in this example; normally it is not easy to find many cavities on a longitudinal section after fracture. With increasing deformation, the first-formed cavities grow larger and eventually several coalesce near the axis of the specimen to produce the small central crack. As this in turn grows larger, it is helped to spread by the planes of intense shear distortion ahead of the crack tip. These planes lie at approximately 45° to the immediately preceding part of the crack; the crack follows one of these directions, which takes it away from the section of minimum area in the neck, so that after travelling some distance in this direction it prefers to follow the other 45° direction back into the section of minimum area. The average direction of the crack is therefore transverse, although in detail it moves in a zig-zag direction. The planes of intense shear distortion help the crack to spread because cavities are formed in them, presumably in exactly the same way that the original cavities were formed. The cup part of a

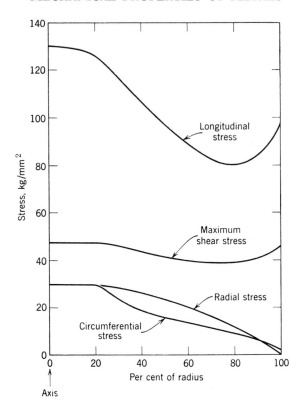

Fig. 7.4. Stress distribution in tensile specimen. 0.25% C steel pulled to fracture at room temperature: YS 33.4 kg/mm², UTS 48 kg/mm², elongation 38% on 2 in., reduction of area 68%. Initial diameter 2¼ in. Stresses determined by drilling axial hole and measuring dimensional changes thereby caused (Ref. 13).

ductile fracture has the appearance then to be expected, since under both optical and electron microscope examination[11, 12] it looks to have formed from numerous holes which were separated by thin walls until these broke.

There has also been some study of ductile fracture in iron and aluminium.[9] In iron, fine sharp cracks extend from each cavity and assist the process of linking up; presumably they are a manifestation of the ease with which brittle cracks can form in iron. Aluminium necks down very much more than copper at room temperature without cavities being

[11] C. J. Beevers and R. Honeycombe, *Conference on Fracture*, Wiley—M.I.T. 1959, p. 474.

[12] C. Crussard et al., *Conference on Fracture*, Wiley—M.I.T., 1959, p. 524.

[13] E. R. Parker, H. R. Davis, and A. E. Flanigan, *A.S.T.M.*, 1946, **46**, 1159.

formed. At least one reason for this is probably that aluminium work hardens less than copper at room temperature and the stress level is therefore lower in the aluminium.

In Fig. 7.3 the main crack is in the centre of the specimen; it is unusual for the crack to start at the surface. The explanation of why it normally starts at the centre is provided by the stress distribution in the neck of a tensile specimen illustrated in Fig. 7.4.[13] These results were obtained by measuring on a necked, but not broken, specimen, the dimensional changes as larger and larger axial holes were drilled. [The measurements yielded slightly different axial and circumferential stresses, although according to a theoretical argument (ref. 7, p. 85) they should be equal.] The chief point to note about these results is that the shear stress is as high on the axis as anywhere else, whereas the tensile stresses are higher. If the assumption is made—for which evidence is given later—that both shear and tension stress help to cause fracture, fracture therefore necessarily starts on the axis. A further point to notice from Fig. 7.4 is that the "true" breaking stress, which is the average value across the section of the longitudinal stress, is the average of a decidedly inconstant quantity.

The cone part of the fracture seems to be a particularly large "zig" or "zag" on the part of the main crack,[14] probably caused by the proximity of the surface. Figure 7.5 illustrates a section through the cone part of a fracture; BC is the specimen surface, AB is the cone part of the fracture, and AC is the other plane of intense shear ahead of the main crack equivalent to AB. The shear along AC has been sufficient to orient many cavities nearly parallel to AC, thus increasing the area across which there is no cohesion, and presumably producing additional cavities. Although the appearance of the cone part of a fracture is smoother than that of the cup part, under the electron microscope it can be seen to contain dimples like those in the latter as well as some smoother areas,[12] and in fact resembles the fracture surfaces of single crystals which have slid apart along a slip plane making an angle with the applied tensile stress.[11, 15] The cone part of a ductile tensile fracture therefore presumably occurs by essentially the same mechanism as the central crack. When adiabatic shear (section 7.15) occurs, it no doubt helps the cone part of the fracture to form, but does not seem to be essential since the cone is still produced when fracture is completed by slow pulling.[9]

Ductile failure also occurs in shear, although it is not much discussed because it is rarely a limiting condition in engineering. As an example of ductile failure in torsion, the mild steel tested in Fig. 7.2, when tested in torsion, failed at a shear stress of 34.6 kg/mm² and a shear strain of 226%.

[14] K. E. Puttick, *Phil. Mag.*, 1960, **5**, 759.
[15] C. F. Tipper, *Metallurgia*, 1949, **39**, 133.

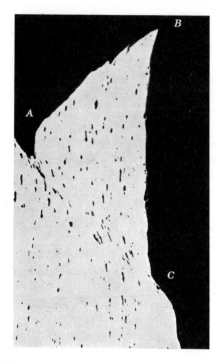

Fig. 7.5.   "Cone" part of ductile fracture (K. Puttick).

This is less than the shear strain of 280% which corresponds to the tensile elongation of 230% in Fig. 7.2.   Possibly the metal withstood a greater shear in tension because the strain could occur in two planes at 45° to the tensile axis, but in a torsion test is concentrated on one plane.   Torsion failure will not be discussed as a problem separate from ductile tensile fracture because a coherent scheme can be made assuming that it occurs in the same way as the latter.

7.3   Effect of Temperature and Speed

Raising the temperature increases the reduction of area in the tensile test,[16] provided hot shortness does not supervene (chapter 9), and a polycrystalline specimen eventually pulls down to a point.   This could well be simply a result of the lower stresses necessary to deform at high temperature, since the lower stress should make fracture less likely unless there occurs a change in the mechanism of fracture giving rise to hot shortness.   Ultimate tensile strengths decrease approximately linearly with rise in

[16] M. J. Manjoine and A. Nadai, *Am. Soc. Mech. Engrs.*, 1941, **63**, p. A77.

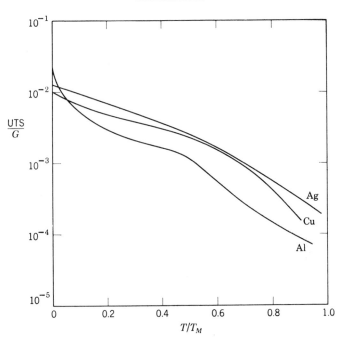

Fig. 7.6. Variation of ultimate tensile strength with temperature. The UTS is normalized against the shear modulus and the test temperature against the melting point on the absolute scale (Ref. 17).

temperature as illustrated in Fig. 7.6, although the rate of decrease is rather faster when the temperature is high enough for thermal recovery to occur during the test. Varying the speed of straining in a tensile test at room temperature over a range of about 10^{-3} to 10^2 in units of unit strain/sec usually has neither a marked nor a consistent effect on ductility as measured by reduction of area,[16, 18, 19] although of course the stress level is raised. At very high speeds, special effects come into operation (section 7.15).

7.4   Effect of Structure and Composition

General experience indicates that with commercial nonferrous metals a reduction in grain size somewhat increases the reduction of area, and the stress level is raised. This combination of effects is probably due to a small increase in the rate of strain hardening with reduction of grain size.

[17] R. P. Carreker and W. R. Hibbard, *T.A.I.M.E.*, 1957, **209**, 1157.
[18] D. S. Clarke and G. Datwyler, *Proc.A.S.T.M.*, 1938, **38**, 98.
[19] H. G. Baron, *J.I.S.I.*, 1956, **182**, 354.

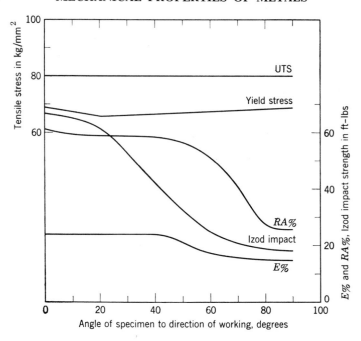

Fig. 7.7. Directionality of mechanical properties of alloy steel (Ref. 22).

In mild steel the "true" breaking stress has been found to vary regularly with grain size,[20] the fracture stress being proportional to $1/\sqrt{\text{grain size}}$.

Cast or fabricated metals generally display directional properties, especially as regards ductility, and usually, a cast metal is less ductile than one in the forged and annealed condition. The fact that cast metals are more ductile along the direction of columnar grains than across them [21] points to the damaging effect of heterogeneity which takes the form of a layered structure, in this case presumably due to segregation at the original dendrite boundaries. It is well known that forged metals are more ductile in the direction of working than across this direction, and Fig. 7.7 shows results bearing on this. The three possible causes of this directionality are a layered or banded structure, the arrangement of inclusions, and crystalline texture. In steel, directionality is enhanced by high inclusion content. Although it is not clear how much of this is due to an effect of inclusions on ductile fracture per se and how much to the un-

[20] N. J. Petch, *Phil. Mag.*, 1956, **1**, 186.
[21] L. Northcott, *J.I.M.*, 1942, **68**, 189.
[22] F. T. Sisco, *Alloys of Iron and Carbon*, Vol. 2, McGraw-Hill, New York, 1937, p. 95.

doubted effect of high inclusion content in promoting the brittle type of fracture, the importance attached to inclusion counts in steel and the large effect of directionality on impact strength both suggest that the latter aspect is rather important in steel. In single-phase metals, crystalline texture seems to be the important factor governing directionality, since after recrystallisation in a way that restores crystalline randomness the directionality of mechanical properties disappears.

Alloying, whether to make a solid solution or a multiphase alloy, although increasing the UTS and sometimes the uniform elongation, probably always decreases the reduction of area except when the effect of some deleterious impurity already present is mitigated by the alloying element. However, the decrease in reduction of area is often small compared with the increase in UTS.

7.5   Criteria for Ductile Fracture

The fact that a triaxial tensile stress exists in the centre of the necked part of a tensile specimen (Fig. 7.4) has given rise to the idea that this triaxial tensile stress initiates ductile fracture. On the other hand, the observation that in hard single crystals fracture may occur at constant resolved shear stress[11] might seem to suggest shear stress as the criterion. Such simple criteria may hold over a limited range of conditions but the following evidence shows that they are not generally adequate. Point 1 and point 2 show that a simple stress criterion is inadequate.

1. If a specimen is stretched while under hydrostatic pressure, the strain at fracture can be greatly increased by increasing the hydrostatic pressure. None of the stress components in Fig. 7.5 remains constant as the hydrostatic pressure is increased.[23]

2. The UTS of tin is 2.0 kg/mm² and the "true" breaking stress is 4.0 kg/mm². However, a thin sandwich of tin stuck to steel pulling rods withstood $12\frac{1}{2}$ kg/mm²[24] (separation then occurred at the tin-steel interface), that is, a considerably higher stress than achieved in the ordinary test.

Nor is a simple strain criterion adequate:

3. In tensile tests carried out with a superimposed hydrostatic pressure, metals can be stretched to strains in the neck of over 100-fold, that is, much greater than in a plain tensile test. If the hydrostatic pressure is large enough, the metal practically draws down to a point. Metals can

[23] P. W. Bridgeman, *Fracturing of Metals*, A.S.M. Symposium 1948, p. 246.
[24] E. Orowan, *Repts. Progr. in Phys.*, 1948–9, **12**, 185.

also be cold worked to much greater reductions of area than they withstand in a tensile test by cold working operations in which a compressive stress is present. Yet even after the heaviest cold work, substantial necking still occurs during a subsequent tensile test, although the elongation is greatly reduced. Table 7.2 gives some data on 18/8 stainless steel which illustrates these points.

Table 7.2

Effect of Cold Work on Mechanical Properties of Stainless Steel[25]

Per Cent of Reduction by Wire Drawing	UTS kg/mm^2	Elongation, % on 2″	RA%
0	67.6	80	71.8
12.5	78	50	70.6
67	153.5	8	53.0
87.6	186.4	5	43.0

The requirements for ductile fracture seem in fact to be a combination of strain and of tensile stress. The evidence is as follows:

4. That shear strain causes damage is shown by torsion tests. Fracture in torsion always occurs on a transverse plane, and the distinctive feature of this plane is that it undergoes more shear deformation than any other plane. Of course, at any one instant the longitudinal plane carries the same shear stress as the transverse plane, but during twisting, different planes in the metal rotate through the longitudinal position, and none of these planes in the metal suffers the full effect. The transverse plane, on the other hand, remains fixed with respect to the metal, so that a transverse section of the specimen undergoes maximum shear deformation from start to finish of a torsion test.

5. The flaws created by shear can evidently be opened by tensile stress or closed by compressive stress. This is shown by two pieces of evidence.[8] First, specimens twisted before being tested in tension show a rapid drop in reduction of area and true breaking stress for large twists exceeding a shear of unity (similarly, stretching before testing in torsion reduces the torsional strain causing failure). A particularly interesting effect is that the damaging effects of torsion are greatly reduced when the specimen is twisted and then untwisted before being tested in tension. Second, in tests under hydrostatic pressure,[26] if the hydrostatic pressure is released

[25] A. B. Kinzel and R. Franks, *Alloys of Iron and Chromium*, Vol. 2, McGraw-Hill, New York, 1940, p. 306.
[26] P. W. Bridgeman, *Rev. Mod. Phys.*, 1945, 17, 3.

before fracture and pulling is continued, a further strain is needed, even though the original strain under hydrostatic pressure exceeds the limit reached in a test made throughout at atmospheric pressure. The further strain increases with increasing hydrostatic pressure for a given strain under hydrostatic pressure. The damage done by the first pulling, therefore, is less the higher the hydrostatic pressure under which the first pulling occurs. This suggests that a hydrostatic pressure prevents the opening of flaws created by the shearing deformation.

It appears, therefore, that during tensile deformation the shear deformation creates flaws which the tensile stress helps to open. Bearing in mind the work from which the photograph in Fig. 7.3 was taken, we must regard the tensile stress as exerting a directing influence on the shear deformation, causing this to enlarge cavities, rather than suppose that the tensile stress makes a cavity spread without help from plastic deformation as it does, for example, during the brittle fracture of glass. The distinction between the ductile and brittle situations is also demonstrated by the fact that the growth of the central cavity during ductile failure—although on the visible scale a rather rapid process that takes place during the last few per cent of deformation—can nevertheless be stopped at any point by unloading to a stress where plastic deformation ceases, whereas the spread of a truly brittle fracture cannot be arrested by any such device in specimens of normal size.

7.6 Theory of Ductile Fracture

A theory of ductile fracture must base itself on the idea that plastic strain and a tensile stress are both required and also on the sequence of events discussed in section 7.2. The first point in such a theory is the way the initial cavities form. They may form at inclusions, as did those in Fig. 7.3, and this kind of site has been proposed a number of times, for example.[15] There is a good reason for cavities to form at inclusions, for when the relatively deformable metal flows past a relatively undeformable inclusion, large tensile forces are set up and sometimes succeed in tearing a gap at the interface where the metal and inclusion join. Expressed differently, the tensile stress around clusters of dislocations pressed against the inclusion breaks the join. Such cavities will occur most easily at those inclusions which have the weakest cohesion to the matrix. The cohesion can be expressed in terms of surface and interface energies, and this leads to an important generalisation discussed in section 7.10. Alternatively, the stresses around the inclusion may break the inclusion itself and form a cavity in this way.

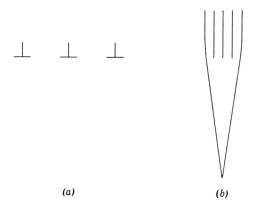

(a)   (b)

Fig. 7.8. This figure and Figs. 7.9–7.11 show ways in which dislocations may combine to make cavities.

However, as already intimated, it seems uncertain that cavities frequently form at inclusions. Moreover, there are several ways in which it is believed that dislocations can combine to produce cracks, one being that just mentioned. It is illustrated in Fig. 7.8; a cluster of dislocations, Fig. 7.8a, is pushed together strongly enough to make the dislocations coalesce into a crack, Fig. 7.8b. The dislocations are supposed to be piled against a barrier such as a grain boundary or inclusion boundary. The second and third kinds of combination do not require any such barrier. The second is illustrated in Fig. 7.9; dislocations of opposite signs and on adjacent slip planes, Fig. 7.9a, coalesce into a crack, Fig. 7.9b. The third combination is illustrated in Fig. 7.10; dislocations with different Burgers vectors run together as in Fig. 7.10a to form the crack in Fig. 7.10b. Expressed slightly differently, slip along the planes A and B (Fig. 7.10b)

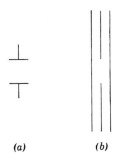

(a)   (b)

Fig. 7.9.

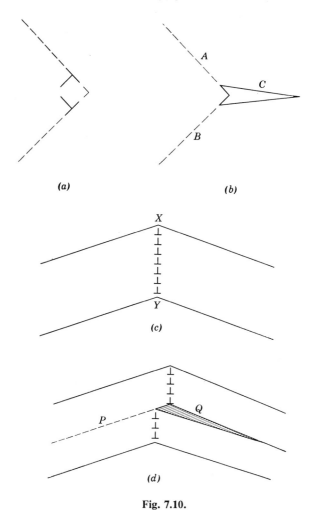

(a) (b)

(c)

(d)

Fig. 7.10.

produces the crack *C*. A fourth method is really a special version of the third and is illustrated in Figs. 7.10*c* and *d*. Slip at a tilt boundary *XY* (Fig. 7.10*c*) along the slip plane *P* (Fig. 7.10*d*) produces the crack *Q*. The crack lies along a slip plane, which makes this method attractive in the case of hexagonal metals that cleave on slip planes. Besides these ways of producing cracks by the combination of dislocations, there are some others which seem specifically related to fatigue fracture and are discussed in chapter 10.

The first, third and the fourth methods have been observed. The first has been observed in MgO[27, 28] and probably in magnesium bi-crystals,[29] and the fourth in zinc.[30]

The third method is a rather general way of producing cracks, and the shearing interfaces A and B in Fig. 7.10b can be slip bands, twins, or grain boundaries. Thus, in crystals of MgO or LiF, A and B are slip bands[31, 32, 33, 34]; in molybdenum,[35] zinc,[36] and steel,[37] A and B are twins (a shear is of course associated with twinning). In creep, A and B are grain boundaries, and C is then a third boundary along which the crack spreads. In the case under consideration, when A and B are slip bands, the first stage is presumably the formation of a single junction dislocation, that is, the dislocations intersect as in Fig. 7.11a to form a junction dislocation as in Fig. 7.11b; the intersection process is here being regarded from a point lying in the plane of the paper in Fig. 7.10. Next, a second pair of dislocations, following the first two, intersect as in Fig. 7.11c; the resulting junction dislocation must also lie along the line of intersection of the slip planes, with the result that the two junction dislocations combine as in Fig. 7.11d to form a length of dislocation with double Burgers vector, assuming that any energy barrier opposing the combination can be overcome by the applied stress. Other dislocations follow, enlarging the Burgers vector of the junctions dislocation, until, if it is of edge type, it can be considered to be a crack, probably after 2 or 3 pairs of dislocations have intersected.

The first and third methods of producing cracks from dislocations thus combine the Burgers vectors in rather similar ways, but with the third the energy saving when the junction dislocation forms should make it possible for a smaller applied stress to produce a crack than with the first method. Remembering the complicated dislocation tangles which are produced by cold work, it would seem that, if the energy barrier which probably opposes the formation of a junction with multiple Burgers vector is not so large as to entirely prohibit the process, many tiny cracks should be produced.

This suggests that eventually several of these cracks are made close

[27] R. J. Stokes, T. L. Johnston, and C. H. Li, *Phil. Mag.*, 1958, **3**, 718.
[28] W. G. Johnstone, *Phil. Mag.*, 1960, **5**, 407.
[29] J. D. Mote and J. E. Dorn, *T.A.I.M.E.*, 1960, **218**, 491.
[30] J. J. Gilman, *T.A.I.M.E.*, 1954, **200**, 621.
[31] E. R. Parker, *Conference on Fracture*, Wiley—M.I.T., 1959, p. 181.
[32] A. S. Keh, J. C. M. Li, and Y. T. Chou, *Acta Met.*, 1959, **7**, 694.
[33] J. Washburn, A. E. Gorum, and E. R. Parker, *T.A.I.M.E.*, 1959, **215**, 230.
[34] A. D. Whapham and M. J. Makin, *Phil. Mag.*, 1960, **5**, 237.
[35] R. W. Cahn, *J.I.M.*, 1954–5, **83**, 493.
[36] R. L. Bell and R. W. Cahn, *J.I.M.*, 1957–8, **86**, 433.
[37] D. Hull, *Phil. Mag.*, 1958, **36**, 1468.

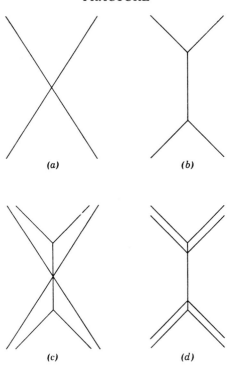

Fig. 7.11.

together and coalesce. In any event, when the crack or cavity is large enough to be regarded as such, there seems no reason why it cannot enlarge simply by dislocations running into it as illustrated in Fig. 7.12. Here, a dislocation is shown extending the crack, but dislocations could also run into the side of the cavity and make it wider. In this way a central crack should be gradually produced which is large enough for

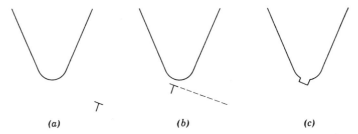

Fig. 7.12. Successive stages of the process of extension of a cavity by addition of a dislocation.

the shear deformation at its tip to be a significant factor in extending it in the way already discussed. If this shear deformation is a significant factor, it accounts for the relatively small number of cavities normally seen on a longitudinal section after fracture, since the first one to grow large has an advantage over others. Also to be explained is the fact that the central crack seems usually to grow from the size at which it can first be seen (on a section) to the full width of the "cup" during a fairly small amount of plastic deformation. Presumably, the intense shear at the edge of the cavity, taking place in the already heavily deformed region of the neck, is responsible for this.

PART B.   BRITTLE FRACTURE

7.7   Incidence of Brittle Fracture

The basic distinction between brittle and ductile fracture from the point of view adopted in this book, in which fundamental processes are the main concern, is that whereas plastic deformation is necessary for the spread of the central crack during ductile failure, plastic deformation is not necessary, although it may occur, during the spread of a crack in a brittle failure. In this respect, brittle failures in metals are akin to brittle failure of glass. As already mentioned, this classification does not always correspond with engineering considerations because some metals fail in a ductile manner after little plastic deformation and are therefore brittle in an engineering sense. The distinction made here, however, corresponds with a noteworthy difference in properties.

Brittle factures nearly always travel along a simple crystallographic plane, the cleavage plane, or along grain boundaries, which makes it relatively simple to decide by examination what part of a fracture surface broke in a brittle fashion. In either case, brittleness is confined to a range of conditions in any given material. Figure 7.13 shows, for example, the effect of varying the temperature on the impact strength of some Cu–Sb alloys. At 0°C those containing about $\frac{1}{2}\%$ Sb show a marked change in toughness, being tough at higher temperatures and relatively brittle at lower temperatures. The change is known as the "tough-brittle transition." This effect is typical of most "brittle" metals, although the temperature of the transition depends on the metal. Usually there is no recovery of toughness as the temperature is reduced (measurements have been made down to 4°K), and no sharp loss of toughness as the temperature is raised, at least until the fracture mechanisms peculiar to creep become possible. However, there are exceptions in which brittle behaviour is confined to a range of temperature (section 7.13). Varying

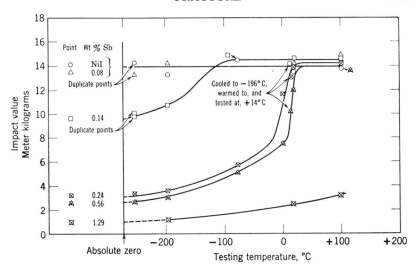

Fig. 7.13.   Results of impact tests on Cu–Sb alloys (Ref. 38).

the temperature is only one of several ways of producing a tough-brittle transition.   Curves like Fig. 7.12 could also be drawn with grain size, (e.g. see Fig. 7.15), speed of test, or composition as abscissa.

Although not all metals exhibit cold brittleness, the phenomenon does not seem confined to metals with particular crystallographic lattices. Thus it occurs in metals with fcc, bcc, hexagonal, tetragonal (white tin), and diamond type (Ge, Si) lattices as well as in many intermetallic compounds.[39, 40]   It is most important in practice in the bcc metals Fe, W, Mo, Cr, Va, and to a lesser extent in Ta, and is so widespread in the first four as often to be a limiting factor.   Although there is no preference for a particular lattice type, there is a close experimental association between a tough-brittle transition such as in Fig. 7.13 and a yield stress which rises steeply as the temperature falls, in the sense that metals which show one behaviour also show the other.   This association gave rise to the engineering theory of brittleness that the tough-brittle transition occurs when the temperature is low enough for the yield stress to exceed the fracture stress, which was supposed to be independent of temperature.   It will be seen in section 7.12 that this idea, applied, however, to the small volume at a crack tip, forms part of a metallurgical theory of brittle fracture.

[38] D. McLean, *J.I.M.*, 1952–3, **81**, 121.
[39] A. M. Savitskii, *Doklady Akad. Nauk. S.S.S.R.*, 1948, **62**, 349 (Report in English in *Metal Progr.*, 1948, **56**, 126).
[40] R. Lourie, *T.A.I.M.E.*, 1952, **194**, 1093.

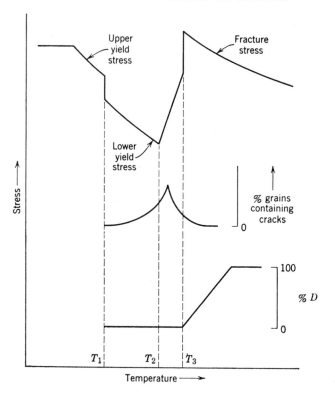

Fig. 7.14. Tough-brittle transition with change in temperature. Schematic variation with temperature of fracture stress, incidence of microcracks, and type of fracture. % *D* represents the percentage of the fracture surface that broke in a ductile manner. Based on experiments on steel (Ref. 41).

7.8 Relation Between Fracture Stress and Yield Stress

The fracture stress is not constant through a tough-brittle transition, but varies systematically. The way it varies with grain size and temperature has proved particularly instructive in formulating a theory of brittle fracture.

The relation found with a rimming steel between fracture stress and yield stress at different temperatures is illustrated by the upper curve in Fig. 7.14. At the top of the temperature range shown, the metal does not break in tension until a stress considerably higher than the yield stress is reached as a result of cold work, and the metal has good ductility. Below

[41] G. T. Hahn, B. L. Averbach, W. S. Owen, and M. Cohen, *Conference on Fracture*, Wiley—M.I.T., 1959, p. 91.

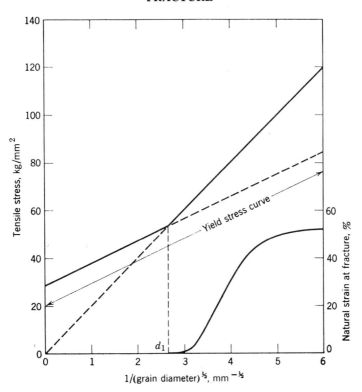

Fig. 7.15. Tough-brittle transition with change in grain size. Relation between brittle fracture stress, yield stress, and grain diameter. Mild steel at $-195°C$ (Ref. 42).

the temperature T_3 the fracture stress drops quickly, and the ductility consequently decreases until at temperature T_2 fracture occurs at the lower yield stress. From T_2 to T_1 the fracture stress rises again, following the lower yield stress as this rises with decrease in temperature. In this temperature range, therefore, fracture is produced during the Lüders strain. At T_1 the fracture stress jumps to the upper yield stress. The only strain that now precedes fracture is the pre-yield strain. At some still lower temperature the curve of fracture stress against temperature shows another break, probably marking the point at which twinning becomes the initiating event.

The way the fracture stress varies with grain size is illustrated by Fig. 7.15. The fracture stress is indicated by the full line curve. Below the break at the grain size d_1 it follows the yield stress curve which had been

[42] J. R. Low, *Relation of Properties to Microstructure*, A.S.M. Symposium 1954, 163.

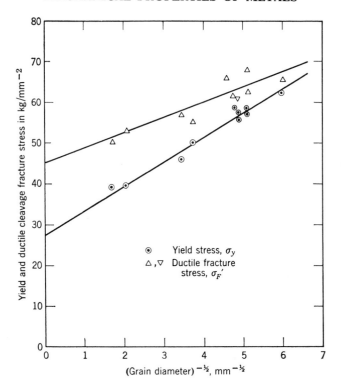

Fig. 7.16. The effect of grain size on the yield and fracture stresses of Mo at $-78°C$. The C and N contents were 80 and 185 ppm respectively (A. S. Wronski and A. A. Johnson).

determined over the whole grain size range in compression tests. At grain sizes smaller than d_1 (to the right in Fig. 7.15) the fracture stress rises above the yield stress curve; in this region strain hardening is necessary to reach the fracture stress and elongations of about 50% are ultimately reached. Thus, increasing the grain size acts like decreasing the temperature, producing a tough-brittle transition. The influence of grain size illustrated in Fig. 7.15 is usually considered to be the general one because, although specific evidence like that in Fig. 7.15 is scanty, much experience shows that large grain sizes tend to be associated with a relatively high degree of brittleness. However, an exceptional behaviour has been found in molybdenum[43] and is illustrated in Fig. 7.16. Here, the yield and fracture stresses diverge more and more as the grain size is increased.

[43] A. S. Wronski and A. A. Johnson, *Phil. Mag.*, 1962, **7**, 213.

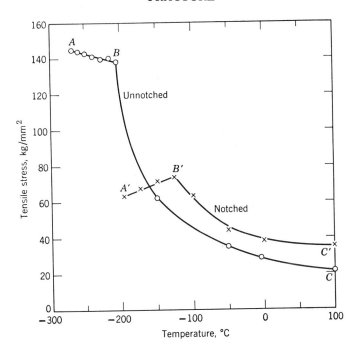

Fig. 7.17. Influence of notch on tensile behaviour of mild steel. AB and A′B′, fracture; BC and B′C′, yield (Ref. 45).

In Fig. 7.14 and 7.15, under the most completely embrittling conditions the fracture stress equals the yield stress. There are, however, instances where this simple result is not found. Thus Fe–P alloys have been prepared in which the fracture stress fell steadily from 12.6 kg/mm² at 100°C to less than 1 kg/mm² at −196°C.[44] The Fe–N alloys mentioned in section 7.1 behave similarly. Au–Bi alloys are possibly another similar example of extreme weakness. As the yield stresses of the two iron alloys are certainly not as low as 1 kg/mm², at low temperature these metals break well below the yield stress. Sharp notches produce the same result, as illustrated by Fig. 7.17. This figure shows how the yield stress, determined in compression tests on unnotched specimens, rose continuously with decreasing temperature. The fracture stress of sharply notched specimens follows this curve down to a certain temperature, and then breaks away in the downward direction. Below this temperature, the fracture stress is less than the yield stress. A similar behaviour seems

[44] B. E. Hopkins and H. R. Tipler, *J.I.S.I.*, 1958, **188**, 218.
[45] E. T. Wessel, *A.S.T.M.*, 1956, **56**, 540.

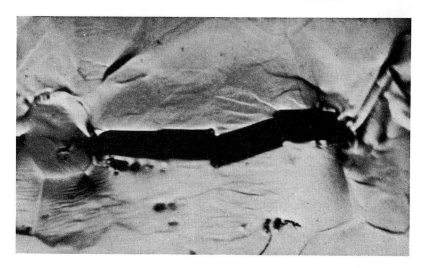

Fig. 7.18. A brittle crack held up at grain boundaries. 0.04% C steel strained at −195°C (J. R. Low).

to occur in experiments on iron single crystals,[46] in which a tough-brittle transition occurs with change in orientation.

It is perhaps the general rule, therefore, that the fracture stress coincides with the yield stress in the brittle condition, but exceptions to this rule exist in which the macro fracture stress is less than the macro yield stress. The exceptions are referred to again in sections 7.10 and 7.12.

7.9 Origin and Spread of Fracture

In the lower part of Fig. 7.14 is shown how the prevalence of visible microcracks and the appearance of the fracture vary with temperature. Although above T_2 the test was stopped before fracture to examine for microcracks, whereas below T_2 fracture occurred at yield and the examination had to be made after fracture, there is no discontinuity in the number of cracks observed between these two regions. Evidently at the point where the microexamination was made above T_2 all the cracks that were going to form had formed and the final stages involved only the spreading of some of these.

The cracks seen are generally between one and two or three grains long. A typical crack is shown in Fig. 7.18. Clearly in this figure the crack has stopped at grain boundaries. The spreading of a crack across a grain

[46] B. Edmondson, *P.R.S.*, 1961, **A264**, 176.

boundary faces in fact much the same difficulty as the spreading of slip does, since cleavage planes in neighbouring grains will not usually co-incide. Very likely the crack spreads by nucleating a fresh crack in the adjoining grain on the latter's cleavage plane and the two cracks join up by a tearing action, thus forming the steps at grain boundaries frequently seen on transverse sections of brittle fractures which could be erroneously interpreted as due to genuine grain-boundary fracture. Sometimes the crack in a single grain is formed by the joining up of several small cracks.[42] The steps where these small cracks join must be the deep "river lines" seen on cleavage fracture surfaces, and, since deep river lines are usually seen, probably much of the enlargement of cracks occurs by this kind of coalescence. It will be seen later in connection with Fig. 7.20 that theory can explain the existence of cracks less than a grain size long.

The tensile component of stress seems to be significant for the cracks registered in Fig. 7.14, since near T_2 85% of them lay within 15° of the normal to the tensile stress. Below T_1 no cracks were seen after fracture, evidently because the first one was no longer stopped by grain boundaries and could propagate under the applied tensile stress right across the speci-men. Neither were cracks seen after loading a specimen very close to the fracture stress below T_1, so that in this temperature range a crack must propagate as soon as it forms. Under particularly brittle conditions, grain boundaries are evidently therefore ineffective, but in a certain region of temperature they play an important part in arresting cracks and encouraging ductile behaviour.

The gradual transition from ductile to brittle behaviour with change in temperature implied by the foregoing is not always found. Extremely sharp transitions are known in polycrystalline iron[2, 47, 48] and perhaps are associated with a large grain size which, by encouraging a large initial crack size, mitigates the power of grain boundaries to halt a crack. In single crystals sharp transitions are similarly to be expected and have been observed.[46]

Besides being associated with yield by slip, fracture is often associated with yield by twinning as mentioned in connection with Fig. 7.10 and 7.14. The details of the association are not certain[49] as it is often difficult to tell whether twins formed before or after the crack, as a result of the stress wave travelling with it. Twins are certainly able to initiate cracks.[46] The general rule is probably that they initiate fracture at low temperature and are initiated by fracture at high temperature.

Once a large enough crack is produced in brittle material, the velocity

[47] W. P. Rees, B. E. Hopkins, and H. R. Tipler, *J.I.S.I.*, 1951, **169**, 157.
[48] N. P. Allen, W. P. Rees, B. E. Hopkins, and H. R. Tipler, *J.I.S.I.*, 1953, **174**, 108.
[49] N. N. Davidenkov and T. N. Chuchman, *Zhur. Tekhn. Fiz.*, 1958, **28**, 2502.

of its tip rapidly accelerates[50, 51] to the limiting velocity. This depends on conditions and has a maximum value of about one-third the speed of longitudinal sound waves. Evidently the crack spreads as a Griffith crack, that is, the external work done during its spread is sufficient to provide the new surface energy and the energy of plastic deformation around the crack tip.[52, 53] An idea of the magnitude of this latter term can be obtained from the tension stress necessary for fracture under conditions where cracks form which are a grain diameter long and have to be spread across the grain boundaries.[42] We insert the known data in the Griffith equation for the breaking stress σ_b

$$\sigma_b = \left(\frac{2E\gamma'}{\pi c}\right)^{\frac{1}{2}} \tag{7.1}$$

E is Young's modulus, γ' is the total energy required per unit increase in area of the crack, comprising true surface energy and plastic work done by the stress concentration at the moving crack tip, and c is the crack length (assumed equal to the grain diameter). This equation gives $\gamma' \sim 10^5$ ergs/cm^2, or about thirty times larger than the likely true surface energy. Nearly all the energy must therefore be used in plastic deformation at the crack tip. This amount of energy, nevertheless, represents a very small amount of plastic work; for example, it is the work done by a stress of 10 kg/mm^2 producing a 10% strain in a slice 10^{-3} cm thick. It is clear from this that a crack can normally spread as a Griffith crack only if very little plastic work indeed occurs during its spread. During propagation across a single grain, that is, during the formation and initial spread of a crack, the grain-boundary barrier has not to be faced and a considerably smaller value for γ is to be expected.

Some experiments on LiF[54, 55, 56] show directly the importance of plastic work during the spread of a crack, in this case across a single grain. It was found that slow moving cracks generated dislocations from which fine "river lines" sprang, and the energy absorbed by this process slowed the cracks still more. It might be added that with a moving crack the stress concentration at the crack tip probably does not increase indefinitely as the crack length d grows, which eq. 7.1 implies happens with a static

[50] N. F. Mott, *Engineering*, 1948, **165**, 16.
[51] J. J. Gilman, *Conference on Fracture*, Wiley—M.I.T., 1959, p. 193.
[52] A. A. Griffith, *Phil. Trans. Roy. Soc. London*, 1920, **A.221**, 163.
[53] E. Orowan, *Repts. Progr. in Phys.*, 1948–9, **12**, 185.
[54] J. J. Gilman, *T.A.I.M.E.*, 1957, **209**, 449.
[55] J. J. Gilman, C. Knudson, and W. P. Walsh, *J.A.P.*, 1958, **29**, 601.
[56] J. J. Gilman, *T.A.I.M.E.*, 1958, **212**, 310.

crack; instead a steady state of stress appears to travel along with the crack tip.[51, 57]

7.10 Importance of True Surface Energy

Despite the usual preponderance of plastic work just referred to, the new surface energy of the surfaces produced during fracture must be decisive for determining the fracture path (in particular, whether it is intergranular or cleavage) and important in determining the fracture stress. These points can be seen by consideration of the situation at the crack tip. The tip advances when the tensile stress there is equal to the cohesive strength of the atoms just ahead, and this is of course measured by the new surface energy. The lower is the new surface energy the lower need the applied stress be and the less plastic work is done. The same conclusions can also be deduced from the Griffith eq. 7.1 by replacing γ' by the true surface energy γ plus a term $\alpha\sigma_b{}^2$ (α being a constant) to represent the plastic work done. Rearranging then gives

$$\sigma_b = \left(\frac{2E\gamma}{\beta\pi c}\right)^{1/2} \tag{7.2}$$

with

$$\beta = \left(1 - \frac{2E\alpha}{\pi c}\right)$$

Equation 7.2 has the same form as eq. 7.1 but with γ now being a controlling term. The new surface energy is therefore a kind of valve that controls the amount of plastic work done although the latter is usually much the bigger quantity. It might be added that for cleavage fracture the term γ in eq. 7.2, that is, the new surface energy, is equal to $2\gamma_s$, where γ_s is the energy per unit area of the cleavage surface. For intergranular fracture γ is equal to $(2\gamma_s - \gamma_B)$, where γ_B is the grain-boundary energy per unit area, since the energy of the two new surfaces is partly offset by the energy of the grain boundary along which fracture is taking place.

The surface energy of solid metals can evidently be reduced by surface adsorption of an element in solid solution, just as detergents reduce the surface energy of water. An example is shown in Fig. 7.19, which illustrates the effect of dissolved antimony on the free surface energy of copper. Consequently, if such a solute concentrates at grain boundaries, the grain boundaries become easy paths for fracture, not because the grain-boundary energy is reduced—this makes fracture along the boundary more difficult—but because the much larger term $2\gamma_s$ is reduced. This effect helps to explain the connection between grain-boundary

[57] C. S. Barrett, *Conference on Fracture*, Wiley—M.I.T., 1959, p. 1.

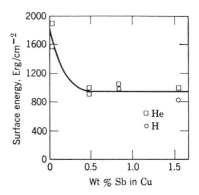

Fig. 7.19.   Effect of Sb on the surface energy of Cu at 950°C in He and in H_2.   (H. R. Tipler and D. McLean; Crown Copyright reserved.)

embrittlement and grain-boundary adsorption, for example, in temper-brittle steels and Al–Mg–Na alloys,[58] or as exemplified more explicitly by a comparison of the influence of antimony on the surface energy of copper in Fig. 7.19 with its embrittling influence in Fig. 7.13; the embrittlement follows grain-boundary paths.   From the point of view of grain-boundary cohesion the ideal solute is therefore one which segregates to grain boundaries because it lowers the grain-boundary energy, but raises the surface energy, for such a solute would increase the grain-boundary cohesion.   As regards cleavage fracture, it is unlikely that adsorption occurs in the way it does at grain boundaries, but an influence of composition on cleavage cohesion is mentioned in the next section.

Extremely large reductions in $2\gamma_s - \gamma_B$ are possible.   Thus, for copper this quantity is about 3000 ergs/cm², and for copper exposed to lead vapour it can be as little as 200 ergs/cm².[59]   Moreover, it can be expected to vary from grain boundary to grain boundary.   Possibly, therefore, in extremely brittle metals like those mentioned in section 7.9, which always break along grain boundaries, extreme weakening of this sort occurs, and at some boundaries $2\gamma_s = \gamma_B$.   Such boundaries would be effectively cracks a grain size long and would enable fracture to take place at an unusually low stress.

7.11   Influence of Composition, Heat Treatment and Test Conditions

Other internal factors besides grain size which affect the brittle behaviour are therefore composition and the heat treatment.   These factors

---

[58] C. E. Ransley and D. E. J. Talbot, *J.I.M.*, 1959–60, **88**, 150.
[59] G. L. J. Bailey and H. C. Watkins, *P.P.S.*, 1950, **B.63**, 350.

determine whether segregation occurs—and hence govern the fracture stress—and also influence the yield strength. As a measure of the strength of these and other effects, the transition temperature in impact tests is frequently used because it is relatively easy to measure. An example of the strong influence composition can have is that 0.01% of oxygen has been found to raise the transition temperature of iron by 200°C, and also to change the fracture path from transcrystalline, along (100) planes, to intergranular.[60] Evidently the oxygen segregates at grain boundaries and makes γ there less than on (100) planes. The important part of a heat treatment is usually the rate of cooling through a certain temperature range; slow cooling allows more time for segregation to occur. The theory of this has been studied.[61] In one examination in which several steels were investigated, slow cooling compared with water quenching raised the transition temperature by 50°C in a typical steel, while the most sensitive composition showed an increase of 600°C. The Fe–P alloys mentioned in section 7.8 were exceptions to this rule, and maximum embrittlement occurred after water quenching from about 700°C; quenching stresses may be important in this case.

In the fcc metals brittle fracture, in the sense in which the term is being used here of fracture taking place with little local deformation along the fracture path, has never been observed except along intergranular paths. Evidently a brittle crack cannot spread in an fcc metal unless γ is reduced substantially below the value characterising the pure metal. In this respect the fcc metals seem to differ from metals with the other common lattices, in which brittle transcrystalline and brittle intergranular fracture both occur. However, in these metals also, the most severe embrittlement is invariably intergranular in character, so that impurities can impair grain-boundary cohesion more than they can impair transcrystalline cohesion.

This association between grain-boundary weakness and impurities concentrated there has led to the view that intergranular brittleness is always the result of a damaging effect of impurities. A practical conclusion is that beryllium, which always fractures along grain boundaries, can be made more ductile by making it purer. Although this may prove to be true, the generalisation involved implies that in a pure metal γ is always greater along grain boundaries than along any crystallographic plane, for which there seems no support in present knowledge.

Although alloying elements can affect grain-boundary cohesion more than they affect cohesion across crystallographic planes, there is evidence

[60] W. P. Rees and B. E. Hopkins, *J.I.S.I.*, 1952, **172**, 403.
[61] D. McLean, *Grain Boundaries in Metals*, Oxford University Press, London, 1957, Chap. V.

to show that alloying elements in the form of precipitates can affect trans-crystalline cohesion, since there is one case where they have been found to strengthen this cohesion. This was in NaCl.[62] When a transmission interference microscope was used and a partly cleaved crystal was ex-amined in a direction perpendicular to the cleavage plane, around each precipitate particle Newton's rings of such character were seen as to prove that the cleavage faces still cohered there.

External factors which affect the transition temperature are the speed of testing, the stress system, and cold work. In some experiments on steel the transition temperature was 100°C higher in impact tensile tests on notched bars than in static tensile tests on similar specimens.[63] This is another example of the equivalence already encountered between lowering the temperature and increasing the strain rate. Raising the hydrostatic tensile component of the stress system increases brittleness.[64] Notched specimens are of course always more likely to be brittle than are smooth ones, partly because the rate of straining at the root of the notch is particu-larly high and partly because there is a large hydrostatic tension there. Cold work usually first lowers the transition temperature but eventually raises it again,[65, 66, 67] provided of course that strain ageing is not allowed to occur before testing.[68]

7.12 Theory of Brittle Fracture

The condition for brittle fracture is evidently that a crack forms which is long enough to spread as a Griffith crack. This generally implies two differences from ductile fracture. First, the initial cracks must be con-siderably longer than those believed to characterise the initiation of ductile fracture. To produce a long crack by the mechanisms of Fig. 7.8–7.11, many dislocations must combine so that long slip distances and metallurgical conditions making it easier to keep an active slip plane going than to start a new one favour brittleness. Alternatively, however, a long crack can be produced by ductile failure itself, and it is known from examination of fractured surfaces that failure of steel, for example, frequently commences in a ductile fashion but transforms to the brittle type as the broken area grows. Second, very little plastic deformation must occur as the crack spreads (for an exception to this rule see section

[62] A. J. Forty, *Acta Met.*, 1959, **7**, 139.
[63] O. Lissner, *Arch. Eisenhüttenw.*, 1953, **24**, 27.
[64] A. Guessier and R. Castro, *Rev. Mét.*, 1949, **46**, 517.
[65] E. J. Ripling and W. M. Baldwin, *A.S.M.*, 1951, **43**, 778.
[66] E. J. Ripling and W. M. Baldwin, *A.S.M.*, 1952, **44**, 1047.
[67] E. J. Ripling and W. M. Baldwin, *Proc.A.S.T.M.*, 1951, **51**, 1023.
[68] E. J. Ripling, *A.S.M.*, 1954, **46**, 184.

7.14). In many brittle metals it appears that a sufficiently low level of plastic deformation is only possible because the yield stress depends sensitively on strain rate, so that a fast moving crack passes any spot before slip can occur there. Since a yield stress which is sensitive to strain rate is also sensitive to temperature, this explains the close experimental association of brittleness and yield stress rising with decreasing temperature. This speed sensitivity may well help to transform a ductile failure into a brittle one, since the edge of the area that is failing by a ductile process in all probability gathers speed as it grows.

There are three theories based on these ideas.

(a) Cottrell's Theory.[69] This theory assumes that dislocations combine as in Fig. 7.10 or Fig. 7.11 so that the energy of combination helps cracks to form. The condition for a crack to form that is long enough to spread as a Griffith crack is worked out, taking into account the energy of the dislocations, the energy of the crack, and the work done by both the tensile and shear stresses as the crack extends. Referring to Fig. 7.10, this is the Griffith condition applied to the crack C assisted by the shear on A and B which also helps to extend the crack. The condition deduced is

$$\sigma n b = 2\gamma' \qquad (7.3)$$

where σ is the applied tensile stress and γ' is the effective surface energy (i.e., including plastic work). The slip displacement, taken to be the amount of slip that relaxes the effective shear stress, is approximately (see eq. 4.6)

$$n b = \left(\frac{\tau - \tau_f'}{G}\right) L \qquad (7.4)$$

where L is the length of the slip band, assumed in the theory to be equal to the grain size, τ is the applied shear stress, and τ_f' is the frictional resistance to slip. Next, rewrite eq. 6.6 using tensile stress $\sigma = 2 \times$ shear stress τ, so that

$$\sigma - \sigma_f' = 2kL^{-\frac{1}{2}} \qquad (7.5)$$

where $k = \tau_s' l'^{\frac{1}{2}}$. Now substitute for nb in eq. 7.3 from eq. 7.4, using eq. 7.5 to replace $(\tau - \tau_f')$ to obtain

$$\sigma = \frac{2\gamma'G}{k} L^{-\frac{1}{2}} \qquad (7.6)$$

as the expression for the fracture stress σ.

[69] A. H. Cottrell, T.A.I.M.E., 1958, 212, 192.

It can also be deduced that the relation between the size c of crack that is formed and the tensile stress is

$$\sigma = \left[\frac{2\gamma'G}{\pi(1 - \nu)}\right]^{\frac{1}{2}} c^{-\frac{1}{2}} \quad (7.7)$$

It is instructive to compare the proportionality factors on the right-hand side of eq. 7.6 and 7.7 with the proportionality factor for the yield stress, which is $2k$ in the present nomenclature when tensile stresses are used. This is done in Table 7.3; values for $2k$ are obtained from Table 6.7. True surface energies are about equal to $Gb/8$; in the table two values have been taken, $Gb/8$ and $5Gb/8$, the latter value implying that some plastic work is done by the stress concentration at the crack tip.

Table 7.3

Proportionality Factor for Fracture Stress and Yield Stress

(The units are kg/mm² for stress and centimeters for length)

	Condition Assumed			
	$-196°C$		Room Temperature	
Factor	$\gamma' = Gb/8$	$\gamma' = 5Gb/8$	$\gamma' = Gb/8$	$\gamma' = 5Gb/8$
$2k$	2×10^{-4}	2×10^{-4}	8×10^{-5}	8×10^{-5}
From eqn. 7.6	6×10^{-5}	3×10^{-4}	1.6×10^{-4}	8×10^{-4}
From eqn. 7.7	5.6×10^{-5}	1.3×10^{-4}	5.6×10^{-5}	1.3×10^{-4}

There are two points to note. The fracture stress (eq. 7.6) rises more rapidly with reduction in grain size than the yield stress (eq. 6.6), except when the dislocation locking factor (i.e., $2k$) is large. And the proportionality factor in eq. 7.7 is smaller than that in eq. 7.6, which means that cracks can spread even though they are smaller than a grain size long.

What is believed to be a typical relation is shown in Fig. 7.20. Everywhere to the left of OC represents the brittle condition. However, no crack can form until the yield stress is reached. Consequently, fracture occurs along AB. The crack corresponding to grain size L_B has the length c_B when first formed, and is smaller than a grain diameter, but can immediately extend. We might, however, expect to see cracks of slightly less than this size after fracture which formed, say, in unfavourably oriented grains. To the right of B the metal must be work hardened to reach the fracture line BC; until BC is reached the cracks produced are smaller than given by OC' and cannot extend as Griffith cracks. Thus, in Fig. 7.15, which is an experimental plot similar to Fig. 7.20, the elonga-

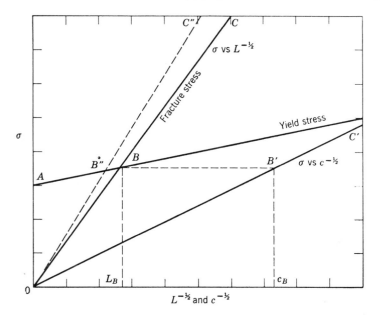

Fig. 7.20. Schematic relation between tensile stress σ and grain size L for yield and fracture, and between σ and crack of length c which can extend under the applied stress. The dashed line OC″ represents the stress required to make cracks cross grain boundaries.

tion begins to rise to the right of the point corresponding to B in Fig. 7.20, and sufficiently far to the right the brittle fracture stress is so high that the metal fails in a ductile way before the condition for brittle behaviour is satisfied.

In section 7.9 it was pointed out that in a certain temperature range cracks are stopped by grain boundaries. This effect can be included in Fig. 7.20 by drawing another line, such as the dashed line $OC″$, to represent the stress required to propagate cracks a grain size long, which makes the abscissa scale for this line $L^{-½}$. In the intermediate range of temperature referred to in connection with Fig. 7.14 the new line lies to the left of OC to correspond to the high value of $γ′$ associated with a crack crossing a grain boundary; the stress must now be raised to $B″C″$ to complete the fracture. At lower temperatures the new line must lie to the right of OC so that the first crack formed can spread across grain boundaries. The very sharp tough-to-brittle transitions with temperature change referred to in section 7.9 possibly correspond to a metal condition such that $OC″$ lies to the right of OC in the temperature region in which the tough-to-brittle transition occurs.

(b) *Stroh's Theory*.[70, 71]   In this theory a group of n dislocations is supposed to be piled up by the applied stress, against a grain boundary for example.   It becomes energetically favourable for the group to convert itself into a crack (Fig. 7.8) when

$$\tau n b = 4\gamma \qquad (7.8)$$

where τ is the applied shear stress.   As before, this can be rearranged to give

$$\tau = \frac{4\gamma G}{k} L^{-\frac{1}{2}} \qquad (7.9)$$

An expression resembling eq. 7.7 can be devised for the crack length. However, analysis shows that, if γ is constant, the crack produced is long enough to be extended as a Griffith crack in a tensile test (tensile stress = $2 \times$ shear stress).   To be able to explain the effects of stress system and grain size on transition temperature it is necessary to suppose that γ increases as the crack extends.   The increase on crossing a grain boundary does not help here as the crack length predicted is more than a grain diameter when the crack is first formed.

(c) *Petch's Theory*.[72]   This theory takes as the criterion for brittle fracture the condition that a fracture which is spreading as a ductile fracture should transform to the brittle type.   At this point the theory bases itself firmly on observation since, as explained earlier, this is frequently known to happen.   It is, however, otherwise similar to the other two theories, especially theory a, which also allows small cracks to form, since it takes ductile fracture as depending on a shear stress criterion and thus makes the transition depend on a shear stress criterion.

The physical situation envisaged is that cracks are formed ahead of the ductile fracture by combination of dislocations.   The condition deduced for such a crack to spread as a Griffith crack is also found to be eq. 7.3. Substituting for nb then gives an equation like 7.6.   It again follows that an expression like eq. 7.7 can be derived for the crack length.

(d) *Discussion of the Theories.*   Relations like those depicted in Fig. 7.20 and proportionality factors similar to those in Table 7.3 therefore can be made to result from all three theories.   All three lead to the following conclusions.

1. The tough-brittle transition with grain size arises solely because the frictional force τ_f' is included in the yield stress but not in the fracture

[70] C. Zener, *Fracturing of Metals*, A.S.M. Symposium, 1948, p. 3.
[71] A. N. Stroh, *Advances in Phys.*, 1957, 6, 418.
[72] N. J. Petch, *Conference on Fracture*, Wiley—M.I.T., 1959, p. 54.

stress, making it possible for the two curves to cross in a diagram like Fig. 7.20.

2. The transition with temperature arises because either τ_f' or the slopes of the curves, or both, alter with temperature, so that the point of intersection occurs at a different grain size at different temperatures. This amounts to making the transition temperature depend on the relative magnitudes of yield stress and fracture stress at the crack tip. The slopes alter both with k, which is related to dislocation locking, and with γ', the effective surface energy. Since γ' largely comprises plastic work, it also depends on dislocation locking. If k is large and γ' small the fracture curve in Fig. 7.20 may always lie below the yield stress curve and the metal is brittle in all grain sizes. According to Table 7.3 this would always be the case at low temperature if no plastic work occurs as the crack extends.

3. The transition with stress system arises because changing the ratio of normal to shear stress alters differently the ordinate scales of the yield curve (ordinate equals resolved shear stress) and fracture curve (ordinate equals resolved normal stress) in Fig. 7.20 so that again the curves intersect at a different grain size.

4. All three theories make use of a relation between yield stress and grain size like eq. 6.10 and are, therefore, subject to the qualifications discussed in connection with this. If this type of equation is used, all three theories predict that the fracture stress is proportional to (grain diameter)$^{-\frac{1}{2}}$, provided γ' and k are unaffected by the changes in heat treatment which change the grain size. Where the fracture stress is not proportional to (grain diameter)$^{-\frac{1}{2}}$ perhaps these conditions are not satisfied.

Certain practical conclusions can also be drawn. The theories assume slip distances about equal to a grain diameter, and so emphasise that severe embrittlement depends on there being long slip distances; otherwise large cracks could not form. Anything which breaks up the slip path therefore increases the ductile range, provided there is not at the same time an increase in τ_f' which more than compensates. Besides fine grain size, precipitate particles break up the slip path. This explains why quenched and tempered plain carbon as well as alloy steels have low transition temperatures. They have a very fine grain size of the order of 1 or 2 microns and are hardened with finely dispersed carbide particles. On the other hand, dislocation locking is probably the most dangerous way of obtaining a high yield stress since it conduces to a large slip distance. Another conclusion is that the ductile range is widened not only by decreasing grain size but also by decreasing the magnitude of k. Decreasing k increases the slope of the fracture stress curve in Fig. 7.20

indirectly, through γ', as well as directly, and also reduces the slope of the yield stress curve, thus shifting the intersection point further to the left. Manganese appears to have these effects in steel.[73] According to chapter 6, k is equal to dislocation locking stress $\times$ (dislocation spacing)$^{1/2}$. Consequently, measures which reduce either of these help to prevent a crack from spreading. There is a limit to the useful reduction in the dislocation spacing, however, because if it is reduced too much the consequential work hardening raises the yield stress and begins to decrease the ductile range again. This reversing effect of dislocation density is probably one reason why small strains reduce the tough-brittle transition temperature and large strains increase it. Small deformations should also have the consequence that, when dislocation locking is strong, then if the metal can survive a little plastic deformation without fracture it becomes much more ductile because relatively easily movable dislocations surround each crack and increase the effective surface energy γ'. This effect may be another factor which conduces to a sharp transition from brittle to ductile deformation. A third conclusion is that to the left of point B in Fig. 7.20 stress concentrations are particularly dangerous, since in this region a crack can spread at a low stress. This, coupled with exceptionally low intergranular cohesion, helps to explain exceedingly low fracture strengths, as intimated in the previous section.

The differences in severity of embrittlement in Fe, Mo, W, V, and Ta may turn out to be explained by such considerations. However, apart from some evidence[69] that k is smaller for Ta than for the other metals, corresponding to its wider ductile range, there seems no good data yet available about the causes of these differences.

The three theories described agree in supposing that cracks are initiated by slip, and therefore that the yield stress is exceeded locally at least. There are cases where this has not yet been proved to occur. Some instances have been mentioned in section 7.8 where the fracture stress was so low that local yield as the initiator is practically out of the question. However, in these instances vanishingly small grain-boundary cohesion can probably be blamed as the source of cracking. Some further examples of this kind will be mentioned in chapter 12. In some substances, surface precipitates seem able to nucleate cracks without slip obviously intervening. Thus, sodium chloride is normally brittle but becomes ductile in water (the Joffé effect) because the surface layer containing cracks is dissolved away. If dried carefully, this ductility can be retained, but usually surface precipitates form and nucleate fracture when a stress is next applied.[74] A more difficult problem is presented by the behaviour of

[73] J. Heslop and N. J. Petch, *Phil. Mag.*, 1957, **2**, 649.
[74] R. J. Stokes, T. L. Johnston, and C. H. Li, *T.A.I.M.E.*, 1960, **218**, 655.

notched steels which (as shown in Fig. 7.17) under appropriate conditions fracture well below the yield stress. One view is that sufficient local plastic deformation occurs at the crack tip under the stress concentration there to initiate a crack.[75] Another view is that this is unlikely, and that some other way of initiating a crack must be found.[76] It has not yet been possible to measure the plastic strain at the crack tip experimentally.

Finally, these theories of brittle fracture go to show that cracks are produced in a similar way when a metal fractures in a ductile fashion. This can be seen, for example, as follows. Adding oxygen to iron introduces brittleness without appreciably affecting the yield stress. Hence, just on the brittle side of the transition cracks of appreciable length form during yield. Moving into the ductile region, it cannot be argued that the cracks failed to form at all, but only that they were shorter because γ' was larger.

7.13 Blue Brittleness

Mild steel generally exhibits partially brittle behaviour in a temperature range in the region of 250°C. This is the "blue brittle" region and ductility improves on either side of this temperature. Titanium, when containing hydrogen, shows a similar effect in a much lower temperature range and hydrogen probably also produces the same behaviour in a low temperature range in steel.[77]

These effects are clearly associated with rates of diffusion. There seem to be two distinct possible mechanisms which can produce blue brittleness.

1. The alloy element, for example, carbon, can diffuse to dislocations which have been temporarily halted quickly enough to lock them before they move again so that cracks are no longer surrounded by unlocked dislocations. The rise in γ' referred to in section 7.12 as occurring as a result of small strains therefore no longer occurs.

2. There is a genuine rise in frictional force because the carbon atoms can diffuse just fast enough to jump from one interstitial position to another as the dislocation stress field passes over them, and absorb energy in so doing (i.e., the Snoek effect discussed in chapter 6).

7.14 Brittle Fracture by the Ductile Mechanism

Some alloys when in the form of large thin sheets are liable to fracture suddenly and, from the point of view of an engineer, in a brittle way,

[75] A. H. Cottrell, Conference on Reacter Pressure Circuits, Iron and Steel Institute, London, 1961, p. 281.

[76] N. P. Allen, Conference on Fracture, Wiley—M.I.T., 1959, p. 123.

[77] E. J. Ripling, T.A.I.M.E., 1956, 206, 502.

although the detailed mechanism of fracture appears to be that described in this chapter as ductile. As might be expected, metals are more liable to this behaviour the more closely the proof stress approaches the UTS or, in other words, the less room there is for general extension. The strain during fracture is then practically confined to the region that necks. The governing situation seems to be that when a metal has a high ratio of proof stress to UTS then, in the form of large thin sheets, the total elastic strain may be greater than the extension occurring during necking.

Consequently, once a crack has grown large enough to satisfy eq. 7.1 with an unusually big value of γ', it will extend very rapidly, even though it extends by the ductile mechanism. The ideas of "fracture dynamics"[78, 79, 80] effectively classify metals as tough or brittle from the engineer's point of view. The experimental procedure involved is to make a measurement of the fracture stress when an artificial crack of known size is present, and to deduce a value for γ' by applying eq. 7.1 to the results. This value is useful in engineering design because it often behaves rather like an invariant property of the metal.

The kind of behaviour in question is best known in aluminium alloys, probably because thin aluminium alloy sheets with a high ratio of proof stress to UTS are used in aircraft, and is also encountered in steels. There seems no reason why it should not occur in other alloys with appropriate properties.

PART C

7.15 High-Speed Effects

During deformation at high speed there are big temperature rises inside a metal. A clear proof of this is that thin layers of martensite have been seen in ferritic steel after rapid deformation,[70] which indicates not only that the temperature there rose above 900°C, but that the heated layer remained thin (and was quenched by the surrounding cool metal). This is to be expected, since the metal softens on heating, inducing the shear to concentrate in a thin layer. Thus, when a metal is deformed rapidly it tends to shear along macroscopically well-defined planes. This kind of fracture has been called adiabatic shear fracture.

[78] G. Irwin, *Fracturing of Metals*, *A.S.M.*, Symposium 1948, p. 147.
[79] G. Irwin, Symposium on *Effect of Temperature on the Brittle Behaviour of Metals*, A.S.T.M., 1954.
[80] G. Irwin and J. E. Srawley, *Conference on Fracture Phenomena*, Würzburg, 1961.

Other effects arise from stress waves.[3, 70] For example, impact on the front of a plate starts off a compression wave, which is reflected from the back face as a tensile wave. If the reflected wave is intense enough, fracture occurs just behind the back face and a piece drops off. This is called "scabbing." The actual fracture presumably occurs by one of the mechanisms already described.

8

Recovery
and Recrystallisation

8.1 Recovery of Mechanical Properties

In a metal cold worked at a low temperature the changes that occur in some physical properties as the temperature is raised (e.g. Fig. 8.9) show that the state of the metal alters below room temperature, but very little change in mechanical properties takes place until the ordinary thermal movements of atoms become significant. This is because the mechanical properties, unlike the physical properties, are relatively insensitive to the movement of vacancies and interstitial atoms in the concentrations in which they are introduced by cold work, and are apparently insensitive to the contraction of stacking faults which also takes place in some metals and requires little thermal activity. The reason for this is that the mechanical properties depend primarily on the density of dislocations and perhaps also on the density of defect jogs, so that recovery of mechanical properties is connected with the elimination of these.

It is geometrically possible for jogs to anneal out (by the meeting of jogs of opposite sign) without the dislocation pattern changing appreciably. Conversely, when dislocations disappear, the density of jogs on the remaining dislocations does not have to diminish for any geometrical reason. Consequently, recovery experiments should help to separate the hardening contributions connected with dislocation density and jog density. For example, if the jogs annealed out first it would be possible to distinguish their contribution to the flow stress. However, recovery of mechanical properties appears to be connected in the main with a reduction in the density of dislocations present. Although this is the opinion widely held, it is worth pointing out that it rests chiefly on generalised comparisons of the temperature ranges of recovery of mechanical properties with, for example, those of polygonisation and of large decreases in stored energy. There are very few specific comparisons showing that mechanical properties recover as the dislocation density falls. If this conclusion is accepted, however, jogs do not contribute very greatly to the flow stress in practice, that is, D in eq. 4.15 is small in cold worked metals. Dislocations can be eliminated either by climb and cross slip or during recrystallisation by the migration of grain boundaries. As recovery is a word restricted to processes preceding recrystallisation, climb and cross slip are then the main events taking place during the process traditionally described as recovery.

Some recovery of mechanical properties occurs in many metals before recrystallisation commences. Some fairly typical hardness results for this group of metals are shown in Fig. 8.1.[1] According to these, about 25% of the hardness of cold worked iron recovers before recrystallisation begins, the beginning of recrystallisation being determined in this case by microscopic examination. The other mechanical properties are found to behave consistently, the proof stress and UTS falling and the ductility rising as the hardness drops.[2] But mechanical recovery does not precede recrystallisation in all metals. Copper, for example, is an exception. In two investigations of the recovery of cold worked copper[3, 4] no change in hardness occurred before recrystallisation (although in an older investigation[5] about 30% of the hardening disappeared before recrystallisation started. The reason for this discrepancy is not clear since the experimental conditions overlapped and recrystallisation was sought in all three investigations by the same method, namely, metallography). Where no recovery precedes recrystallisation, then, according to the view explained earlier, except in the recrystallisation nuclei themselves no dislocations disappear until the spreading of the boundaries of these nuclei enables them to do so. Slow climb of dislocations is probably the cause of this behaviour.

These two kinds of behaviour, of softening before recrystallisation and

[1] C. R. Austin, L. A. Luini, and R. W. Lindsay, *A.S.M.*, 1945, **35**, 446.
[2] H. Kofler-Valencak and H. Krainer, *Arch. Eisenhüttenw.*, 1956, **11**, 725.
[3] M. Cook and T. Ll. Richards, *J.I.M.*, 1946, **73**, 1.
[4] V. A. Phillips and A. Phillips, *J.I.M.*, 1952–3, **81**, 185.
[5] N. R. Pilling and G. P. Halliwell, *A.S.T.M.*, 1925, **25**, 97.

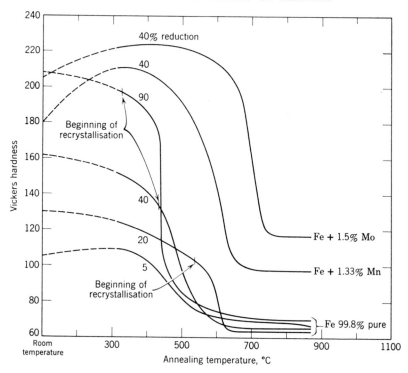

Fig. 8.1. Change of hardness on heating cold rolled Fe and Fe alloys (Ref. 1).

of retaining full hardness up to the recrystallisation temperature, probably represent the effects of the behaviour of dislocations in a pure metal. Not infrequently, and especially in alloys, the first effect of heating after cold work is to cause an increase in hardness, and the results for the iron alloys in Fig. 8.1 show this behaviour. As a rule, this seems to be a strain-ageing effect, although it may sometimes be connected with vacancies (see section 8.3).

Alloying elements are believed either to have no effect on the temperature at which recovery commences, or, more usually, they raise it. An exception is that magnesium has been found to double the speed of softening of aluminium,[6] an effect not yet understood. As far as the normal effect is concerned, the potency of different elements varies widely. For example, Fig. 8.1 shows that manganese and molybdenum markedly raise the softening temperature of iron, whereas some other elements studied in the same investigation had a much smaller effect.

If, instead of the hardness test, a more delicate test is used, evidence can

[6] E. C. W. Perryman, *T.A.I.M.E.*, 1956, **8**, 1247.

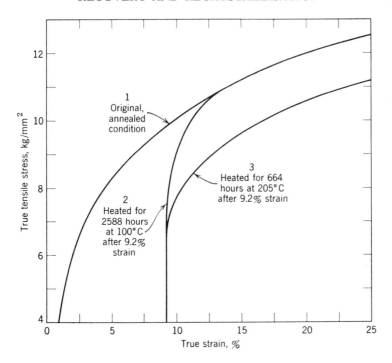

Fig. 8.2. Effect of annealing, after a strain of 9.2%, on the stress-strain curve of 2S–O Aluminium (Ref. 7).

be found for two stages of mechanical recovery occurring at different temperatures. A detailed study of the influence of heating on the stress-strain curve of cold worked 2S-O aluminium has demonstrated this[7] and some results of the investigation are illustrated in Fig. 8.2. Curve 1 is the stress-strain curve of an annealed sample. The first stage of recovery, curve 2, produced by heating at 100°C after straining, consists of a drop in yield stress which is much bigger than the drop normally found on reloading; however, the original stress-strain curve was quickly regained on further straining. The drop in yield stress takes place quickly at first during the recovery anneal but soon becomes a slow change. The second stage, curve 3, produced by heating at a higher temperature, consists of a lowering of the whole subsequent stress-strain curve, such that if it is slid backwards along the strain axis it roughly coincides with the original curve for the annealed condition. The rate of recovery was again rapid at first but became progressively slower. As far as other metals are

[7] T. V. Cherian, P. Pietrokowsky, and J. E. Dorn, *T.A.I.M.E.*, 1949, **185**, 948.

concerned, the first stage has been observed in zinc,[8] while a study of the stress-strain curve of decarburised iron after recovery showed that the two stages overlapped,[9] so that it cannot be expected that two stages should always be distinguished. This is referred to again in section 8.2. In the 2S-O aluminium, for stage 2 an activation energy of 1.44 ev was found, the temperature range studied being 247–318°C. Another investigation of aluminium, using hardness measurements, also found recovery over the temperature range of 180–300°C to be characterised by virtually the same activation energy, namely, 1.4 ev.[10] This activation energy is similar to that for self diffusion in aluminium and hence for climb.

Formal theories of recovery have been developed based on the idea that the rate of recovery diminishes exponentially with decrease in the internal stress.[8, 11] As might be expected from this assumption, they give the result in accordance with experiment that the rate of recovery changes progressively from an initial fast rate to a very slow one.

8.2   Recovery of Structure

Metallographic studies have revealed no change occurring prior to recrystallisation in those metals that do not soften before they recrystallise. In the ones that do, the visible structural changes which seem to occur in the temperature range of traditional recovery consist of a reduction in dislocation density and of polygonisation in one form or another.[12, 13, 14]

The way these structural changes occur depends on conditions. In single crystals oriented for single slip, conditions are especially simple. Thus, on heating bent Fe-Si single crystals[12] of such orientation that the bending produced only edge dislocations, there was first observed a redistribution of the dislocations along their slip planes under their mutual interaction. The redistribution involved only glide, and not climb, and evidently occurred in this metal because at room temperature there is a substantial resistance to dislocation movement which diminishes on raising the temperature. At a higher temperature, the dislocation density fell because climb became possible and led to a large amount of mutual annihilation of dislocations of opposite signs. At a still higher temperature, the remaining dislocations collected into walls perpendicular to the

[8] A. H. Cottrell and V. Aytekin, *J.I.M.*, 1950, **77**, 389.
[9] H. L. Couch and J. D. Lubahn, *T.A.I.M.E.*, 1959, **215**, 433.
[10] E. C. W. Perryman, *T.A.I.M.E.*, 1955, **7**, 369.
[11] D. Kuhlman, G. Masing, and J. Raffelsieper, *Z. Metallk.*, 1949, **40**, 241.
[12] W. R. Hibbard and C. G. Dunn, *Acta Met.*, 1956, **4**, 306.
[13] P. A. Jacquet, *Acta Met.*, 1954, **2**, 770.
[14] E. C. W. Perryman, *Acta Met.*, 1954, **2**, 26.

Fig. 8.3. Three-dimensional network and patches of two-dimensional network in Fe after cold work and recovery   × 27,000. (Crown copyright reserved.)

original slip planes. It was such simple conditions that first suggested the name polygonisation.[15]

When there has been multiple slip, as in polycrystals, the dislocation density is still greatly reduced during recovery,[16] but polygonisation now involves the formation of networks comprising dislocations of different Burgers vectors (section 2.1h).   Figure 8.3 is an electron micrograph of cold worked iron after recovery which shows the regular networks produced by heating. Comparison with Fig. 5.24 and 5.25 reveals the reduction in dislocation density that has taken place.   Examination at lower power by the etch-pit method discloses some very striking patterns during the early stages of recovery; one is shown in Fig. 8.4.   It seems from this that metastable arrangements of the arrays exist.   Later, the well-known, more clearly defined subcrystal structure develops, and Fig. 8.5 is an example.   Such clearly defined subcrystals appear to develop the most readily in metals with relatively unextended dislocations.   In

[15] R. Cahn, *J.I.M.*, 1949, **76**, 121.
[16] A. Saulnier and P. Miraud, *Compt. rend.*, 1959, **248**, 2871.

Fig. 8.4. Complicated subboundary patterns produced in Fe−4% Si alloy by heating after 10% elongation. (The "needles" are mechanical twins.)   × 1000. (Crown copyright reserved.)

copper, for example, which does not normally recover before it recrystallises and has extended dislocations, polygonisation is slow.[17]   However, purity plays a part here, for whereas polygonisation to an advanced stage has only been observed in copper of 99.999% purity after heating at 1000%C,[18] after still further purification by zone refining polygonisation has been seen to take place at 600°C.[19]

The mechanism of recovery after multiple slip is clearly more complicated than that after single slip since dislocations of several Burgers vectors are involved.   A simplifying factor is that the subboundary networks and the three-dimensional networks joining them are probably produced by similar dislocation movements.   At all events, both could be produced by the movements now to be discussed.

There are a number of distinguishable elementary events during recovery after cold work that has involved multiple slip.   First and possibly most frequently there is the simple formation of junctions with the help of

[17] A. Franks and D. McLean, *Phil. Mag.*, 1956, **1**, 101.
[18] F. W. Young, *J.A.P.*, 1958, **29**, 760.
[19] J. Montuelle, to appear.

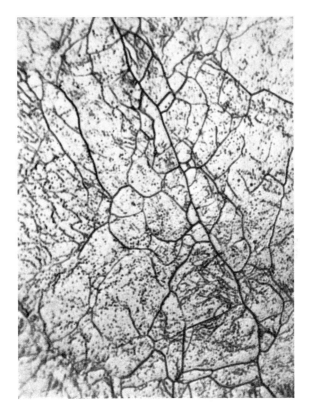

Fig. 8.5. Subgrain structure in Fe−4% Si alloy heated to 650–700°C after 10% elongation. ×1250. (Crown copyright reserved.)

cross slip or climb. Since the formation of an attractive junction entails a reduction in dislocation line length, it is a recovery process. It cannot reduce the dislocation content beyond a certain limit, however, without elimination of dislocations of opposite sign. The most frequent form of the encounter of two dislocations of opposite sign is probably the cutting intersection (section 2.1*i*). Concurrently with this, what is really involved now is the problem of the stability of dislocation networks, which is analogous to the problem of the stability of a network of grain boundaries.

There are probably several processes whereby three-dimensional dislocation networks reduce their dislocation content, that is, display the phenomenon of network growth, analogous to grain growth, and two can be picked out. The underlying driving force is, of course, the energy of

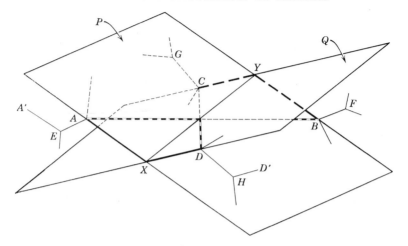

Fig. 8.6. Intersection of dislocations with opposite Burgers vectors.

dislocations which continuously drives the networks toward the nearest most stable state. For stability, the requirements that have to be satisfied are that at each junction point, or node, the Burgers vectors must add vectorially to zero and there must be line tension equilibrium, and dislocations must join the nodes by the shortest paths (elastic anisotropy and the difference between the energies of edge and screw dislocations modify this statement somewhat without affecting the principle behind it) compatible with line tension equilibrium, in general, no doubt by curved paths. In the attempt to reach this state the dislocations and nodes migrate by climb and slip, and it must sometimes happen that two nodes meet before line tension equilibrium is reached at both of them. Then it will usually happen that equilibrium is badly upset, and the struggle to reach it commences afresh. This is one process by which the dislocation density is reduced.

Another may be the climb following a cutting intersection, which is another event violently upsetting the approach to equilibrium. This can be described with the aid of Fig. 8.6, in which dislocations of opposite Burgers vector AB and CD lying in planes P and Q respectively have intersected and have glided into positions AXD and BYC; at A, B, C, and D these dislocations are attached by the attractive junctions shown to the rest of the dislocation network. Since the Burgers vectors of the dislocations AXD and BYC must lie along the line XY of intersection of the planes P and Q for cutting to have occurred, the dislocations AXD and BYC are largely of edge type. The process of shortening their length by straightening along AD and BC respectively therefore involves climb.

This straightening movement is likely to upset equilibrium at nodes A, B, C, and D. For example, it may increase the angles there, so that AXD and BYC can glide and climb until A and D become coincident with E and H respectively, and similarly C and B can become coincident with G and F respectively, thereby reducing the total length of dislocation. The whole dislocation of which AD is a part, i.e., ——A'—D'—— can now reduce its length by moving in the general direction YX with the aid of glide and climb. During this movement attractive junctions beyond A' and D' are liable to be undone as were the junctions at A and D. It must be possible to trace out in the crystal a continuous loop of dislocation including $A'D'$, which may be successful in shrinking to nothing in this manner. Put another way, the dislocation ——A'—D'—— continues moving in the general direction YX until it meets its opposite (i.e., another dislocation like ——CB——) moving in the direction XY. Even if the two are on different planes they will be attracted to and may annihilate each other. The whole process described may also take place with CYB and with the other dislocations at junctions broken by the movement of ——CB—— and ——A'—D'——.

Recovery obviously does not go to completion in the sense of eliminating all dislocations, although the undislocated crystal has the lowest free energy. A metastable state must be reached even in metals in which climb is easy. As already implied in describing the last event, annealing of a network is liable to be stopped at a junction where the available movement is insufficient to break it. The network is then in a metastable state since any small movement involves an increase in energy, and a higher temperature or a longer time is necessary to overcome the energy barrier. This is analogous to the metastable state that is reached with grain boundaries during grain growth. It will be clear from what has been said that when recovery occurs at one point it will tend to spread unless halted by such a metastable locking point, which is again similar to the situation in grain growth. Consequently, once recovery is well under way it should tend to be a homogeneous affair.

In the cold worked condition, sharp bends in dislocations (as in AXD in Fig. 8.6) must have the result that line tension helps to reduce the activation energy for climb, and the stress field of nearby dislocations may be large enough to have some effect. But these factors should attenuate as recovery proceeds and the activation energy should rise to that for self diffusion, which explains why recovery is rapid at first but progressively slows down.

These mechanisms allow cross-slip to play a limited part in recovery, and of course cross-slip will come into operation at a lower temperature than climb. What was called stage-2 mechanical recovery in connection with Fig. 8.2 clearly represents a general reduction in dislocation density because it affects the entire stress-strain curve. Both this fact and the activation energy involved indicate that climb is then the important process. What was called stage-1 recovery is more limited and perhaps commences when recovery by cross slip commences.

The explanation of the final arrangement of the dislocations after recovery, partly in subboundaries and partly in a three-dimensional network, is a somewhat different problem from that of how they are eliminated. The mechanisms discussed will clearly have as their result a three-dimensional network which grows coarser and coarser as recovery proceeds. If the dislocations were homogeneously distributed after cold work this three-dimensional network would probably be the only structural result of recovery. But the breadth of X-ray reflections from cold worked metals (see below) as well as the cell structure seen with the electron microscope shows that the dislocations are not homogeneously positioned either as regards density or distribution of dislocations of different Burgers vectors, and that little blocks of metal are rotated with respect to each other. A subboundary present after recovery probably represents the net local excess of Burgers vector that was present before recovery. For clearly, if little blocks of the metal are rotated with respect to each other, there must be contained in the subboundary regions, although these are ill-defined before recovery, the dislocations which can produce appropriate subboundaries. These dislocations need only move short distances not exceeding the width of the initially ill-defined subboundary zone to form a subboundary network, but must move much larger distances of one or more subgrain diameters to escape doing this. Given the initial misorientation between little blocks, the recovered subcrystal structure therefore seems inevitable. Of course, the subboundaries when formed may have some mobility and there may be some growth of subgrains.

Although the final arrangement of the dislocations in a subboundary must be that having lowest energy, the process of assembly of dislocations into a two-dimensional subboundary and the possibility of the existence of intermediate metastable arrangements has not been studied. (The only studies of groups of dislocations so far made are of piled up groups and of isolated polygonised arrays.) Presumably small patches of fairly regularly arranged dislocations such as those in Fig. 8.3 form at certain places, and they grow because their stress fields attract other dislocations. It is reasonable to expect that these nuclei occupy the same positions as walls of the cold worked cell structure, although not every wall becomes a proper subboundary since the latter are about ten times as far apart as the former.

Impurities may reduce the rate of polygonisation even at very high temperature.[20] Since climb must be the rate-controlling process here, this seems convincing evidence that impurity atoms can reduce the rate of climb. Two conceivable ways in which they might be effective are by attaching themselves to jogs and blocking movement of the latter, and widening the stacking fault with extended dislocations.[21, 22] The former effect should require smaller concentrations than the latter, because there are relatively few jogs and because the binding energy between an impurity and a jog is likely to be higher than that between an impurity and a stacking fault. If blocking of jogs is important, the binding energy must in fact be quite high to explain the high temperature up to which impurities may be effective. For example, lithium, sodium, and iron in amounts of around 0.02–0.2 at % retard the rate of polygonisation of aluminium up to 630°C.[23] If the elements in such small quantities are to be still attached to jogs at this temperature and not to become uniformly dispersed, their binding energy to jogs must be about 1 ev. As might be expected, impurities differ widely in their potency; for example, in contrast with the elements just mentioned small amounts of manganese (0.022 at %) and even large amounts of zinc (15 wt %)[24] appear to have little effect in aluminium.

Other structural studies of recovery have been made with X rays. Two effects have been discovered. The longer known effect is the sharpening of the diffraction lines before softening starts.[6, 25] It probably signifies a reduction in internal stress on the microscopic scale, presumably by some changes where the dislocation network is particularly densely packed. Figure 8.7 shows that recovery of line breadth is not necessarily associated with softening. If it is correct to ascribe line breadth to stresses on the microscale, that is, to the stress fields of all the dislocations, the results here clearly show that these stresses do not account for the whole of work hardening. The other effect is that the stacking faults produced in many metals by cold work shrink at relatively low recovery temperatures—e.g. around room temperature in copper and silver.[26] The recovery behaviour of the stacking faults so far observed is not quite that which simple arguments would suggest since although cold work produces

[20] J. Montuelle, *Conference on Properties of Very Pure Metals*, C.N.R.S., Paris, 1959.
[21] N. F. Mott, *Dislocations and Mechanical Properties*, John Wiley and Sons, New York, 1957, p. 350.
[22] D. McLean, *Symposium on Point Defects in Metals*, Inst. Metals, London, 1958, p. 159.
[23] J. Montuelle, *Compt. rend.*, 1935, **241**, 1304.
[24] J. Montuelle, *Rev. Mét.*, 1957, **54**, 781.
[25] E. C. W. Perryman, *T.A.I.M.E.*, 1955, **203**, 1053.
[26] B. E. Warren and E. P. Warekois, *J.A.P.*, 1953, **24**, 951.

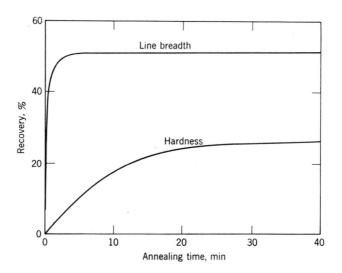

Fig. 8.7. Recovery of aluminium at 281°C after 20% cold work (Ref. 25).

less area of stacking fault in nickel or aluminium than in copper or silver, implying that stacking faults have higher energy in the former pair, in nickel the stacking faults are more difficult to anneal out than in copper or silver.[27] Alloying may stabilise the stacking faults to higher temperatures; zinc and silicon added to copper have this effect.[28, 29, 30]

8.3 Recovery of Physical Properties

Figure 8.8 shows how several physical properties of nickel recover on heating after cold work at room temperature. In this figure, the escape of energy curve represents a continuous measurement, during heating at a rate of 6°C/min, of the rate of heat evolution. The other properties, hardness, electrical resistance, and density, were measured intermittently at room temperature after heating at this rate to various temperatures. The heat evolution consists of a fairly steady background evolution from 100°C to 550°C, a small peak centred on 260°C, and a large peak centred on 610°C. The combination of measurements of several properties makes the interpretation of the two peaks fairly certain. The large peak is clearly due mainly to the elimination of dislocations during recovery

[27] C. N. J. Wagner, *Rev. Mét.*, 1958, **55**, 1171.
[28] C. S. Barrett, *T.A.I.M.E.*, 1950, **188**, 123.
[29] C. N. J. Wagner, *Acta Met.*, 1957, **5**, 427.
[30] C. N. J. Wagner, *Acta Met.*, 1957, **5**, 477.

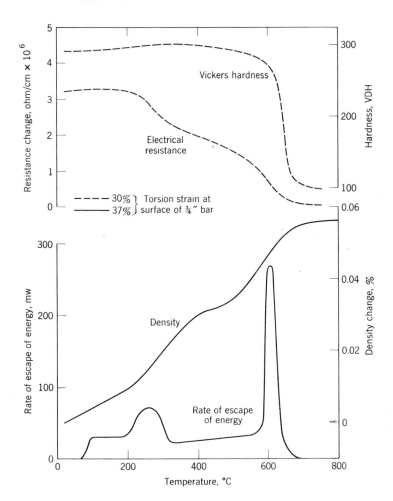

Fig. 8.8. Change in physical properties on heating cold-worked nickel (99.6% pure) (Ref. 31).

and recrystallisation, as is shown by the drop in hardness (at a slightly higher temperature since the hardness specimens were cold worked less). The associated changes in density and electrical resistance make it possible to check the mutual consistency of calculations of the energy of dislocations and their effect on density and electrical resistance (chapter 2). These simultaneous changes in the region of 600°C are an example of the

[31] L. M. Clarebrough, M. E. Hargreaves, and G. W. West, *Phil. Mag.*, 1956, **1**, 528.

kind of specific correlation referred to in section 8.1 as indicating that recovery of mechanical properties depends on a reduction in dislocation density. The smaller peak at 260°C evidently concerns vacancies since the concomitant changes in density and electrical resistance both lead to similar estimates of vacancy concentration. Presumably, most of the vacancies collect into clusters rather than disappear at dislocations, and the slight increase in hardness confirms the expectation that as clusters they should more effectively impede dislocations (but see section 8.1 for another cause of such hardening). The explanation of the background heat evolution is less certain. Possible causes are rearrangement of dislocations, gradual elimination of the vacancy clusters, and elimination of stacking faults.

It might reasonably be expected that such a set of curves would be generally typical of metals except that when vacancies are mobile below room temperature the "vacancy peak" will not be detected in experiments over the range room temperature upward, as seems to be the case with copper.[32] With aluminium somewhat surprisingly, a peak is observed at the relatively high temperature of about 70°C,[33] and seems to be due to vacancy elimination as can be seen by calculating the vacancy concentration obtained in this work. For the concentration deduced from the heat evolution of 0.8 cals/mol after 45% compression, namely, 0.0056 at % (assuming 0.6 ev per vacancy) is confirmed reasonably well by electrical resistance measurements.[25] Thus, after 20% cold work the resistance fell by 0.0135 μ ohm cm on heating at 74°C, which corresponds to a vacancy concentration of 0.0014 at % (assuming that 1 at % vacancies increase the resistance by 1 μ ohm cm), or, assuming linearity, 0.022 at % for 40% strain. A curious feature is that electrical resistance anneals out faster in an aluminium–magnesium alloy than in aluminium.[6] This feature has not been explained but, as already mentioned, magnesium also accelerates softening.

However, the background or continuous heat evolutions are sometimes more substantial than Fig. 8.8 indicates. An example of a large continuous heat evolution is shown in Fig. 8.9. The results here record the residual stored energy after the annealing treatments indicated on the curves, not the rate of energy evolution as the temperature is continuously raised, as in Fig. 8.8. Nevertheless, the two results can be fairly compared and there is either a large background evolution of energy or a succession of peaks, especially for the specimen deformed at −196°C. In either case, the amount left to be evolved during mechanical recovery and annealing is relatively small.

[32] L. M. Clarebrough, M. E. Hargreaves, and G. W. West, *P.R.S.*, 1955, **A.232**, 252.
[33] H. A. Aström, *Acta Met.*, 1955, **3**, 508.

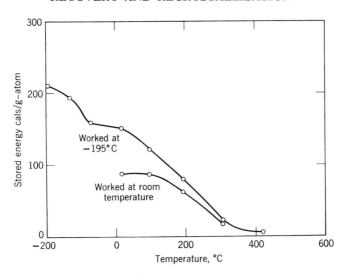

Fig. 8.9. Stored energy remaining in cold-worked 82.6% Au–17.4% Ag alloy after heating at different temperatures. The alloy was cold worked by drilling (the drillings forming the sample) (Ref. 34).

8.4 Recrystallisation

Recrystallisation evidently occurs because of the extra energy present in the cold worked state in the form of dislocations, since it is this energy which is eliminated during recrystallisation. Nevertheless, it has laws of its own[35] not at present related to the rest of this book. It will only be relevant here to refer to particular points.

The relation between the temperatures of recrystallisation and of polygonisation probably depends on the amount of cold work in the way depicted in Fig. 8.10. According to this, with increasing cold work the recrystallisation temperature falls more than the temperature of polygonisation. With metals of type *A* (Fig. 8.10), recrystallisation precedes polygonisation after heavy cold work, and thus prevents polygonisation by removing the strain energy that is its driving force, and vice versa after light cold work. Metals of high stacking fault energy such as aluminium and iron seem to belong to this group. In metals of type *B*, recrystallisation precedes polygonisation under most conditions; metals of low stacking fault energy like copper seem to belong to this group. Improving the purity seems to shift both the polygonisation and recrystallisation curves to the left, but the former is shifted more than the latter and,

[34] P. Greenfield and M. B. Bever, *Acta Met.*, 1956, **4**, 433.
[35] W. M. Williams and R. Eborall, *J.I.M.*, 1952–3, **81**, 501.

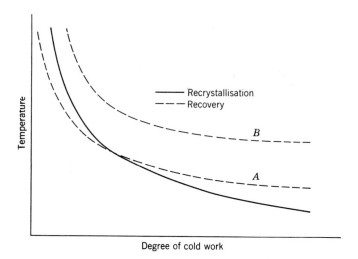

Fig. 8.10. Effect of degree of cold work on recovery and recrystallisation temperatures of different types of metal, *A* with high stacking fault energy, *B* with low stacking fault energy.

for example, polygonisation begins to precede recrystallisation even in a metal like copper.

Impurities have at least three notable effects on recrystallisation even in trace amounts. The most important is the powerful influence that some have in raising the recrystallisation temperature, which is perhaps most strikingly shown by the fact that zone-refined aluminium has been produced which recrystallises at $-79°C$ [36] after cold work at $-196°C$, whereas aluminium of 99.99% purity recrystallises at about 200°C. Different impurities have quite widely different effects,[37] and their separate influences on the rate of nucleation and the rate of grain growth can be distinguished.[36] Figure 8.11 and Fig. 8.12 illustrate the separate influences of copper in aluminium. Since other impurities were also eliminated to about the 10^{-5}% level, the fact that the curves become independent of copper content toward the left implies that aluminium has here been prepared sufficiently pure that the true recrystallisation properties of the pure metal are being revealed.

A second effect of impurities is that they influence the critical strain required for recrystallisation.[35, 38] A third effect is that impurities affect the ease with which single crystals are produced in some metals by the

[36] O. Dimitrov, *Conference on Properties of Very Pure Metals*, C.N.R.S., Paris, 1960.
[37] J. C. Blade, J. H. W. Clare, and H. J. Lamb, *J.I.M.*, 1959–60, **88**, 365.
[38] F. Erdmann-Jesnitzer and R. Krumpholz, *Metall.*, 1958, **12**, 891.

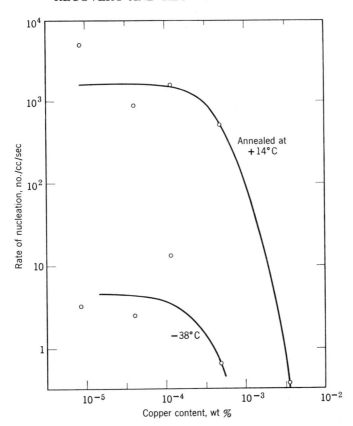

Fig. 8.11. Rate of generation of recrystallisation nuclei in Al. Influence of Cu content (Ref. 36).

strain anneal method. Thus, it is easier to produce single crystals by this method in iron and aluminium of normal purity than after zone re-fining,[20, 39] or than in impure samples. Since the requirement for producing a single crystal is that a recrystallisation nucleus form in one place while the surrounding matrix is still strained enough to provoke growth, small amounts of impurity must be able to develop the necessary heterogeneity either during recovery or during the preceding cold work. In zone-refined or impure iron and aluminium this heterogeneous situation evidently does not easily arise. Instead, in zone-refined specimens the whole matrix polygonises rather uniformly and completely enough so that

[39] J. Talbot, *Conference on Properties of Very Pure Metals*, C.N.R.S., Paris, 1959.

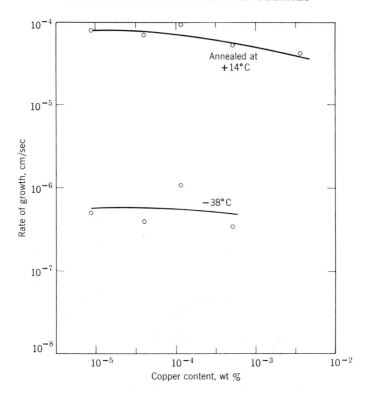

Fig. 8.12. Rate of growth of recrystallised nuclei in Al. Influence of Cu content (Ref. 36).

insufficient strain energy is left to provoke migration of grain boundaries. The recrystallisation at such a low temperature as −79°C referred to earlier is probably aided by the point defects created by the cold work, as well as by high purity, since without their help the activation energy for the processes involved, for example, for the migration of grain boundaries, would surely be too high to permit recrystallisation. Since point defects are not eliminated from aluminium by thermal diffusion at −79°C, they doubtless remain until swept up by migrating grain boundaries. This should mean that as soon as the purity is high enough for recrystallisation to occur before vacancies are eliminated, recrystallisation will occur at much lower temperatures. In other words, there is a purity barrier the surpassing of which permits recrystallisation at remarkably low temperature.

The theory of recrystallisation is really a question of the structural

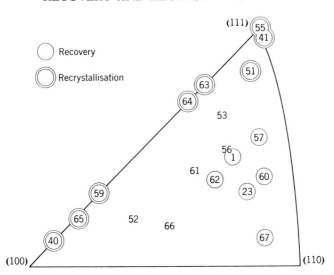

Fig. 8.13. Single-crystal specimens of Al elongated 10%, then heated for 30 min at 620°C. Shows influence of orientation on recovery and recrystallisation. (Jaoul, Bricot, and Lacombe, *Rev. Mét*, 1957, **54**, Fig. 18, p. 89.)

relation between recovery and recrystallisation. There is a certain amount of evidence for the hypothesis that polygonisation provides the nuclei for recrystallisation.[40]   One piece of evidence is that slip must occur on two systems if recrystallisation is to take place. This has been shown[41] by the method illustrated in Fig. 8.13. Single crystals of aluminium of the orientations shown were elongated 10% and annealed. Those oriented for double slip recrystallised, but those oriented for single slip simply recovered. Since with dislocations of two Burgers vectors it is possible to surround a nucleus on all sides with boundaries of identical misorientation—that is, to produce a subcrystal that is rotated with respect to its environment—but it is not possible to do this with dislocations of only one Burgers vector, this result is consistent with the polygonisation hypothesis. It also explains why single crystals of those hexagonal metals which slip extensively on only one plane at room temperature can be deformed so much without recrystallisation, why after small deformations recrystallisation in a polycrystalline sample nucleates mainly at grain boundaries (the slip is more complex there); and hence the observation with aluminium[35] that the finer the initial grain size the finer is the recrystallised grain size after small deformation, other things being equal.

[40] R. W. Cahn, *P.P.S.*, 1950, **A.63**, 323.
[41] B. Jaoul, I. Bricot, and P. Lacombe, *Rev. Mét.*, 1957, **54**, 81.

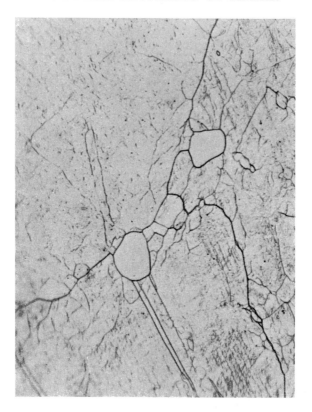

Fig. 8.14. Recrystallisation nuclei in Fe–4% Si alloy heated to 700°C after 12% elongation. × 1250. (Crown copyright reserved.)

Another piece of evidence is that when, after cold work and recovery, the specimen consists mostly of subcrystals as in Fig. 8.5, here and there are subcrystals which possess the distinguishing feature of having somehow got rid of their dislocations and which can apparently grow.   Figure 8.14 shows such a region.   These apparent nuclei have every appearance of forming part of the normal subcrystal structure with, however, this added feature, that they have lost their dislocations, which is clearly necessary to provide a net driving force for growth.   The same behaviour has been found in nickel using transmission electron microscopy.[42]

Recrystallisation frequently produces a preferred orientation.   Two ideas have been used to explain this, and both correctly predict the observed orientations.   The older idea is simply that the recrystallisation

[42] W. Bollman, *J.I.M.*, 1958–9, **87**, 439.

nuclei have these preferred orientations. Put into modern terms, the sub-crystals produced by polygonisation have them. The orientation relationship between a subcrystal and the surrounding matrix is determined by the Burgers vectors of the dislocations which comprise the subboundaries in question. In the simplest case, when dislocations of only two different Burgers vectors are involved, by applying eq. 2.8 it can be seen that the misorientation is equivalent to a rotation about a $\langle 111 \rangle$ axis in the fcc lattice, about a $\langle 110 \rangle$ axis in the bcc, and about a $\langle 0001 \rangle$ axis in the hexagonal. These are, in fact, the observed orientation relationships between recrystallised grain and cold worked matrix for the three lattices.[43, 44] The inclusion in the dislocation networks of dislocations of other Burgers vectors produces some deviation from the ideal rotation axes, and deviations are of course found experimentally. The other idea is that the recrystallised metal consists of grains of those orientations which grow fastest in the cold worked matrix.[45] This idea also satisfactorily explains the observed orientation relationships. For example, in the fcc lattice those grains grow fastest which are separated from the cold worked matrix by a boundary across which there is a rotation about a $\langle 111 \rangle$ axis; it might be added that for such grains the tilt boundaries migrate faster than the twist,[46] and certain directions of tilt boundaries migrate faster than others.[43] Apart from their ability to predict orientation changes on recrystallisation, the situation as regards these hypotheses is ambiguous. It would seem that speed of grain growth must necessarily be an important factor determining the final result. On the other hand, the importance of the orientations of the nuclei is uncertain. In three experiments[46, 47, 48] in which the orientations of the individual recrystallisation nuclei were measured, they were found to be randomly disposed with respect to the cold worked matrix, implying either that very many extra dislocations were included in the networks, or that nuclei were not formed by polygonisation. But in another set of experiments[49] it was found that the orientations of the recrystallisation nuclei depended on the method of cold working, presumably through the Burgers vectors of the dislocations activated.

Quite a different idea about recrystallisation nuclei is that they form at impurity particles, much as solid nuclei do during freezing from the liquid

[43] P. A. Beck, *Conference on Grain Boundaries*, Commissariat for Atomic Energy, Saclay, Paris, 1960.
[44] H. Hu, *T.A.I.M.E.*, 1959, **215**, 320.
[45] P. A. Beck, *Acta Met.*, 1953, **1**, 230.
[46] B. Liebman, K. Lücke, and G. Masing, *Z. Metallk*, 1956, **47**, 57.
[47] H. Yushida, B. Liebman, and K. Lücke, *Acta Met.*, 1959, **7**, 51.
[48] M. N. Parthasarthi and P. A. Beck, *T.A.I.M.E.*, 1961, **221**, 831.
[49] K. Lücke and F. Hässner, *Acta Met.*, 1955, **3**, 204.

state.[50] For example, a piece of matrix contained in a cavity in a hard inclusion might remain relatively unstrained during cold work, and grow into the strained matrix on annealing. There is no experimental proof yet that this idea applies during recrystallisation.

It is worth noting that during the process of grain growth that takes place after recrystallisation is just complete, the dislocation networks will anneal in the sense already discussed of reducing the total line length. Since annealing of the network depends on self diffusion, whereas grain growth appears to depend on grain-boundary diffusion and this requires only about half the activation energy of self diffusion, the rate of annealing of the network should be more sensitive than the rate of grain growth to the annealing temperature. Moreover, during grain growth boundaries sweep through grains, presumably reducing the dislocation content in doing so. Consequently, when a range of grain sizes is produced for some experiment, it is probable that the dislocation densities also vary widely. This may sometimes be important, for example perhaps in determinations of the grain size dependence of the yield stress.

[50] D. Turnbull, *Acta Met.*, 1957, **5**, 502.

9

Creep

9.1 Introduction

When a load that is greater than the yield stress is applied to a metal, after the work hardening of the kind discussed in Chapter 5 the metal continues to deform slowly for an indefinite time. This is the pheno- menon of creep. Creep occurs from very low temperatures, probably from 0°K, to the melting point. The most important sort, the slow creep encountered by engineers, has a practical temperature range of about 0.4 to 0.7 times the melting point (of the basis metal) on the absolute scale.

There are three main kinds of creep: logarithmic creep, high tempera- ture or recovery creep, and diffusion creep. Their normal temperature ranges and some of their characteristics are depicted in Fig. 9.1. Loga- rithmic creep occurs at low temperatures where no recovery of mechanical properties is possible. In this region the creep strain effectively work hardens the metal and the creep rate attenuates. It is called logarithmic creep because the extension is proportional to log (time). At higher temperatures mechanical recovery becomes possible and the creep rate declines less rapidly or not at all with increasing strain. Engineering creep and hot working are in this category. At very high temperatures creep which is apparently due directly to diffusion is found. The creep rate is fairly insensitive to stress in logarithmic creep, extremely sensitive in recovery creep, and probably linearly sensitive in diffusion creep. The creep rate is also fairly insensitive to temperature in logarithmic creep and

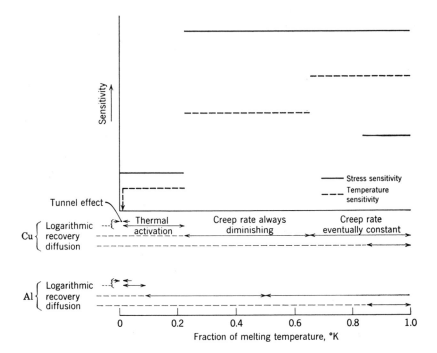

Fig. 9.1. Temperature ranges and stress and temperature sensitivities of the different types of creep. The sensitivity-temperature plot in the upper part of the figure relates to Cu.

extremely sensitive in recovery creep, but it remains extremely sensitive in diffusion creep.

The wide range of creep rates encompassed in technology is indicated in Fig. 9.2 and covers about twelve orders of magnitude from slow engineering creep to fast hot working. The fast rates are associated with higher temperatures, but the range still remains very large, at about seven orders of magnitude, if allowance is made for this, since a rate of $10^6\%$ per hour at 0.9 times the melting point is equivalent to 10% per hour at 0.6 times the melting point.

9.2 Logarithmic Creep

Even at very low temperatures creep is produced by stresses greater than the yield stress. It is found that in the low temperature region the creep rate decelerates with time approximately according to the equation

$$\dot{\epsilon} = \frac{\alpha}{t} \qquad (9.1)$$

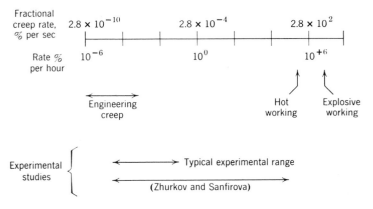

Fig. 9.2. Range of deformation rates used in technology and in experiments. The experimental studies refer to metallurgical and physical studies, not to studies aimed at assessing service behaviour. Zhurkov and Sanfirova data from Ref. 1.

so that

$$\epsilon = \alpha \ln t + \beta \qquad (9.2)$$

where α and β are constants. It is from eq. 9.2 that the name logarithmic creep is derived, although the equation clearly does not apply at zero time. This is not a serious difficulty since measurements can only be made after a finite time and the constant β in eq. 9.2 is then adjusted to make the two sides of the equation agree. As already indicated in Fig. 9.1, logarithmic creep is fairly insensitive to changes in stress and temperature, and specific data for copper illustrating this point is shown in Fig. 9.3. According to this figure an increase in stress of three times, or an increase in temperature of 200°C, increases the creep extension in a given time by only about three times.

The form of eq. 9.2 shows that creep soon becomes very slow. For this reason logarithmic creep is important practically only in such things as high precision components where minute creep caused by locked-up stresses would impair the dimensional accuracy. To obviate this a stabilising heat treatment may be necessary. The other significance of logarithmic creep is to provide a method of studying work hardening processes. With this end in view, logarithmic creep has been studied in aluminium,[2, 3] copper,[2, 4] cadmium,[2, 5] magnesium,[6] and copper–silver

[1] S. N. Zhurkov and T. P. Sanfirova, *Soviet Phys. JETP.*, 1959, **3**, 1586.
[2] O. H. Wyatt, *P.P.S.*, 1953, **66**, 459.
[3] H. Blank, *Z. Metallk*, 1958, **49**, 27.
[4] H. Conrad, *Acta Met.*, 1958, **6**, 339.
[5] J. W. Glen, *Phil. Mag.*, 1956, **1**, 400.
[6] H. Conrad and W. D. Robertson, *T.A.I.M.E.*, 1958, **212**, 536.

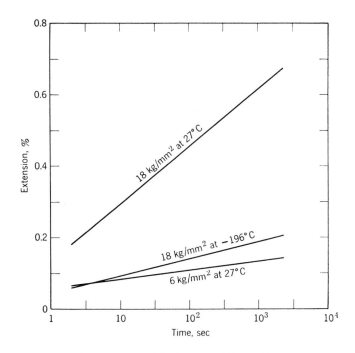

Fig. 9.3.   Logarithmic creep of Cu (Ref. 2).

alloys.[7, 8]   In the rest of this section, the connection between work hardening and logarithmic creep is discussed.   It might be mentioned here that a typical feature of the experiments in question is the smallness of the creep strain compared with the instantaneous extension.   This arises from the fact that a stress much larger than the yield stress in the annealed condition is applied (e.g. Fig. 9.3) and produces a large instantaneous strain but nevertheless a small creep strain.

The starting point for an understanding of logarithmic creep is a feature of the cold worked structure discussed in Chapter 5.   After the initial rapid strain, some pieces of dislocation, for example, where the dislocation density is low, will be on the verge of moving, whereas others, for example, where the density is high, will need a considerable increase in stress before they can move.   Different pieces of dislocation thus require different activation energies to make them move.   This can be represented as in Fig. 9.4 where the number n of pieces of dislocation requiring

[7] M. Davies and N. Thompson, *P.P.S.*, 1950, **B.63**, 847.
[8] G. C. E. Olds, *P.P.S.*, 1954, **B.67**, 832.

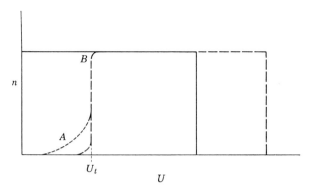

Fig. 9.4. Illustrating change during creep of number n of dislocations requiring thermal activation U to move along slip plane.

an activation energy U is plotted against U. The full line curve shows the initial condition. For simplicity, n is taken as constant up to the limiting value of U. Any creep causes strain hardening, which means that in Fig. 9.4 the whole rectangle slides to the right as indicated by the dashed curve. As far as individual pieces of dislocation are concerned, at any instant those of lowest U are most likely to move, and when eventually stopped again they may lie anywhere in the permissible range of U. They presumably cause some redistribution of the U values of other dislocations they come near by, for example, altering the stress field or the distance between junctions. Because of the strain hardening, that is, the steady increase in dislocation density as deformation proceeds, on average the whole n–U curve slides to higher U.

This model can be treated quantitatively.[9] Suppose that a stress τ is applied and immediately work hardens the material up to the flow stress τ. Slow creep then occurs with the aid of thermal activation and work hardens the material still further up to the stress τ'. For one of the thermally activated dislocation processes discussed in section 4.7 the activation energy U required at this stage is

$$U = v(\tau' - \tau)$$

where v is the "activation volume," equal to xbd in eq. 4.4, and where a "square-topped" process (section 4.7) has been assumed. If the strain-hardening coefficient is h, then

$$\tau' - \tau = h\epsilon$$

so

$$U = vh\epsilon$$

[9] N. F. Mott, *Phil. Mag.*, 1953, **44**, 742.

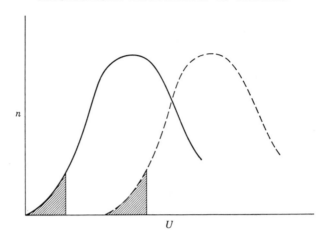

Fig. 9.5.   More probable n–U relation than Fig. 9.4.

Hence the creep rate is

$$\dot{\epsilon} = NAbve^{(-vh\varepsilon/kT)} \qquad (9.3)$$

where N is the number of pieces of dislocation likely to slip at any moment, that is, N is a group of pieces of dislocation at the left-hand end of the n–U curve in Fig. 9.4 spanning a small range of U; A is the average area swept out by a dislocation each time it slips and is equal to Lx in section 4.7; b is the Burgers vector; and v is the frequency of vibration of dislocations.   Equation 9.3 yields the relation

$$\epsilon = \frac{kT}{vh} \ln \left[\frac{vh}{kT} NAbvt + 1 \right] \qquad (9.4)$$

Since, even for small t, the left-hand term in the bracket $\gg 1$, eq. 9.4 is equivalent to eq. 9.2 with $\alpha = kT/vh$ and $\beta = (kT/vh) \ln (vh/kT)NAbv$. It might be remarked that eq. 9.4 expresses the experimental fact that logarithmic creep is relatively insensitive to temperature and stress, since ϵ varies only directly as T and not exponentially, and varies with stress only through variation in $1/vh$.

The assumption made in Fig. 9.4 that n is constant over the whole range of U is no doubt incorrect, but the error should not usually be serious.   For suppose n varies with U initially as shown by the full line in Fig. 9.5.   This distribution has been produced by the cold work required to raise the yield stress to the applied stress so that, as cold work is continued by creep, there seems no reason why the shape of the distribution curve should alter much as it slides to the right.   Consequently, the same number of dislocations, indicated by the hatched areas, are likely to slip at any instant. Of course if the number of active dislocations does change systematically during creep, the extension-time relation will deviate from the logarithmic form of eq. 9.4. Some deviations have been discovered.[10]

An earlier theory of logarithmic creep, known as the exhaustion theory,[11, 12] used the idea that hardening occurred because the dislocations which can slip most easily are gradually used up, which is equivalent to assuming that there is no redistribution among the other dislocations. The situation is represented again by Fig. 9.4, but now each dislocation that slips is taken from the left-hand end of the n-U distribution and placed somewhere at the right. The rectangle in Fig. 9.4 therefore again slides to the right and the two theories must be very similar. The analysis using the exhaustion idea is as follows: if n is the number of dislocations per unit of activation energy,

$$\epsilon = nU_t Ab \qquad (9.5)$$

where U_t is the value of U at the left-hand end of the n-U distribution at time t. Now, U_t is determined approximately by

$$vte^{-U_t/kT} = 1$$

or

$$U_t = kT \ln vt \qquad (9.6)$$

Substituting for U_t in eq. 9.5, we have

$$\epsilon = nAbkT \ln vt \qquad (9.7)$$

which is essentially of the same form as eq. 9.4.

It is not certain whether strain hardening is more important than exhaustion hardening always, but it appears to be so in two sets of experiments. In these, magnesium single crystals[6, 13] and copper single crystals[4] were employed, and the strain-hardening coefficient h obtained when the data were inserted into an equation like 9.3 was the same as that obtained from stress-strain curves. This seems to mean that ordinary strain hardening moves the curves to the right in Fig. 9.4 and 9.5 faster than exhaustion hardening would. In the experiments just mentioned, the creep strains employed ranged from 0.1–1.0%, which is usually enough to cause appreciable strain hardening. Since these strains are

[10] H. Blank, *Arch. Eisenhüttenw.*, 1958, **29**, 301.
[11] N. F. Mott and F. R. N. Nabarro, Conference on Strength of Solids, *Phys. Soc. London*, 1948, 1.
[12] A. H. Cottrell, *J. Mech. and Phys. Solids*, 1952, **1**, 53.
[13] H. Conrad and W. D. Robertson, *T.A.I.M.E.*, 1957, **9**, 503.

typical of logarithmic creep experiments, perhaps strain hardening is usually the important thing. Whether it is also more important for the much smaller and much slower creep strains that can be troublesome in precision components cannot be decided with certainty.

At the absolute zero of temperature creep cannot occur by thermal agitation. However, it is theoretically possible for creep to occur down to absolute zero by the quantum mechanical tunnel effect,[14] and theory yields the relation

$$\epsilon \sim \frac{2\pi h}{\sqrt{2MU}} \qquad (9.8)$$

where h is Planck's constant, a is the atomic spacing along the dislocation, and M is the mass of the dislocation per atom length. As eq. 9.8 shows, tunnel creep is independent of temperature. Inserting appropriate values into eq. 9.8 yields the result that creep due to thermal agitation should become slower than tunnel creep below a few degrees K. Creep has been observed down to $1.2°K$ [15] and may be tunnel creep.

Three kinds of experiment have been made to extract information about slip processes from logarithmic creep. They consist of measuring the effect on the creep rate of small changes in temperature or stress, or of making stress relaxation experiments. To analyse these effects, express $U(= vh\epsilon)$ as

$$U = W - v(\tau - \tau_0) \qquad (9.9)$$

where W is the energy required for the temperature sensitive components of the flow stress and the term τ_0 represents those components, such as the stress field of all the dislocations, which are scarcely affected by temperature and which have to be overcome by the applied stress τ without help from thermal agitation. It can be seen from eq. 9.9 that direct measurement of U by altering the temperature thus measures a rather complicated quantity which can vary from zero to W and in practice takes the value that gives the experimental value of $\dot{\epsilon}$ at the temperature of measurement. In fact, the situation is probably sometimes more complicated than this, as can be illustrated by reference to the type of dislocation junction exemplified in Fig. 4.25 by curve A. When such a dislocation junction gives way, the released dislocations move on until they make new junctions of greater strength. Before reaching such a position many must form transitory junctions of weaker strength, that is, where the dislocation spacing x is too large. Figure 9.6 illustrates these events. Thermal agitation releases the dislocation from a junction such as A in Fig. 9.6,

[14] N. F. Mott, *Phil. Mag.*, 1956, **1**, 568.
[15] J. W. Glen, *Phil. Mag.*, 1956, **1**, 400.

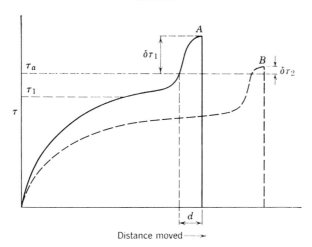

Fig. 9.6. Force-distance relationship for two dislocation junctions. *A* is stronger than *B*.

requiring an activation stress $\delta\tau_1$. Before similar or stronger junctions are made again, the released dislocations pass through weaker junctions such as *B* which requires an activation stress of $\delta\tau_2$. At the original temperature T_1 these junctions offer no resistance. But on lowering the temperature those for which $\delta\tau_2$ is large enough will do so. That is to say, the effect of lowering the temperature is to enable weaker junctions that were formerly "transparent" to become important. Consequently, slip that occurs after the temperature is lowered alters a diagram like Fig. 9.4, producing something like the dotted extension at the left-hand end of the distribution. The value of N in eq. 9.3 and 9.4 changes, becoming a function of the ordinate n at some point *A* instead of at some point *B* (Fig. 9.4). A further complicating effect is the change, with change in temperature, of τ_0, due to the associated change in elastic modulus (see appendix). Determination of U by change-in-temperature experiments have been made, but the interpretation of the results obtained is therefore not simple.[16, 17]

Change-in-stress experiments yield simpler results. By substitution of the expression for U in eq. 9.9 into eq. 9.6, the effect of changing the stress is obtained. Equation 9.6 applies of course to logarithmic creep due to ordinary strain hardening as well as to exhaustion hardening since it merely states how long the next event will take if the activation energy has

[16] J. L. Lytton, L. A. Shepard, and J. E. Dorn, *T.A.I.M.E.*, 1958, **212**, 220.
[17] Y. A. Rocher, L. A. Shepard, and J. E. Dorn, *T.A.I.M.E.*, 1959, **215**, 316.

a certain value. Consequently, deductions made from change-in-stress experiments are independent of which of the two logarithmic creep theories is adopted. Making the substitution and differentiating τ with respect to ln t, we have

$$v\, \partial\tau = kT\, \partial(\ln t)$$

or

$$v = kT \frac{\partial(\ln t)}{\partial T} \qquad (9.10)$$

The quantities on the right-hand side of eq. 9.10 are experimentally measurable, so the activation volume v can be determined. If the dislocation spacing is then deduced, say from the flow stress, an activation distance d is determined. Measurements of this kind have been made,[18] and results for several metals are given in Table 9.1.

Table 9.1

Value of d From Stress Increment Experiments, Expressed in Terms of that for Cu

Metal	Al	Ag	Au	Cd	Co	Cu	Ni	Pb	Pt	Zn
d	0.8	0.8	0.9	0.1	2.1	1.0	0.7	0.3	0.9	0.1

These are average values for dislocations in different situations and perhaps undergoing different processes.

The third type of experiment, consisting of following the stress relaxation at constant strain,[19, 20] can be analysed using eq. 9.3 and 9.4. In these experiments, as the specimen slowly extends, elastic strain is gradually replaced by plastic strain, and the stress applied steadily decreases. This effect is easily incorporated into eq. 9.3. The decrease in applied stress $\Delta\tau$ is equal to ϵG, where G is Young's modulus, and, following the discussion in section 4.7, an additional thermal agitation energy of amount vGE is required to compensate for this. The exponent in eq. 9.3 becomes $-(vh\epsilon + vG\epsilon)/kT$. Since G is many times larger than h, the original term can be neglected and the exponent $-vG\epsilon/kT$ used. An equation similar to eq. 9.4 can then be derived but with the factor kT/vh replaced by kT/vG. Consequently, the equation for stress relaxation is

$$\Delta\tau = G\epsilon = \frac{kT}{v} \ln\left[\frac{vG}{kT} NAbvt + 1\right]$$

[18] P. R. Thornton and P. B. Hirsch, *Phil. Mag.*, 1958, **3**, 738.
[19] P. Feltham, *Phil. Mag.*, 1961, **6**, 259.
[20] P. Feltham, *J.I.M.*, 1960–61, **89**, 210.

Comparing this equation with eq. 9.4, we see that the ratio of the factors outside the logarithm is h. Experimental measurements of stress relaxation and logarithmic creep on brass show that this is so.[19]

The distance d is a distance such as that indicated for the intersection process in Fig. 9.6. At low temperatures it, and therefore also v, should be smaller than at high temperatures because thermal activation contributes less and the stress comes higher up the curve; this should be true for any "round topped" process. Experiment shows that v does decrease with temperature,[18] which helps to explain two points of apparent disagreement between the theories of logarithmic creep outlined earlier and experiment. In eq. 9.4 it tends to make the constant term kT/vh independent of temperature, as has been found in experiments on copper at low stress[4] or low temperature.[2] It tends also to make the effect of stress changes independent of temperature. For using the expression for U in eq. 9.9, we see that

$$\dot{\epsilon} \propto \exp \left[\frac{-W - v(\tau - \tau_0)}{kT} \right]$$

The more nearly v varies as does T, the more accurately this can be written:

$$\dot{\epsilon} \propto \exp -\frac{W}{kT} \exp \left[\text{const. } (\tau - \tau_0) \right]$$

A behaviour conforming to this equation has been found in copper single crystals[4] and magnesium single crystals.[6]

Since no recovery occurs during logarithmic creep, the physical state of the material depends only on the strain, provided the contribution to the strain hardening of an element of strain is independent of the temperature at which the strain occurred. In eq. 9.3 this proviso requires that h be independent of temperature, as it nearly is in the temperature range of logarithmic creep. The strain rate is therefore a unique function of strain, stress, and temperature. This is what is meant when it is said that a mechanical equation of state is obeyed in the domain of logarithmic creep.

An exceptional behaviour observed in some logarithmic creep experiments[3] was that, after the applied stress was increased, the creep rate rose slowly over a period of up to 3 min to a maximum value instead of rising immediately. It is tempting to think that impurities were responsible in some way.

9.3 Recovery Creep

Above a certain temperature mechanical recovery becomes possible and offsets some of the strain hardening, with the result that $\dot{\epsilon}$ declines less

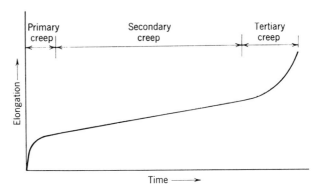

Fig. 9.7. The three stages of the elongation-time relation in high-temperature creep.

rapidly. This is equivalent to saying that before a large enough thermal agitation arrives to allow a dislocation to move once more, the flow stress is reduced by recovery. The local situation can be illustrated by reference to Fig. 9.6. The applied stress is τ_1 and the full line curve represents conditions before recovery. A large activation energy is needed to complete the intersection and is moreover sensitive to dislocation spacing. Recovery occurs locally, increasing the dislocation spacing and conditions are now represented by the dashed line curve. The smaller activation energy now needed is easily supplied. But the ensuing slip increases the dislocation density again, and so on. Clearly, the same kind of situation obtains with other dislocation events which give other shapes of curves in a diagram like Fig. 9.6.

The typical relation between elongation and time during high temperature creep is shown in Fig. 9.7 and has three stages, primary or transient creep, secondary or steady state creep, and tertiary creep. Sometimes a fourth is added at the beginning to include the instantaneous extension on loading. The primary stage does not seem to be fundamentally distinct from the secondary stage, but merely represents the period during which strain hardening and recovery approach a balance (section 9.7). In the bottom temperature range of recovery creep a balance is never reached, and the creep rate continuously decreases with the passage of time (see Fig. 9.1); but in the upper temperature range a balance is eventually reached and the creep rate becomes constant as depicted in Fig. 9.7; this is the stage of steady-state creep. It is characteristic of recovery creep that the creep extension (primary plus secondary) is generally considerably larger than the instantaneous extension on loading. In this respect recovery creep differs strongly from logarithmic creep. Beyond some time, which in engineering practice may be years, the creep rate begins to

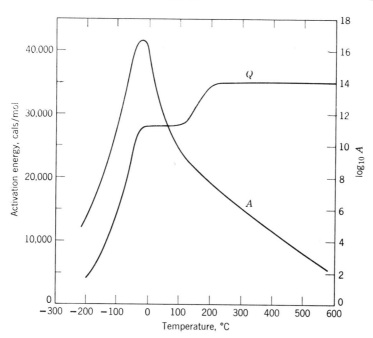

Fig. 9.8. Variation with temperature of Q and A in the creep rate equation $\dot\epsilon = Ae^{-Q/RT}$ for pure aluminium. The factor A is calculated for a creep rate of $10^{-5\%}$ per sec (Ref. 21).

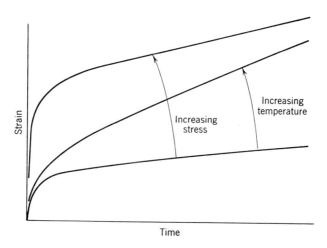

Fig. 9.9. Different effects of stress and temperature on the primary and secondary parts of recovery creep.

[21] O. D. Sherby, J. L. Lytton, and J. E. Dorn, *Acta Met.*, 1957, **5**, 219.

accelerate to start the tertiary stage, which usually ends in fracture. The acceleration can have many causes, of which metallurgical changes and the formation of internal cavities (section 9.10) are probably the commonest. In some metals, however, tertiary creep is caused by recrystallisation. This does not necessarily lead to fracture but may initiate a fresh cycle starting again with primary creep.

Several pieces of evidence show directly that recovery does occur and help identify the recovery processes in the primary and secondary stages. In some experiments on magnesium single crystals,[6] interrupting the creep straining for rests at zero stress had no effect on the creep curve in tests at 78 and 203°K but resulted in an increase in creep rate in tests at 25 and 91°C. The behaviour of aluminium and copper polycrystals has been found to follow the same pattern.[2] Evidently some recovery took place at the two higher temperatures, which are toward the bottom end of the temperature range of recovery creep. Three experimental results help to identify the recovery process in this region as cross slip. First, the temperature at which recovery creep commences is about the temperature at which stage 3, which is also associated with cross slip, begins, and is lower the higher the stress, as is to be expected for cross slip. For example, in copper at a stress of 6 kg/mm², recovery creep starts between 27°C and 70°C, and at a stress of 18 kg/mm² between −72°C and 27°C; in aluminium it starts at a lower temperature, for example, at −196°C at a stress of 8 kg/mm².[2] Second, in experiments on carefully oriented single crystals of aluminium, cross slip was detected on the surface when the creep could reasonably be identified as recovery creep, but not at lower temperatures.[16, 17] Third, measurements on aluminium polycrystals of the activation energy for creep by the change-in-temperature method gave the result shown in Fig. 9.8. The intermediate plateau at 28 kcals/mol lies at a level appropriate to cross slip[22] and extends over the lower part of the temperature range of recovery creep. The high frequency factor also shown in Fig. 9.8 to occur in this region is likewise appropriate to cross slip. It is referred to again in section 9.7.

But cross slip eliminates only screw dislocations so that only about half of the dislocations are eliminated by this recovery process. In the temperature range where cross slip is the only substantial recovery process, complete recovery is therefore impossible and a steady state stage not to be expected. It is thus consistent with the absence of this stage in the bottom half of the temperature range of recovery creep to suppose that cross slip is here the important recovery process. However, at higher temperatures climb becomes possible and the edge dislocations can be

[22] G. Schoeck and A. Seeger, Conference on Defects in Crystalline Solids, *Phys. Soc.*, 1954, 340.

eliminated as well.   Complete recovery is then possible and gives rise to
a constant creep rate (section 9.7).   This tacit identification of the rate-
controlling process for steady-state creep as consisting of climb will be
generally accepted in this chapter.   Apart from the reasonableness of
the idea in accounting for complete recovery, the experimental evidence in
its favour is that in several metals the measured activation energy is that
expected for climb, and that climb of dislocations does occur in the
temperature range concerned.   This idea is discussed further in section 9.6,
together with exceptions.

The temperature range in which steady-state creep occurs is the most
important range in engineering simply because creep is a bigger problem
the higher the temperature.   As already mentioned, recovery creep is very
sensitive to temperature and stress.   Steady-state creep in particular is
highly sensitive to temperature with the result that the qualitative effects
of stress and temperature changes are as indicated in Fig. 9.9.

At very high temperatures the creep rate of aluminium has been found
to vary with stress as shown in Fig. 9.10.   Up to a stress of 10 gram/mm²

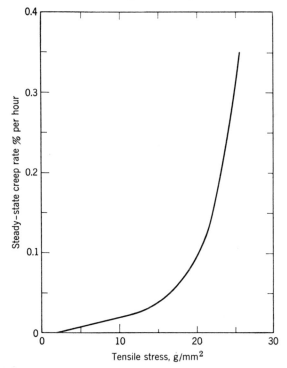

Fig. 9.10.   Effect of stress on the creep rate of Al at 647°C (Ref. 23).

[23] J. Harper and J. E. Dorn, *Acta Met.*, 1957, **5**, 654.

Fig. 9.11. Al after 50% extension at 200°C in 900 hr. Load 0.79 kg/mm². ×86. (Crown copyright reserved.)

Fig. 9.12. Annealed Al. ×87. (Crown copyright reserved.)

$\dot{\epsilon} \propto \sigma$, and above about 20 grams/mm² $\dot{\epsilon} \propto \sigma^4$. Although in the low stress region in Fig. 9.10 $\dot{\epsilon}$ was linearly related to the stress, several features showed that diffusion creep (section 9.9) was not in question; for example, the creep rate was one thousand times too fast, and occurred at about the same rate in single crystals.[23]

9.4   Structural Changes in Simple Metals during Recovery Creep

The most obvious structural change in pure metals is that polygonisation occurs in some and recrystallisation in others. Of pure metals, re-crystallisation has been found to occur in lead,[24] nickel,[25] copper,[26] and gamma iron,[27] whereas aluminium,[28] alpha iron,[29] magnesium,[30] cad-mium, tin, and zinc[31] do not recrystallise but polygonise. An example of the polygonised structure is shown in Fig. 9.11; Fig. 9.12 shows the initial annealed structure. The metals which polygonise are believed to contain relatively unextended dislocations, so that polygonisation in them is understandable, requiring as it does cross slip or climb, or both. In fact, clearly defined polygonisation seems to occur only when the tempera-ture is high enough for steady-state creep, and becomes clearly defined at a time roughly coinciding with the end of transient creep. On the other hand, polygonisation is not so evident in metals believed to contain relatively extended dislocations. In copper it is very slow in tests at 400°C[32] and in lead in tests at room temperature,[33] whereas in gamma iron polygonisation is slower than in alpha iron.[34] The metals in which polygonisation is slow eventually recrystallise. There is an obvious parallel here to the behaviour discussed in Chapter 8 with regard to polygonisation and recrystallisation during recovery on heating after cold work.

It is simplest first to discuss the metals which polygonise. The sub-boundaries formed by polygonisation are two-dimensional networks, which at first are similar to that in Fig. 8.3 but in which the dislocations

[24] R. C. Gifkins, *J.I.M.*, 1958–9, **87**, 255.
[25] W. G. Jenkins, T. G. Digges, and C. R. Johnson, *J. Research Natl. Bur. Standards*, 1954, **53**, 329.
[26] P. Feltham and J. D. Meakin, *Acta Met.*, 1959, **7**, 614.
[27] P. Feltham, *P.P.S.*, 1953, **B.64**, 865.
[28] G. R. Wilms and W. A. Wood, *J.I.M.*, 1948–9, **75**, 693.
[29] C. H. M. Jenkins and G. A. Mellor, *J.I.S.I.*, 1935, **132**, 179.
[30] J. W. Suiter and W. A. Wood, *J.I.M.*, 1952–3, **81**, 181.
[31] D. McLean and M. H. Farmer, *J.I.M.*, 1956–7, **85**, 41.
[32] A. Franks and D. McLean, *Phil. Mag.*, 1956, **1**, 101.
[33] R. C. Gifkins, *J.I.M.*, 1953–4, **82**, 39.
[34] C. Crussard and R. Tamhankar, *T.A.I.M.E.*, 1958, **212**, 718.

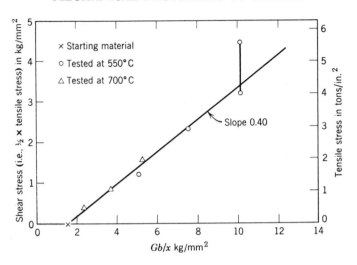

Fig. 9.13. Relation between stress and dislocation spacing x during creep of α Fe (Ref. 36).

soon become too closely packed to be resolved with the electron microscope. Moving dislocations evidently join the subboundaries they encounter. They could rarely pass through, since the dislocation spacing in the subboundaries is normally far too fine for this to be possible. Measurements of the misorientation θ at the subboundaries as a function of strain corroborate this[31, 35] by showing that the relation is

$$\theta \sim \epsilon \tag{9.11}$$

For suppose that n dislocation loops spread across each subgrain of area l^2. Since there are l^{-3} subgrains per cc the strain produced is $\epsilon = nb/l$. Since the misorientation at the subboundary is also nb/l, eq. 9.11 follows. It makes no difference to this reasoning of course if mutual annihilation of parts of loops occurs inside a subgrain since a single loop is then formed, and when this has reached the subboundary the strain produced is exactly that which would have been produced had this loop started as a single loop from a single source. In between the subboundaries is a three-dimensional dislocation network similar essentially to those in Fig. 8.3 or 2.4. According to measurements made during recovery creep of iron, the dislocation density here does not change much during steady-state creep. Moreover, in steady-state creep the spacing between dislocations is inversely proportional to the applied stress as illustrated in Fig. 9.13. This relation

[35] D. McLean, Symposium on Creep and Fracture, *H.M.S.O.*, London, 1956, p. 73.

[36] D. McLean and K. F. Hale, Symposium on Structural Processes in Creep, *Iron & Steel Inst.*, 1961, p. 86.

is similar to those in Fig. 5.29, with much the same slope, except that in Fig. 9.13 the line passes below the origin probably because recovery is here involved.

These observations suggest the following picture of the recovery creep process in simple metals which polygonise. The flow stress is mainly governed by the dislocation density inside the subgrains, which remains constant during steady-state creep. Dislocations move across the subgrains, however, making and breaking junctions and locally altering the stress field as they go, and join a subboundary on the other side of the subgrain, where they are largely rendered inactive. However, unless the subboundary is in the ideal plane specified by eq. 2.8 it will exert a long range stress field which will contribute to the flow stress.

In the metals which tend to recrystallise rather than polygonise probably much the same process occurs, although the incipient walls are presumably relatively irregular as well as ill-defined and may throw out a stronger stress field. Conceivably, they are also more transparent to dislocations, some of which might then travel right across a grain.

Since the relation in eq. 9.11 has been derived from the assumption that the strain was produced by slip it is evidence that the strain is indeed caused by a slip mechanism. This is useful because direct proof in other ways is lacking. For example, the amount of slip seen on a previously polished surface often accounts for only a small part of the total strain[37]; evidently, therefore, much of the slip is too fine to be detectable as slip lines.

The structural changes discussed in this section are important in simple metals. In strong, creep-resistant metals the important changes occur on the finer scale implied in sections 9.8 and 9.10.

9.5   Grain-Boundary Movements during Recovery Creep*

Grain boundaries become glissile at high temperature so that grains can slide over each other. Since grain boundaries inclined at 45° to a tensile stress axis slide the most,[39] the sliding is evidently directly caused by the applied stress and so contributes to the creep extension. Individual grain boundaries slide jerkily[40] like individual slip bands, but on average there is a smooth increase. Given the proviso just mentioned this smooth increase contributes a strain ϵ_{gb} to the total extension ϵ_t.

* A very full review of measurements of grain-boundary sliding is given in Ref. 38.

[37] D. McLean and M. H. Farmer, *J.I.M.*, 1954–5, **83**, 1.
[38] R. C. Gifkins, *Conference on Fracture*, Wiley—M.I.T., 1959, p. 579.
[39] J. G. Harper, L. A. Shephard, and J. E. Dorn, *Acta Met.*, 1958, **6**, 509.
[40] H. C. Chang and N. J. Grant, *T.A.I.M.E.*, 1953, **197**, 1175.

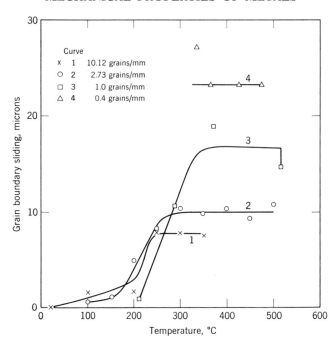

Fig. 9.14. Grain boundary sliding in Al after 10% elongation. Curves 2, 3, and 4 from surface measurements. Curve 1 from change in grain shape on a section (Ref. 41).

The magnitude of this has been measured in two ways: by averaging the measurements of surface displacements at many grain boundaries, and by measuring the change in grain shape in the interior of the specimen. With the latter method, assuming the grains elongate on average by an amount equal to the extension caused by ordinary crystallographic slip, then, subtracting this from the total extension gives the extension due to grain-boundary sliding. These two different methods have both been applied to pure aluminium and give similar results.[41] Figure 9.14 shows how the amount of sliding as measured by the two methods varies with temperature at different grain sizes, while Fig. 9.15 shows that the height of the plateaux in Fig. 9.14 varies with grain size; there is evidently a unique relation here that is independent of the method of measurement.

The most important result of such measurements is the steady increase in sliding throughout a given test. In several experiments using Al,[35, 39, 42]

[41] D. McLean and R. C. Gifkins, *J.I.M.*, 1960–61, **89**, 29.
[42] B. Fagan, O. D. Sherby and J. E. Dorn, *T.A.I.M.E.*, 1954, **200**, 919.

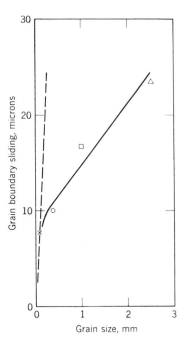

Fig. 9.15. Influence of grain size on height of plateaux in Fig. 9.14.
— — — — — Calculated sliding if grain boundary sliding accounted for all the extension. (Ref. 41.)

some Al alloys,[37] Cu, Fe, Sn, Zn,[31] and an Fe–Ni alloy[43] a linear relation between grain-boundary sliding and elongation was found. Figure 9.16 shows how the linear relation was maintained in a Cu–Be alloy in spite of a sudden deceleration in the creep rate. With beta brass, however, a square root relation was obtained.[44] With Pb, a linear relation has been found to persist to about 10% elongation and at higher elongations the curve bends toward the elongation axis.[45] In any event the ratio between sliding and elongation can be regarded as roughly constant over quite a wide range of creep strain, and its variation with conditions studied. Figures 9.14 and 9.15 show the influence on this ratio of temperature and grain size, since these results relate to a constant elongation. Increasing

[43] V. M. Rosenberg, *Izvest. Akad. Nauk S.S.S.R.* (Div. of Tech. Sci., Metallurgy and Heat), No. 1, 1960, p. 105.

[44] J. A. Martin, M. Herman and N. Brown, *T.A.I.M.E.*, 1957, **209**, 78.

[45] R. C. Gifkins, *Properties of Reactor Materials*, Central Electricity Generating Board, London, 1962, p. 335.

the stress reduces the ratio except in the high temperature experiments of Fig. 9.10, in which the ratio increased in proportion to log (stress) in the temperature range where the creep rate was linearly proportional to stress. In hexagonal metals the ratio tends to be high.[38] Alloy elements have not been found to greatly alter the ratio. In engineering creep, grain-boundary sliding seems to account for a substantial fraction of the total strain.

Since the total strain is the sum of the separate strains due to crystallo-graphic slip and grain-boundary sliding, the close connection in any given test between sliding and total strain (e.g. Fig. 9.16) shows that there is an equally close connection between crystallographic slip and sliding. Two experiments show in fact that slip controls sliding. With beta brass, experiments over a range of temperature straddling the order-disorder temperature of this alloy showed that on going from the ordered to the disordered state the total creep rate increased nearly ten times, but ϵ_{gb} increased in the same ratio. In the Cu–Be alloy used for Fig. 9.16, strain ageing evidently set in after 16 hours and slowed down slip and also slowed down sliding in the same ratio. As in both cases the metallurgical change involved obviously affects the grain interior, the fact that the rates

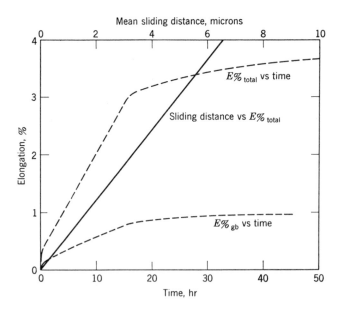

Fig. 9.16. Linear relation between grain boundary sliding and elongation for a Cu–0.37 wt % Be alloy. Creep curves shown dashed (Ref. 31).

of sliding and slip were reduced in equal proportions demonstrates that the former is controlled by the latter.

There appear to be two kinds of interaction between sliding and slip which produce this result.[31] One is simply that grain-boundary sliding is impeded by ledges or protuberances in the grain boundaries, which must be sheared through. The rate of sliding is then controlled by the rate at which the crystals can be deformed. This explanation meets some objections, for instance the difficulty about the implication that the first bit of sliding is relatively unimpeded, and that the protuberances must be sheared under a fairly heavy stress concentration. Another explanation proposes a mechanism whereby screw dislocations arriving at a grain boundary and thus enforcing sliding increase the stress concentration on a particular ledge and eventually cause it to give way,

However, whatever the precise mechanism connecting slip inside the grains with sliding at grain boundaries, the fact that the former controls the latter means that from the point of view of resistance to deformation sliding is not very important, since measures taken to restrain slip also restrain sliding. The main importance of sliding at grain boundaries lies in its connection with fracture in creep.

The creep rate is often increased by reducing the grain size. The simple explanation of this, that it is merely the result of the larger number of sliding interfaces, is incorrect, however. Sometimes the increase is far too large to be accounted for in this way, for example, a 1000:1 increase for a 15:1 change in grain size.[46] Moreover, measurement of grain-boundary sliding in two aluminium specimens differing in grain size by 9:1 showed practically the same average rate of sliding in both[47] and the ratios of ϵ_{gb}/ϵ_t were 0.02 and 0.17, nearly 9:1. The creep rates, however, differed by 2:1, so that the grains themselves were deforming faster in the finer grain sized specimen. An alternative reason is that the alteration of heat treatment required to change the grain size also changes the grain interior structure (section 8.4).

Besides sliding, grain boundaries migrate during creep. At each grain boundary separately this is an irregular movement like the sliding. There are two somewhat distinct possible causes of migration. One is that creep stores a certain amount of deformation energy in the grains in the form of dislocations, and grain boundaries will tend to migrate into the grain having the larger stored energy. The other is that, since grain boundaries hold up dislocations, dislocations push grain boundaries. Grain-boundary migration does not contribute to creep strain but may be important in alleviating tensile stresses across a grain boundary.

[46] J. McKeown, R. Eborall, and R. D. S. Lushey, *Metallurgia*, 1954, **50**, 13.
[47] D. McLean, *J.I.M.*, 1952–3, **81**, 293.

9.6   Activation Energy for Recovery Creep

Measurements of the activation energy of recovery creep have been made on simple metals to throw light on the creep process. Similar measurements on complex alloys meet some doubt about whether they are useful since simultaneous metallurgical changes, for example, changes in precipitate particle spacing, are likely to obscure the kinetically simple processes. The discussion in this section relates to simple metals.

The activation energy of recovery creep can be measured either by the rapid change-in-temperature method in which the creep rate is measured just before and just after changing the temperature, or by running creep tests at different temperatures and measuring the creep rate at corresponding points, such as in the steady-state region. The former method requires a small correction for modulus change with temperature (see appendix). Both methods can be expected to give results differing slightly from that of the controlling recovery process since the balance point between flow and recovery is shifted on changing the temperature,[48] but this error seems usually to be quite small. When carefully compared, the two methods give similar results.

The first method has been used to make measurements over a wide range of conditions. The variation of activation energy with temperature for aluminium was shown in Fig. 9.8 and that for copper is similar[49] (for copper the measurements at high temperature were made by the second method). In the upper half of the temperature range explored, both sets of results show two plateaux which have been thought to be associated with cross slip (the lower one)[50] and climb (the upper one) as being the controlling processes. The gradual change below the lower plateau has in effect already been discussed in the section on logarithmic creep.

It has been mentioned that in the recovery creep range the creep rate is very sensitive to the applied stress. It is necessary to know how this stress-sensitivity arises if a correct choice of model for recovery creep is to be made. Some workers believe that the stress influences the creep rate $\dot{\epsilon}$ by affecting the activation energy, leading to an expression of the form

$$\dot{\epsilon} = Ae^{-(Q-\alpha\sigma)/kT} \qquad (9.12a)$$

where A and α are constants, Q is the activation energy at zero stress, and σ is the applied stress. Others think that the stress mainly affects the frequency factor, leading to an expression of the form

$$\dot{\epsilon} = B\sigma^n e^{-Q/kT} \qquad (9.12b)$$

[48] D. McLean, Symposium on Point Defects & Mechanical Properties, *Inst. Metals*, 1958, p. 159.
[49] P. R. Landon, J. L. Lytton, L. A. Shepard, and J. E. Dorn, *A.S.M.*, 1959, **51**, 900.
[50] G. Schoeck, Symposium on Creep and Recovery, *A.S.M.*, 1957, 199.

where B and n are constants.   Of course, direct stress should always affect the creep rate through the rate of climb (section 2.1c), but this by itself is expected to be a sufficiently small effect at the stress levels applied to pure metals at high temperatures as simply to have the effect of multiplying the frequency factor by σ/kT.[51]   Some experimental results are plotted in Fig. 9.17 according to eq. 9.12b (in Fig. 9.17 the stress is normalised by dividing by the shear modulus G) in such a way that results following eq. 9.12b would yield straight lines.   The plotted lines tend to be straight lines with $n \sim 5$ toward the left of the diagram, that is, at high temperatures and low stresses, and concave towards the abscissa at the right of the diagram, that is, at high stresses and low temperatures.   One interpretation of this is that eq. 9.12b generally applies in pure metals when climb is the controlling process (high temperatures) and eq. 9.12a when the creep rate is controlled by cross slip (low temperatures in the recovery creep range).   It is in fact to be expected that when the creep rate is controlled by cross slip the measured activation energy will be sensitive to stress, as this is the situation with cross slip itself.

Certain measurements of activation energy by the change-in-temperature method at first sight seem conflicting with regard to the point at issue. According to some of these results the activation energy is sufficiently insensitive to stress at high temperature that the very high stress sensitivity of the creep rate cannot be ascribed to a change in activation energy with change in stress.   This independence is illustrated by line a in Fig. 9.18. But in another set of experiments a different result was obtained.   These experiments covered a range of strain rates of up to $10^8:1$ at each temperature with several metals, so that at each temperature a large range of stress, usefully of about $4:1$, could be explored.   With all the metals used, the activation energy was found to be altered substantially by such large changes, as illustrated for aluminium by line b in Fig. 9.18.   However, this variation may well arise from a different cause from that just discussed.   It seems likely that over such wide ranges of creep rate the controlling process does not remain the same, as was implied in the discussion of Fig. 9.17.   As far as high temperature recovery creep in pure metals is concerned it therefore seems at present that the activation energy is relatively insensitive to stress.

At ordinary creep rates and at temperatures corresponding to the higher plateau in Fig. 9.8, activation energies similar to those for self diffusion are usually found.[52]   Table 9.2 gives some comparisons.   This similarity between the two activation energies has been used to support the view that climb is the rate-controlling process at high tempera-

[51] N. F. Mott, Symposium on Creep and Fracture, $H.M.S.O.$, 1956, p. 21.
[52] J. Dorn, Symposium on Creep and Fracture, $H.M.S.O.$, 1956, p. 89.

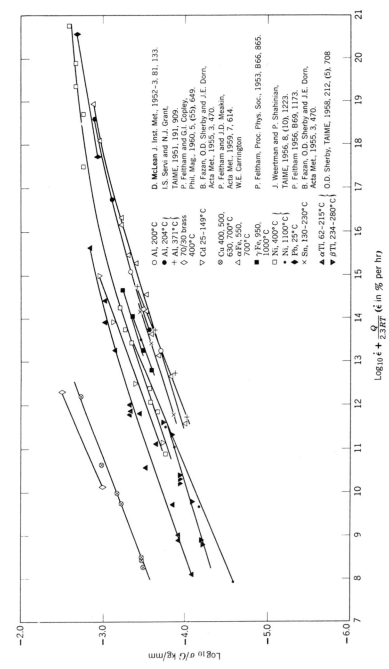

Fig. 9.17. Creep data on twelve metals plotted in accordance with eq. 12*b*.

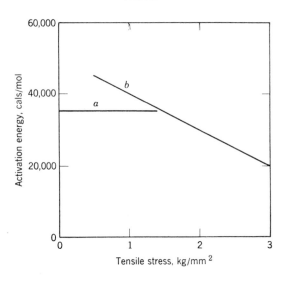

Fig. 9.18. Effect of stress on activation energy for creep of Al. *a*—Ref. 21; *b*— Ref. 1.

Table 9.2

Activation Energies in Electron Volts for High Temperature Creep and for Self-Diffusion

	Al	Cd	γFe	In	Mg	Ni	Pb	Sn
Creep	1.55	0.91	3.2	0.72	1.26	2.83	0.93	0.91
Diffusion	1.4	0.8	2.95	0.78	1.39	2.90	1.12	0.26
								−0.46

tures. There are, of course, exceptions where special circumstances appear to prevail. For example for zinc the activation energy over the temperature range 70 to 120°C was found to be 21 kcals/mol, which is about the value for self diffusion, and at higher temperatures rose gradually to a higher plateau at 38 kcals/mol stretching from 330 to 400°C.[53] Since this value coincides with that found for prismatic glide in zinc,[54] it prompts the suggestion that in polycrystalline zinc prismatic glide becomes the controlling process at high temperature.[53] This implies that only basal slip and twinning occur at lower temperatures.

[53] W. J. M. Tegart and O. D. Sherby, *Phil. Mag.*, 1958, 3, 1287.
[54] J. J. Gilman, *T.A.I.M.E.*, 1956, **206**, 1326.

Applying the change-in-temperature method to aluminium, the activation energy has been found to be independent of strain over a wide range up to 40%.[21] On the other hand, according to results obtained by the minimum creep method the activation energy is high at the beginning of primary creep, which throws some confusion into the relation between the primary and secondary stages.

9.7 Theory of Recovery Creep

There are two sorts of theory which have been developed about recovery creep, the phenomenological type which relates creep rate to strain hardening and recovery, and the type which considers particular dislocation models. The former will be discussed first.

It would be incorrect to derive an equation for recovery creep by starting with eq. 9.3 and writing $U = v(h\epsilon - rt)$, where r is the rate of recovery, since this would amount to assuming that the controlling process is the arrival of a thermal agitation large enough to liberate again a halted dislocation. The basic idea of recovery creep is that recovery takes place before the thermal agitation necessary for slip arrives and holds down the rise in flow stress that would otherwise occur. That is to say, an extension $\delta\epsilon$ produces an increase of flow stress due to strain hardening of $h\delta\epsilon$ and in time δt the recovery, at a rate r, causes the flow stress to drop by $r\delta t$. Consequently in steady state creep

$$\dot{\epsilon} = \delta\epsilon/\delta t = r/h \tag{9.13a}$$

or
$$\epsilon = \gamma t \tag{9.14}$$

where γ is a constant. Experiments on zinc in which $\dot{\epsilon}$, h, and in effect also r, were measured directly confirm eq. 9.13.[55]

An equation for transient creep has been derived along different lines.[9] Suppose that slip takes place at a flow stress of τ, but that the strain ϵ has raised the average flow stress to $\tau + h\epsilon$. Then for slip to occur at any point there must be local recovery of amount $= h\epsilon$. Suppose further that a dislocation movement in the vicinity is equally likely to increase or decrease the local flow stress by amount $\delta\tau$. Then to reduce the flow stress by $h\epsilon$ requires on average $(h\epsilon/\delta\tau)^2$ dislocation movements, requiring a time $\delta t = \alpha(h\epsilon/\delta\tau)^2$, where α is here the time required for a single movement. A further strain $\delta\epsilon$ can then occur, so that

$$\delta\epsilon/\delta t \propto (\delta\tau/h\epsilon)^2$$

or
$$\epsilon = \beta t^{\frac{1}{3}} \tag{9.15}$$

where β is a constant. The derivation of this equation differs in kind

[55] A. H. Cottrell and V. Aytekin, *J.I.M.*, 1950, **77**, 389.

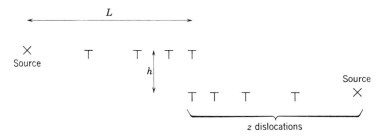

Fig. 9.19.   Model used in one theory of recovery creep.

from that of eq. 9.13 in that recovery is connected not with time but with strain.   But the derivation contains what appears to be the essential feature of transient creep, namely, that the processes concerned do not change in kind but slow down as a result of strain hardening, until eventually a steady state is reached.

Some careful experiments have shown that in the recovery creep range the strain can indeed be separated into two components, one $\propto t^{1/3}$ after eq. 9.15 and the other $\propto t$ after eq. 9.14.[55, 56, 57]   The strain can be separated into these two components in the sense that the total creep strain can be expressed as the sum of two such terms.   The total creep strain is also frequently found to be quite accurately represented by the form $\dot{\epsilon} \propto t^n$ where n takes values between $\frac{1}{4}$ and nearly unity.[58-62]

As regards theories of the mechanism of recovery creep, attention has been focussed on steady-state creep, and the recovery process has been taken to be climb for the reasons already given (i.e., climb is necessary for complete recovery and the measured activation energies are often correct for climb).   Such theories lead to equations of the form of eq. 9.12.   One theory worked out in some detail[63, 64] uses the model illustrated in Fig. 9.19.   Here, the dislocations from two sources on different slip planes halt each other.   The leading dislocations are supposed to be mutually eliminated by climbing toward each other, when another dislocation is emitted by each source and each dislocation in the two rows of z moves up

[56] E. N. da C. Andrade, *P.R.S.*, 1910, **A.84**, 1.

[57] E. N. da C. Andrade, *P.R.S.*, 1914, **A.90**, 329.

[58] S. Bhattacharya, W. K. A. Congreve, and F. C. Thompson, *J.I.M.*, 1952-3, **81**, 83.

[59] D. O. Thompson, *J.A.P.*, 1955, **26**, 280.

[60] E. H. Weinberg, *J.A.P.*, 1953, **24**, 734.

[61] E. P. Tyndall, R. A. Artman, C. A. Wert, and R. Eisner, *J.A.P.*, 1955, **26**, 286.

[62] L. Slifkin and W. Kauzmann, *J.A.P.*, 1952, **23**, 746.

[63] J. E. Weertman, *J.A.P.*, 1957, **28**, 362.

[64] J. E. Weertman, *J.A.P.*, 1955, **26**, 1213.

one place. The controlling process, and therefore the measured activation energy, is that for climb. With this model a fairly high stress sensitivity of the form $\dot{\epsilon} \propto \sigma^n$ (as in eq. 9.12b) is obtained in the following way: (a) Because the activation energy in this model is strictly of the form $Q_{climb} - z\sigma b^3$, but the second term is small compared with kT and can be written outside the exponential. Since $z \propto \sigma$, this gives a strain rate $\propto \sigma^2$. (b) An argument leads to a slip area $L^2 \propto \sigma$. (c) The distance of climbing h is deduced to be $\propto 1/\sigma$. The result is that the strain rate is proportional to about the fourth power of the stress, which is on the low side. With this kind of model the equivalent of a large number of jogs is necessary to reproduce observed rates of creep,[51] assuming that vacancies are emitted or absorbed only at jogs, and is perhaps supplied if vacancies migrate very quickly along a dislocation to a jog so that in effect every atom site along a dislocation becomes a capturing (or emitting) site. The number necessary works out to about one every 10 to 1000 atoms sites along each dislocation[48] to give frequency factors (see eq. 9.12b) $B\sigma^n \sim 10^8$, which is the order of magnitude shown in Fig. 9.8 for steady-state creep.

Combination of intersection and stress field hardening with the cutting intersection recovery process results in another model.[36] In the steady state the dislocation density is supposed to be such that the flow stress is slightly greater than the applied stress. The three-dimensional dislocation network is then strained by the applied stress to such a point that thermal agitation can break junctions in it, which means that individual junctions are within about 1 ev of breaking, compared with the energy released when an attractive junction forms of several hundred ev. When a junction breaks as a result of a successful thermal agitation, the subsequent movement is presumably accompanied as usual by strain hardening; that is, there is an increase in dislocation line length and the average value of the network spacing x decreases. Without recovery, bigger and bigger thermal agitations would be necessary and creep would slow down. However, recovery occurs and offsets the increase in dislocation line length. Suppose the key recovery process is the climb following a cutting intersection which causes recovery in the way described in section 8.2. Because many junctions are strained nearly to breaking point, the amount of climb needed to spread the recovery action will often be small. In this way the stress accelerates the recovery process, and hence the creep rate, without altering the activation energy of climb, in accordance with eq. 9.12b. The recovery process reduces the total length of dislocation and so increases the average spacing and lowers the flow stress. The balance between strain hardening and recovery implied in eq. 9.13 thus applies at the level of dislocations; dislocations are made by strain and destroyed by recovery at exactly equal rates. The balance is maintained through the size of thermal agitation needed, which depends very sensitively on the dislocation density. The dislocation density must necessarily adjust itself so that the balance is preserved. Equation 9.13*a* can therefore be rewritten as

$$\dot\epsilon = \frac{\partial\varrho}{\partial t} \Big/ \frac{\partial\varrho}{\partial\epsilon} \qquad (9.13b)$$

where ϱ is the dislocation density.

Two factors help produce a high-stress sensitivity besides the one just mentioned, which is an effect of stress on average velocity: (*a*) the small influence of stress on activation energy mentioned above, which is also an effect on velocity; and (*b*) the dislocation density should be proportional to (stress)^2, as Fig. 9.13 indicates is so.

Insofar as primary creep has a similar activation energy to steady-state creep, the mechanism of primary creep is presumably the same as that of steady-state creep. In the second model just described, primary creep is that part of creep during which the thermal activation for further strain increases from zero to the level characterising the steady state. It is zero at the end of the instantaneous work hardening occurring on loading, by which the flow stress is raised to the level of the applied stress. Then follows the kind of situation envisaged in the derivation of eq. 9.15; the activation energy steadily increases and the creep rate decreases until the balance point is reached.

In a lower temperature range, cross slip is believed to be the controlling process as already described. Since all experience indicates that fresh strain generates fresh dislocations, and since cross slip can only eliminate the screw components, the dislocation density steadily increases. The creep rate should therefore steadily decrease, without reaching a steady state if climb cannot occur. Since only one activation is needed for a single cross slip event, such as mutual annihilation, whereas many activations are needed for climb over a given distance, the frequency factor for creep controlled by cross slip should be considerably greater than that for creep controlled by climb. The upward bend of the curve for the frequency factor A in Fig. 9.8 as the temperature is lowered into the range where cross slip is thought to be the controlling process is therefore the behaviour to be expected.

A third idea about high-temperature recovery creep is that it may sometimes be controlled by the movement of screw dislocations containing jogs which create vacancies as the dislocations move.[51] At high temperature the situation is different from that envisaged earlier (sections 4.7*d* and 5.10), because thermal agitation enables a vacancy to detach itself from the dislocation as soon as it is produced. The energy required for this is the energy of migration of vacancies. The total energy involved at each jog as the dislocation moves forward is therefore the sum of $Q_f + Q_m$, the energies of formation and migration of vacancies respectively, which is equal to the activation energy for self diffusion Q_d. Consequently, the creep rate $\dot{\epsilon}$ is given by an equation of the form

$$\dot{\epsilon} = A(e^{-(Q_d - \alpha\sigma)/kT} - e^{-(Q_d + \alpha\sigma)/kT}) \tag{9.16}$$

where A and α are constants. As, in this theory, $\alpha\sigma$ will be large compared with kT, this equation reduces to eq. 9.12a.

The relatively fast creep in aluminium at very high temperature and very low stress (Fig. 9.10), although exhibiting the same activation energy as creep under other conditions, seems from the sharp difference in stress dependence and grain boundary behaviour to be controlled by a different process. In these specimens the grains filled the specimens thickness so that many dislocations could travel across a grain and not meet the obstruction of a grain boundary. If they could come out of the grain at the surface, climb would not be necessary to maintain a constant dislocation density, which perhaps suggests the movement of screw dislocations just discussed as a likely rate-controlling process.

9.8   Role of Solutes and Precipitates in Creep

Alloying elements are added partly to slow down the creep rate and partly to delay fracture (section 9.10). Some remain in solution, but others are added to produce precipitates.

Solutes added to restrain creep operate mainly through their effect on the rate of recovery. Theoretically, this can be seen from eq. 9.13, since alloying elements can have much bigger effects on the rate of recovery than on the rate of strain hardening, and their effect on creep rate is usually very much greater than their effect on strain hardening. The direct contribution of solutes to the flow stress, by producing a friction stress, is probably seldom significant at creep temperatures. There are probably three distinguishable recovery effects. One is illustrated by Fig. 9.20 which shows the flow stress, measured at the temperature of the abscissa, after the specimens had been strained 5% also at the temperature of the abscissa. Clearly, in Al, even small amounts of Mg and Cu usefully impede recovery up to a temperature of 200–300°C. Several other elements which are closer in atomic size to aluminium had a weaker effect.[65]   From the discussion in section 9.7, we conclude that the alloys hamper climb, probably by blocking the jogs in the way discussed in section 8.2, an effect which would be expected to depend on difference in atomic size.

[65] O. D. Sherby, R. A. Anderson, and J. E. Dorn, *T.A.I.M.E.*, 1951, **191**, 643.

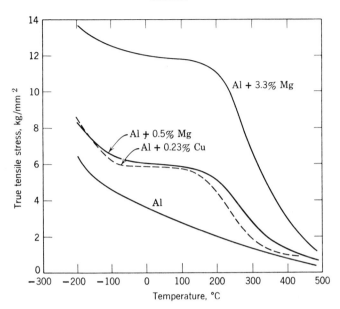

Fig. 9.20. Strengthening effect of solutes at elevated temperatures. The ordinate is the stress after 5% strain in a tensile test at the temperature of the abscissa. Alloy content in at % (Ref. 65).

The second effect is that it should be possible to hamper climb by the Suzuki mechanism as well as by solutes blocking jogs, since solute atoms which are attracted to the stacking fault of extended dislocations widen the stacking fault and make climb, and also cross slip, more difficult. With a considerable amount of solute present, this effect would persist to a high temperature even if, as perhaps is likely, the attraction to the stacking fault is fairly weak. Many creep-resistant alloys based on gamma iron contain about 30% cobalt, and nickel base alloys contain similar amounts of chromium and sometimes also cobalt. Since large amounts of solute are here found useful—chromium increases the creep strength of nickel slowly but steadily up to 30 to 40%,[66, 67]—and since no strong atomic interactions seem likely, perhaps the Suzuki effect is the operative one here. Some examples of alloying elements widening the stacking fault have been given earlier (chapter 6). It might also be noted that according to Table 9.3 the best alloys based on gamma iron are superior to any based on alpha iron and the dislocations in gamma iron,

[66] W. Rosenhain and C. H. M. Jenkins, *J.I.S.I.*, 1930, **121**, 225.
[67] N. T. Domotenko and I. I. Kornilov, *Izvest. Akad. Nauk S.S.S.R.*, 1957, (10), 36.

especially in solid solutions based on gamma iron, are almost certainly more extended than those in alpha iron.   The third effect is that solutes may alter the average strength of the atomic binding, at least when added in quantity.   An example is probably the rise in the creep strength of iron–nickel alloys at the composition of the Ni_3Fe compound.   This compound starts to precipitate out at 500°C; above this temperature there is a wide solubility range.   Nevertheless, the peak in creep strength is still found at 800°C,[68] suggesting that the extra atomic binding manifested by the compound is still operative.   The effect probably sometimes accounts for a variety of solutes having a greater combined effect than any single one—for example, the progressive increase in the creep strength as first Ti, then Cr, W, and Al are added to Ni.[69]   If atomic binding affects creep rate through the rate of diffusion as the ideas of section 9.7 indicate, there ought sometimes to be a correspondence between the effects of solutes on creep rates and diffusion speeds.   Such a correspondence has been found between the diffusion coefficients and creep rates at different temperatures of Ni–Ti, Ni–Ti–Cr, and Ni–Ti–Cr–W–Al alloys.[70]   Another example of this effect, though not involving solutes, seems to be the change in the creep rate of iron and thallium at the temperature of the phase change.   The difference in creep rate for a given stress, for example of alpha and gamma iron at the temperature of the alpha–gamma phase change, is very similar to the change in the rate of self diffusion.[71, 72]   The effect of atomic binding should be experimentally distinguishable from the first effect (Fig. 9.20) by not suffering a sudden attenuation at a certain temperature.   It will also need relatively large amounts of solute.

Apart from an effect with precipitates mentioned below, it seems unlikely that other known ways in which solutes hamper dislocation movement will be effective in engineering alloys during steady-state creep.   The operating temperature, up to about two-thirds the melting point of the base metal, is too high.   For example, the drag of an atmosphere should have an upper limit to its effective temperature range at about half the melting point, even when it remains attached to the dislocation.[48, 73]   Often, however, atmospheres will evaporate below this temperature, and Fig. 9.21 illustrates some results probably due to this.   The big peak

[68] I. I. Kornilov, Conference on Creep and Fracture, H.M.S.O., 1956, p. 215.

[69] I. I. Kornilov and L. I. Pryakhina, Proc. Acad. Sci. U.S.S.R., Sect. Chem., 1957, 112, 5.

[70] I. I. Kornilov and A. Ya. Shinyaer, Izvest. Akad. Nauk S.S.S.R., 1957, (9), 50.

[71] O. D. Sherby and J. L. Lytton, T.A.I.M.E., 1956, 206, 928.

[72] O. D. Sherby, T.A.I.M.E., 1958, 212, 708.

[73] A. H. Cottrell, Relation of Properties to Microstructure, A.S.M. Symposium, 1954, p. 131.

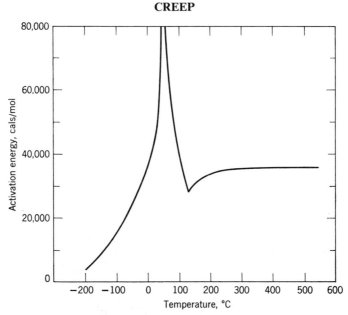

Fig. 9.21. Variation with temperature of the activation energy for creep of an Al–3.2 at % Mg alloy (Ref. 74).

slightly above room temperature is just the behaviour to be expected when the solute atoms are evaporating from the dislocation line itself, since altering the temperature then not only alters the creep rate through the normal effect of temperature, but also alters the state of the dislocations.

The creep-resistant alloys used in engineering practice evidently depend on a finely dispersed precipitate for much of their strength. Although practical experience makes it quite clear that precipitates vary widely in their effectiveness, no systematic work has yet been done in this important field. What seem to be the salient desirable features must therefore be picked out with guidance from general practical experience. The Nimonic and Inconel type alloys are especially valuable in this connection since they give particularly clear pointers.

The straightforward idea of the role of precipitates is that they act as obstacles to dislocations, which must therefore climb or cross slip to get past the particles, and that they may precipitate on and anchor dislocations against both slip and climb. Although, theoretically, it is not entirely clear that climb should be the controlling process in precipitation hardened metals, some experimental evidence that this is so is given by the observation that the activation energy for recovery creep at high temperature in

[74] N. R. Borch, quoted in *A.S.M.*, 1959, **51**, 900.

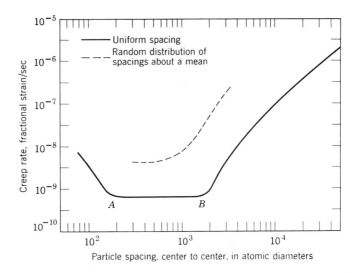

Fig. 9.22. Calculated variation of creep rate with particle spacing. Spherical particles.

aluminium alloys containing precipitate is the same as that for pure aluminium.[75]　This role for precipitates also assumes that they are hard enough at the service temperature to act as obstacles to slip. The hardness of large pieces of a number of precipitate compositions has been found to be greater at 800°C than that of the matrix.[76]

With this kind of model, particle spacing will be an important variable. Suppose that dislocations glide quickly until they are stopped by particles and then have to climb before they can move forward again.　Calculation yields the relation between creep rate and particle spacing shown as the full line in Fig. 9.22, in which a fixed volume fraction of precipitate is assumed.　In the calculation a dislocation density and a rate of climb were assumed which resulted in engineering creep rates.　The curve has three branches.　There is a horizontal part AB, where the creep rate is independent of particle spacing because, as the spacing is increased, the precipitate size increases in proportion, so that the free run distance between particles increases in exactly the same ratio as the distance that has to be climbed.　Toward the fine spacing end to the left of A it becomes faster for the dislocations to push the particles through the matrix than to climb over them.　However, this happens at such close spacings

[75] W. H. Giedt, O. D. Sherby, and J. E. Dorn, *A.S.M.E.*, 1955, **77**, 57.

[76] J. H. Westbrook, *T.A.I.M.E.*, 1957, **209**, 898.

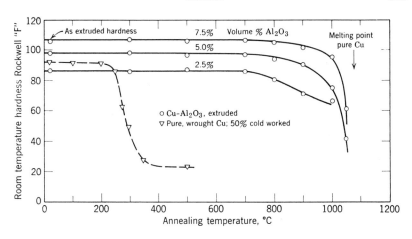

Fig. 9.23. Softening of strained Cu and Cu–Al₂O₃ alloy (Ref. 77).

that it can hardly be important in practice. At large spacings beyond B three things happen which increase the creep rate.

1. Dislocations loop between widely spaced particles, leaving a ring around the particles. This process is assumed to go on until enough dislocation rings surround each particle to make the spacing between the rings around neighbouring particles too small for another dislocation to loop between.

2. More than one dislocation can be pressed into the space between particles. They all climb together and the creep rate increases in proportion to this number.

3. Because dislocations have a certain flexibility, only a length near a precipitate particle need climb. Thus, the length that has to climb tends to remain constant as the interparticle spacing is increased beyond a certain amount. These three factors come into operation at about the same spacing, and lead to the rapid increase in creep rate on the right of Fig. 9.22. The critical spacing of course decreases as the stress becomes bigger.

This simple idea of the role of precipitates is incomplete, however, because it does not account for two things. One is the experimental association not only between closely spaced particles and slow creep rate, but also between closely spaced particles and high resistance to recovery from cold work. This latter is shown very well by the results in Fig. 9.23, which illustrates how copper containing a fine dispersion of Al₂O₃ particles retains the hardness of cold work nearly to the melting point of copper.

[77] O. Preston and N. J. Grant, *T.A.I.M.E.*, 1961, **221**, 164.

Evidently a fine dispersion has a powerful retarding effect on the rate of recovery. The other neglected thing is the dislocation density. The simple action of particles described earlier does not really give any satisfactory way, even if only in principle, of determining the dislocation density. As the creep rate $\dot\epsilon$ can be written

$$\dot\epsilon = \varrho b v$$

where ϱ is the **dislocation** density, b is the Burger's vector, and v is the average **dislocation** velocity, an indeterminate dislocation density means an indeterminate creep rate. In practice, of course, creep rates are determinate in the sense of being reproducible, and a more complete theory must therefore fix the dislocation density, even if only in principle. In such a theory, with a given alloy at a given temperature the dislocation density must therefore depend on the stress as the only remaining variable.

We can incorporate both points into the theory if we consider the structure of a dispersion hardened alloy after it has been made to creep. Although the structure has not yet been experimentally investigated, proceeding from the known fact that particles hinder dislocations it seems inevitable that dislocations moving in different, and sometimes opposite, directions are bound to form some kind of tangled network connecting the particles. If we make the reasonable assumption that this network contributes to the flow resistance, its formation is a process of work hardening and connects dislocation density with applied stress. Because such a network would also be anchored by the particles, so long as these remained finely dispersed the network should not easily migrate, and without migration there is a limit to the amount of dislocation that can be eliminated. Such a structure should therefore resist recovery, as experiment shows dispersion hardened alloys do.

It therefore seems that with these dispersion hardened alloys, just as with simple metals, there is work hardening during primary creep, and a balance is eventually reached between work hardening and recovery, when steady-state creep commences. According to this, eq. 9.13a and 9.13b both apply to dispersion hardened metals as well as to simple ones. It would, of course, be quite reasonable to draw this conclusion directly from the occurrence of steady-state creep in dispersion hardened metals. A major reason for the success of a stable fine dispersion in retarding creep is therefore its effect on r in eq. 9.13a, that is, its ability to stabilise the work hardened structure.

Thus, besides being hard, the precipitate particles should be fine and stable. It is relatively easy to produce a fine dispersion; the problem is to prevent the particles and therefore the spacing between them from growing at high temperature. The rate of particle growth depends on the rate of diffusion of particle material and on the particle-matrix interface energy, which is the driving force for growth.   Here therefore are two structural principles, both of which seem to be used in practice.   The simple Al + Al_2O_3 alloy known as SAP evidently uses the first, for the solubility of Al_2O_3 in Al is believed to be extremely small and interparticle diffusion of oxygen must be very slow indeed.   The Nimonic and Inconel alloys use the second.   In these alloys the precipitate that restrains the creep rate is mostly Ni_3Al, which is isomorphous with the matrix and differs from the latter in parameter by only about 0.5%.   Although this mismatch is enough to create appreciable strains around and inside the particles, and so augment their effectiveness as barriers, it is equivalent to an interface energy of only about 0.5% that of an ordinary grain boundary.   This reduction in driving force would be offset by a 200°C rise in temperature and so must enable these alloys to operate 200°C higher for the same degree of particle stability than an alloy hardened with a precipitate having a normally large interface energy.   Solutes can influence the mismatch and thus influence the creep rate indirectly.   Ideally, both principles should be applied simultaneously, but this may be impossible since substances which have a low interfacial energy are likely to be rather similar to the matrix and have a considerable solubility.   It seems more realistic to think of the two principles as somewhat mutually exclusive alternatives.

The first principle has been somewhat the more successful to date as Table 9.3 illustrates.   This table gives the ratio between the top service temperature and the melting point (in °K) of several commercial alloys.

Table 9.3

Ratio T/T_M between Top Service Temperature and Melting Point in °K

Basis Metal of Alloy	αFe	γFe	Ni	Mg	Al	
T/T_M	0.48	0.59	0.68	0.62	0.56*	0.72†

* Complex alloy.   † SAP.

The relative superiority of SAP on this scale presumably arises from the stability of the Al_2O_3 particles in it.   Several SAP-type materials have been   investigated,   namely   Al–Al_2O_3,[78, 79, 80, 81]   Cu–Al_2O_3,[77, 82, 83]

[78] A. von Zeerleder, Z. Metallk., 1950, 41, 228.
[79] R. Irmann, Metallurgia, 1952, 46, 125.
[80] G. S. Ansell and F. V. Lenel, T.A.I.M.E., 1961, 221, 452.
[81] G. S. Ansell and J. Weertman, T.A.I.M.E., 1959, 215, 838.
[82] K. M. Zwilsky and N. J. Grant, T.A.I.M.E., 1961, 221, 371.
[83] M. Adachi and N. J. Grant, T.A.I.M.E., 1960, 218, 881.

Cu–SiO$_2$,[77, 83] Ni–Al$_2$O$_3$,[84] and Cr–Al$_2$O$_3$.[85] The ability of these alloys to retain strength at high temperature depends on how successful the particular method of manufacture is in producing a fine and uniform dispersion. The best so far are the original SAP quoted in Table 9.3, containing about 12 volume % of alumina, and copper containing about 7$\frac{1}{2}$ volume % of alumina. These are equally successful in proportion to the melting points of their metallic matrixes.

SAP-type materials are therefore a particularly promising immediate line of development, but whether they will remain so in the future is not certain. With an alloy based on a high melting point metal such as, say, niobium, operating at the same fraction of its melting point as the alloys in Table 9.3, refractory compounds are likely to be more soluble than at the lower temperature at which SAP can be used. Consequently it may not be possible to use this type of material at as high a fraction of its melting point as that at which SAP can be used. There is no reason, on the other hand, why the principle of low particle-matrix interface energy should not continue to be used with as much success as in the Nimonic and Inconel alloys.

There is also another advantage of this principle not yet mentioned. The more second phase that can be incorporated in an alloy without causing room temperature brittleness and creating handling and operational problems the better, because the free slip distance is thereby reduced and a given critical spacing B (Fig. 9.22) can be achieved with larger particles that grow relatively more slowly than smaller ones. Within this limit it should be possible to incorporate more of a second phase that is similar to the matrix than of one which is very different from it, and this consideration should gather strength as the gap between service and room temperature grows and makes room temperature brittleness a more serious problem.

An alternative to a single fine and stable precipitate is a succession of precipitates of different compositions, each of which grows but is succeeded or superseded by another fine precipitation. This seems to be the characteristic at least of a number of iron base alloys evolved over a long period of time. A succession of precipitates has been observed,[86] and the form of some creep curves, by showing sudden decelerations of creep rate, suggests that fresh precipitation takes place during service.[87] When "warm working" benefits creep resistance it does so presumably by bringing down a fine precipitate. Precipitation which is accelerated by

[84] L. J. Bonis and N. J. Grant, *T.A.I.M.E.*, 1960, **218**, 877.

[85] A. Gatti, *T.A.I.M.E.*, 1960, **218**, 437.

[86] K. F. Hale, *Proc. Intern. Conf. Electron Microscopy*, Berlin, 1958.

[87] J. Glen, *J.I.S.I.*, 1958, **190**, 114.

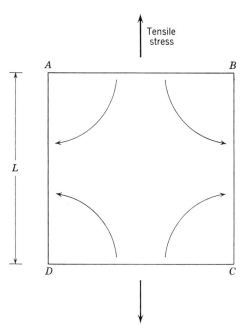

Fig. 9.24. Stress-directed flow of vacancies inside a grain $ABCD$.

straining is likely to come down on dislocations and possibly this is a particularly effective location for a time because the particles are located where they are needed. However, eventually, the dislocations will detach themselves from these precipitates—for example, because the particle spacings increase—and thereafter the precipitates act like those discussed. The observation that in some alloys a composition just inside a two-phase field has a greater creep resistance than neighbouring compositions[68] is perhaps connected with such selective precipitation. Of course, alloys which depend on continuing fresh supplies of precipitate will fail in the end because the supply cannot be inexhaustible, and are unlikely to last as long as stable alloys like SAP.

9.9 Diffusion Creep

Since diffusion occurs, creep due to stress directed diffusion is possible.[88, 89, 90] Thus, if a tensile stress is applied, material is trans-

[88] F. R. N. Nabarro, Conference on Strength of Solids, *Phys. Soc. London*, 1948, p. 75.
[89] C. Herring, *J.A.P.*, 1950, **21**, 437.
[90] R. O. Williams, *Acta Met.*, 1957, **5**, 55.

ported from the sides to the ends of a specimen to lengthen it. Vacancies flow in the opposite direction. Since grain boundaries can act as sources and sinks for vacancies, the path length to consider is related to the grain size.

Figure 9.24 shows an imaginary square sectioned grain of side L to which a tensile stress is applied. Vacancies flow in the directions indicated. Along AB and CD the vacancy excess is

$$c - c_0 = c_0 \frac{\sigma b^3}{kT} \qquad (9.17)$$

where c is the actual concentration and c_0 is the equilibrium vacancy concentration, and there is a similar deficit along AD and BC. The diffusion coefficient for vacancies is D/c_0, where D is the self diffusion coefficient of the metal. If a mean diffusion length of $L/2$ for each of the four diffusion paths shown in Fig. 9.24 and an average cross-sectional area of $L^2/8$ is assumed, the rate at which vacancies migrate from the ends to the sides and hence the rate at which atoms migrate from the sides to the ends is $\partial v/\partial t = 2\sigma b^3 LD/kT$ in units of volume/unit time. The creep rate is $(1/L^3)(\partial v/\partial t)$ and therefore is

$$\dot{\epsilon} = \frac{2\sigma b^3 D}{L^2 kT} \qquad (9.18)$$

According to eq. 9.18 diffusion creep is distinguished from slip creep by depending on the stress linearly instead of to a higher power. Experimentally it should therefore be found at low stresses. High temperatures are of course also needed to produce a measurable rate of extension. In suitable experiments, wires or foils of Ag,[91] Au,[92] Cu,[93] and Cu–Sb alloys[94] have in fact been found to creep at a rate within an order of magnitude of that predicted by eq. 9.18. There is also some support for the form of the equation since in the very high temperature range concerned the creep rate varies linearly with the stress, varies with grain size in the manner predicted by eq. 9.18,[93, 94] and single crystals of silver creep at a relatively negligible rate.[91]

The metals referred to in the preceding paragraph contain extended dislocations. As mentioned in section 9.3, in aluminium, which contains relatively unextended dislocations, a form of creep linear in stress is observed at very low stress and high temperature, but for the reasons given there cannot be diffusion creep.

[91] A. P. Greenough, *Phil. Mag.*, 1952, **43**, 1075.
[92] F. H. Buttner, E. R. Funk, and H. Udin, *T.A.I.M.E.*, 1952, **194**, 40.
[93] A. L. Pranatis and G. M. Pound, *T.A.I.M.E.*, 1955, **203**, 664.
[94] H. R. Tipler, to appear.

Fig. 9.25. Crack at triple-grain boundary junction during creep. Nimonic 90
alloy stressed at 12½ kg/mm². × 500. (Crown copyright reserved.)

9.10 Fracture in Creep

Most creep resistant metals, and some others, break during creep in
quite a distinctive way.   Small cavities appear at grain boundaries, grow
and coalesce, and eventually there is a grain-boundary fracture.   Some
metals instead draw down to a point, or at least draw down a long way.
The first behaviour is the serious kind since it can and usually does happen
at low elongation, perhaps only about 1%.
The theory of this kind of fracture is believed to be largely understood
in principle.[48, 95, 96, 97, 98, 99]   It is best thought of in two parts.   The
simpler part deals with cracks produced at grain corners, such as that in
Fig. 9.25.   These cracks are evidently produced by sliding along grain
boundaries as in Fig. 9.26, which produces a stress concentration at O.
This is a similar situation to that in Fig. 7.10.   Since the stress concentration factor is limited by the length of the grain boundaries OA and OB,

[95] J. N. Greenwood, *Bull. Inst. Metals*, 1952, **1**, 104 and 121.
[96] I. A. Oding and W. S. Iwanowa, *Doklady Akad. Nauk S.S.S.R.*, 1955, **103**, 77.
[97] I. A. Oding and W. W. Burdukski, Conference on Deformation and Flow of Solids,
Springer, Berlin, 1956.
[98] R. W. Baluffi and L. L. Seigle, *Acta Met.*, 1957, **5**, 449.
[99] A. H. Cottrell, Symposium on *Structural Processes in Creep, Iron and Steel Inst.
London*, 1961, 44.

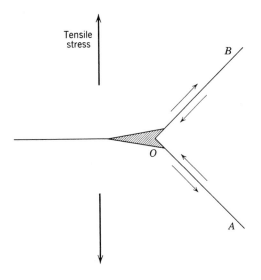

Fig. 9.26. Generation of a crack at a grain corner by grain boundary sliding.

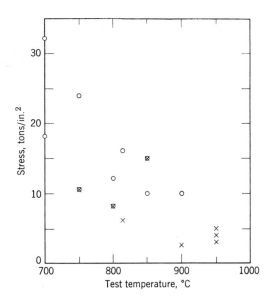

Fig. 9.27. Types of cavity found in Nimonic 90 after creep at different stresses and temperatures.   ○ Wedge-shaped crack based on grain corner (Fig. 9.25); × separate cavities occurring at any point along grain boundaries (Fig. 9.28); ⊗ both types.

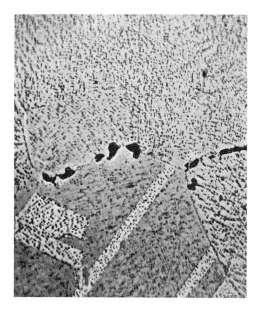

Fig. 9.28. "Cavitation" during creep. Nimonic 90 alloy stressed at 3.9 kg/mm².
× 500. (Crown copyright reserved.)

there should be a certain minimum stress necessary to produce a crack at O. This seems to be the case[100]; Fig. 9.27 shows some results illustrating this point.

Grain-boundary fracture still takes place at lower stresses, however, but in a somewhat different way. Cavities form at various points along the grain boundaries. They now show no preference for grain corners but have a marked preference for grain boundaries approximately perpendicular to an applied tensile stress. The cavities grow in size, coalesce, and eventually fracture occurs. Figures 9.28 and 9.29 show two stages in this sequence. The second part of the theory of creep fracture deals with this process.

It is believed that the cavities form at nuclei whose nature will be discussed below. For the moment it will help description of the process to suppose that they are ledges in the boundaries which are opened into holes by sliding as illustrated in Fig. 9.30. When the cavities are big enough they can be enlarged by precipitation into them of vacancies and the sequence described in the preceding paragraph follows. The critical size at which vacancies can commence to precipitate into the cavities is important since the bigger it has to be the less likely are nuclei of that size

[100] D. McLean, *J.I.M.*, 1956–7, **85**, 468.

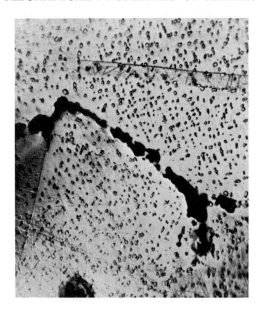

Fig. 9.29. "Cavitation" during creep.   Nimonic 90 alloy stressed at 3.9 kg/mm².
× 1000.   (Crown copyright reserved.)

to be produced.   It can be calculated as follows.   The energy of a hole
of radius r and surface energy γ (approximately equal to $2\gamma_s - \gamma_B$, where
γ_s is the surface energy and γ_B the boundary energy) is

$$W = 4\pi r^2\gamma - \tfrac{4}{3}\pi r^3 F \tag{9.19}$$

where F is the free energy liberated per unit volume of vacancies precipitated.   In the present case,

$$F = \frac{kT}{b^3} \ln \frac{c}{c_0} \tag{9.20}$$

where c/c_0 is the ratio of actual to equilibrium vacancy concentration
given by eq. 9.17, since at transverse grain boundaries the tensile stress σ
produces this degree of supersaturation.   The energy W starts to decrease,

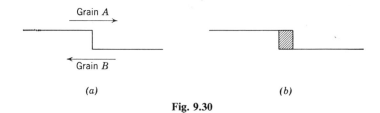

Grain A

Grain B

(a)   (b)

Fig. 9.30

that is, the given vacancy supersaturation can make the cavities grow, when

$$r > \frac{2\gamma}{\sigma} \qquad (9.21)$$

(The relation of this equation to the Griffith eq. 7.1 is discussed in section 9.11.) For $\sigma = 5$ kg/mm^2 and $\gamma = 1500$ ergs/cm^2, the holes must exceed about 10^{-5} cm diameter to grow by precipitation of vacancies. Here the only source of vacancy supersaturation has been assumed to be the tensile stress, acting as in section 9.9. The important part the tensile stress plays accounts for the preference of the cavities for grain boundaries that are transverse to the tensile stress. If for some other reason the vacancy concentration is raised, the critical radius will be smaller and the preference for transverse boundaries might not be so marked. Neutron irradiation might be sufficiently effective, particularly where the temperature is not too high and the supersaturation produced by the stress is therefore relatively small.

There is experimental evidence that the vacancy concentration, the tensile stress, and grain-boundary sliding play the roles assigned to them in this theory. That vacancies help the formation of cavities is shown by experiments in which brass and copper were heated in a vacuum.[101, 102] By volatilising zinc from the brass, vacancies would be formed, but none would be generated in the copper. Correspondingly, cavities appeared in the brass but not in the copper. Moreover, the cavities did not appear when the brass was heated in nitrogen presumably because the atmosphere hindered the evaporation of zinc. In other experiments[103] in which the ratio of tensile to shear stress was varied, when the shear stress was kept constant the rupture time decreased with increase in tensile component, whereas substituting a compressive stress for the tensile stress produced the result that no cavities were formed. These are the effects which eq. 9.17 and 9.21 imply should happen. The measured temperature coefficient of the time-to-rupture corresponded to the activation energy for diffusion along grain boundaries, as is rather to be expected since the tests were carried out at a relatively low temperature between 400 to 500°C where grain-boundary diffusion provides faster transport than grain interior diffusion.

As regards the influence of grain-boundary sliding, there are two general observations. One is that at any protuberance in the boundary, sliding will produce a powerful stress concentration which may overcome the cohesion there just as it does at the grain corner in Fig. 9.25; a numerical estimate of this effect is made in the next paragraph. The other is that

[101] L. M. T. Hopkin, *J.I.M.*, 1956-7, **85**, 422
[102] L. M. T. Hopkin, *Nature*, 1957, **180**, 808.
[103] D. Hull and D. E. Rimmer, *Phil. Mag.*, 1959, **4**, 673.

when vacancies are generated in the absence of an applied stress, as in some of the experiments on brass mentioned earlier or in other Kirkendall-type experiments (in which a vacancy supersaturation is produced by a diffusion process), the resulting cavities show no preference for grain boundaries. Evidently there are nuclei within the grains which are efficient enough to operate at the vacancy supersaturations concerned. But in creep, the cavities have an overwhelming preference for grain boundaries. From this it can be argued that sliding at grain boundaries develops still more efficient nuclei, but it can also be argued that the cavities then form at grain boundaries simply because the vacancies are produced there by the tensile stress. In addition to these general points, there are two specific experimental results which seem to point to an influence of grain-boundary sliding. The first is that in the experiments on brass it was found that applying a small stress had the effect of suppressing cavity formation inside the grains and concentrating it at grain boundaries. The interpretation of this seems to be that sliding developed nuclei at grain boundaries which were more efficient than those already existing, and kept the vacancy supersaturation below the value necessary for precipitation on these. The second is that, in experiments on copper bi-crystals at high temperature,[104] when a tensile stress was applied perpendicularly to the boundary so that there should be no sliding while the tensile stress was applied, no cavities formed along the boundary (or elsewhere) except in specimens which had previously been sheared parallel to the boundary. Again it appears the sliding developed nuclei which could be fed by the vacancy supersaturation generated by the applied stress.

A problem in the theory is the nature of the grain-boundary nuclei, which so far have been supposed to be ledges as depicted in Fig. 9.30.[105] Something can be said about the dimensions such protuberances would involve. The previous estimate led to a typical critical diameter of cavity of about 10^{-5} cm. Supposing the theoretical rupture stress at a ledge is 500 kg/mm^2 and the applied tensile shear stress parallel to the boundary (nearly normal to the tensile stress) is 1 kg/mm^2, a stress concentration factor of 500 fold is needed. If the ledge is 10^{-5} cm high and also 10^{-5} cm deep, its cohesion would then be overcome by shear stress on an area of boundary about $2\frac{1}{2}$ microns square. Protuberances of normal cohesion therefore have to be rather large or numerous to avoid being broken. In addition, it is possible to envisage mechanical growth from a much smaller size,[106] when the chance of reaching the stable size would

[104] C. W. Chen and E. S. Machlin, *T.A.I.M.E.*, 1957, **9**, 829.
[105] R. C. Gifkins, *Acta Met.*, 1956, **4**, 98.
[106] D. McLean, *Grain Boundaries in Metals*, Oxford University Press, London, 1957, p. 120.

be less the larger this is. Reduction in γ encourages the formation of cavities because it amounts to a reduction in cohesion, so that ledges are broken more easily, and reduces the minimum stable size. There is experimental support for this effect since rupture is faster in antimony-bearing copper than in antimony-free copper,[102] and antimony lowers the surface energy of copper in the way shown in Fig. 7.19. Another possibility is that inclusions act as ledges. Here again a low value of γ encourages cavity formation and seems a likely explanation of the effect in this direction that ZnO particles have in brass.[107]

This discussion suggests two main ways of controlling grain-boundary cavitation. Strongly cohering grain-boundary precipitates (large γ) should act as pinning points and reduce the free lengths of grain boundary and hence the stress concentrations at nucleating points. Since it is found that grain-boundary precipitation of suitable particles increases the time to rupture of Ni–Cr base alloys,[108] this effect seems to be used in current alloys. The beneficial effect of zirconium and boron in the Ni–Cr base alloys[108] may be an example of an element increasing the quantity $(2\gamma_s - \gamma_B)$ by segregating to the grain boundary and lowering the grain-boundary energy by more than it lowers the surface energy; but other explanations are obviously possible here. The discussion also throws up two other points. If the alloy flows easily, stress concentrations are alleviated, but this can obviously rarely be used as a way of increasing rupture life. This kind of consideration, however, probably goes some, but doubtless not all, of the way to accounting for the different behaviours among metals; for example, copper is brittle in creep and aluminium is not, and a higher stress is needed for equal rates of flow under comparable conditions in copper than in aluminium. In this connection it is worth noting that if aluminium is alloyed to bear higher creep stresses it tends to become more brittle in creep. Grain-boundary migration should mitigate stress concentrations by smoothing out ledges and spreading out the stress concentration at grain corners; there is an inverse correlation between rupture life and extent of grain-boundary migration which may arise in this way.[109] This idea is also difficult to use in practice, since fast migration occurs only in metals that flow easily at high temperature.

9.11 Eq. 9.21 and the Griffith Eq. 7.1

Equation 9.21 and the Griffith eq. 7.1 both give the stress required to extend a cavity of a certain size but yield quite different values for this

[107] R. Resnick and L. Seigle, *T.A.I.M.E.*, 1957, **209**, 87.

[108] C. W. Weaver, *J.I.M.*, 1959–60, **88**, 462.

[109] N. J. Grant, Symposium on Creep and Fracture, *H.M.S.O.*, London, 1956, p. 317.

stress. The reason is that they deal with spreading under different conditions.[99, 110] The complete expression for the energy W associated with a cavity comprises three terms. (a) The increase in surface energy of amount $\alpha \pi r^2 \gamma$ where α is 2 for a disc-like cavity and 4 for a spherical one. (b) The change in energy obtained by subtracting the elastic strain energy around the cavity from the work done by the applied stress as the cavity is formed. This is a net decrease of about $\frac{4}{3}\pi r^3(\sigma^2/2E)$. (c) The work done by the applied stress because the cavity increases the overall volume; this is σV where V is the volume of the cavity. The cavity starts to extend when

$$W = \alpha \pi r^2 \gamma - \tfrac{4}{3}\pi r^3 \frac{\sigma^2}{2E} - \sigma V$$

begins to decrease with increase in r. The Griffith situation is concerned with a disc-shaped cavity for which V is small and in any case envisages no volume expansion other than that involved in the elastic strain term b. The first two terms are then the only ones and lead to eq. 7.1 (i.e., if the exact expression for (b) is used). At high temperatures, the cavity is approximately spherical and the third term (c) is then much larger than the second term (b); combined with the first term it leads to eq. 9.21. By inserting appropriate values into eq. 7.1 and 9.21 it is easily seen that the Griffith stress is greater than that given by eq. 9.21 for stresses for which r is greater than an atomic diameter. Moreover, the effective surface energy is usually much larger than the true surface energy during the spread of a disc-shaped cavity, and this enhances the difference.

It is therefore the possibility of enlarging by diffusion that enables cavities to grow at small stress when the temperature is high, because this means that the stress can do much more work on them than when this possibility is absent, as in the situation envisaged by eq. 7.1.

[110] D. McLean, Conference on Grain Boundaries, Commissariat de l'Énergie Atomique, Saclay (Paris), 1960.

10

Fatigue

10.1 Survey*

A metal can be broken by a stress considerably smaller than the normal breaking stress if the stress is applied many times. This is the behaviour known as fatigue. The relation between peak stress S and number of cycles N of tensile and compressive stress needed for failure has the form shown in Fig. 10.1, in which the number of cycles needed increases as the peak stress decreases. Millions of cycles are often involved in engineering practice. An indication of the severity of the fatigue effect is that the peak stress required to cause failure in 10^6–10^7 cycles of stress alternating between equal tensile and compressive values usually lies between $\frac{1}{3}$ and $\frac{3}{5}$ of the UTS. Consequently, it is often a limiting factor in engineering design.

---

* The engineering problems in fatigue have been reviewed,[1, 2, 3, 4, 5] and there is also a general review.[6]

[1] P. G. Forrest, *Fatigue*, Butterworths, Oxford, 1962.

[2] H. J. Gough, *The Fatigue of Metals*, Scott Greenwood & Son, London, 1924.

[3] R. Cazaud (trans. by A. J. Fenner) *Fatigue of Metals*, English edition published by Chapman & Hall, London, 1953.

[4] H. J. Grover, S. A. Gordon, and L. R. Jackson, *Fatigue of Metals and Structures*, Department of the Navy, Washington, 1954.

[5] G. Sines and J. L. Waisman, *Metal Fatigue*, McGraw-Hill, New York, 1959.

[6] N. Thompson and N. J. Wadsworth, *Advances in Phys.*, 1958, **7**, 72.

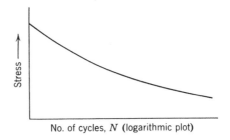

Fig. 10.1. Typical *S–N* curve.

10.2 Types of S/N Curve. Coaxing and Damage

Among metals two types of fatigue behaviour are generally distinguished. Iron and mild steel have a definite "fatigue limit"; the "S/N curve" in Fig. 10.2 illustrates this behaviour. At a stress S_0 (i.e., alternating between $+S_0$ and $-S_0$) and a value of N which is usually between 10^5 and 10^7, the curve becomes horizontal, as stresses less than S_0 do not cause fracture. A similar type of behaviour has also been found to occur with some strain-ageing aluminium alloys, superpure aluminium,[7] some titanium alloys,[8] and some magnesium alloys[9]. Most metals, however, show the behaviour depicted in Fig. 10.1 in which the S/N curve falls continuously, though usually with a decreasing slope, up to the highest number of cycles that have been applied in fatigue experiments, about 10^{10}. With such metals there is no definite fatigue limit, so the "fatigue strength," as it is called, is quoted for a specified number of cycles. A fatigue limit is therefore a special effect.

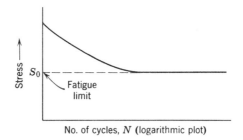

Fig. 10.2. *S–N* curve for mild steel and some other metals.

[7] P. G. Forrest, private communication.
[8] S. M. Bishop, J. W. Spretnak, and W. G. Fontana, *Trans. A.S.M.*, 1953, **45**, 993.
[9] E. F. Emley, *J.I.M.*, 1954–5, **83**, 531.

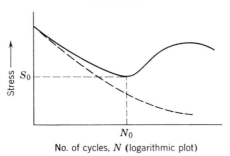

No. of cycles, N (logarithmic plot)

Fig. 10.3. Suggested effect of "coaxing."

The definite fatigue limit has been ascribed to the phenomenon of "coaxing" in which the fatigue limit is raised by gradually increasing the fluctuating stress, starting at a level below the fatigue limit.[10, 11] Coaxing in turn is thought to be the result of strain ageing, as appreciable plastic strain (e.g. 0.01–0.1% per half cycle in iron or mild steel) still occurs after many cycles at fluctuating stresses just less than the fatigue limit. To explain the sharp fatigue limit, coaxing is supposed to occur during the early part of the test and to change an S/N curve that would have shown no fatigue limit, such as the dashed curve in Fig. 10.3, into the full line curve in Fig. 10.3 by the time N_0 cycles have been applied. A definite fatigue limit is therefore found at the fatigue stress S_0.

The fatigue limit is only raised if coaxing is done at stresses that are not too high. Otherwise, the fatigue limit is lowered and the fatigue life at a given stress is reduced; "damage" is then said to have occurred. Not only steels but all metals are subject to damage by overstressing. The metallurgical sign of damage seems to be the presence of "persistent slip bands" or tiny cracks (section 10.5).

10.3 Effects of Test Conditions

(*a*) *Surface Layers and Environment.* Since fatigue cracks normally start at the surface (section 10.5), the surface condition might be expected to be important. This is true, both from an engineering point of view since the smoother the surface the higher the endurance in general,[12] and also from a metallurgical point of view, for the condition of the surface layer affects the endurance. The fatigue strength of $\frac{1}{3}$ to $\frac{3}{5}$ of the UTS quoted in section 10.1 applies to smooth specimens. Several results

---

[10] P. G. Forrest and J. Holden, private communication.
[11] J. C. Lery and S. L. Kanitkar, *J.I.S.I.*, 1961, **197**, 296.
[12] G. A. Hankins and M. L. Becker, *J.I.S.I.*, 1931, **124**, 387.

illustrate the effect of metallurgical surface condition. For example, hardening the surface of steel by carburising, nitriding,[13] or by shot peening[14] raises the endurance, and a thick anodised layer on aluminium also helps to prevent fatigue failure.[15] On the other hand, arranging for a soft surface layer by decarburising the surface layer of steel[12] or by coating an aluminium alloy with aluminium (i.e., the metal known as Alclad)[16] lowers the endurance. The effect of electroplated coatings, which are sometimes harder and sometimes softer than the basis metal, cannot be specified so clearly[13, 16] and it seems that additional effects such as the degree of protection afforded against atmospheric attack or stress in the coating may be important. Excluding plated coatings, the effect of surface layers can reasonably be interpreted in terms of the resistance to slip of the surface layers; residual compressive stresses will also help (see section 10.3b). Some experiments on mild steel[17] confirm the importance of slip resistance rather directly by showing that the weakening effect of a decarburised layer is removed by a preliminary overstrain, which would cold work the layer. Surface layers show the effects mentioned whether tests are done in a machine that applies a uniform alternating stress or in one of the more usual bending type of machines, which shows that fatigue damage starts at the surface because it is a free surface in contact with some other medium and not because the stress is highest at the surface.

It is worth emphasising that the improvement conferred by hardening the surface can be large. For example, some results on case-hardened steel showed improvements of 15 to 230%, the average being 60%.[13] Such results seem to mean that if the formation of a crack at the surface of a metal can be stopped, at least half as high a stress again would be needed to produce internal fatigue failure.

Because of this remarkable weakness of the surface, contamination of the surface by the atmosphere might reasonably be suspected to be an essential part of normal fatigue. It is doubtful, however, if this is really so. Tests in vacuum or inert atmosphere sometimes show an improvement, and sometimes do not,[18] but anyhow tests in a normal vacuum are not decisive, since even in a vacuum of 10^{-6} mm of mercury each surface

[13] E. R. Gadd, Discussion on Fatigue, *Royal Aeronaut. Soc.*, September 1953, p. 565.
[14] G. Sines, Technical Note 3495, National Advisory Council for Aeronautics, Washington, 1955.
[15] T. H. Alden and W. A. Backofen, *Acta Met.*, 1961, **9**, 352.
[16] Battelle Memorial Institute, Prevention of the failure of metals under repeated stress, John Wiley and Sons, New York, 1941.
[17] J. A. Pope and C. W. Parson, International Conference on Fatigue of Metals, *Inst. Mech. Engrs. London*, 1956, p. 557.
[18] M. Hempel, A. Kochendörfer, and A. Tietze, *Arch. Eisenhüttenw.*, 1959, **30**, 211.

metal atom is hit once a second by a gas molecule in an experiment at room temperature. The gas molecules would therefore be able to contaminate the surface or enter cracks. However, fatigue occurs in liquid helium, and there seems to be no discontinuous improvement in fatigue strength on reducing to liquid helium temperature by doing the test with the specimen immersed in liquid helium. In view of the weak binding forces around a helium molecule, this result makes it unlikely that surface attack is necessary for fatigue to occur.

(b) *Stress System.* Because many engineering components are subjected to various combinations of shear, tensile, and compressive stress, fatigue under complex stress systems is an important engineering problem and has been extensively investigated.[1] Most of these investigations are outside the scope of this book and only some relevant ones are summarised in this section.

A steady shear stress applied to a specimen tested in alternating shear has very little effect on the fatigue strength,[14] provided the steady shear stress is not large enough to introduce the extra complication of substantial extra work hardening. A steady direct stress applied to a single crystal specimen tested in alternating shear has been reported[19] to have no effect on the time for inception of a crack but to retard its subsequent rate of spread if compressive and to accelerate it if tensile. These results suggest that the time or number of cycles for the inception of a crack is determined by the range of shear stress and not by the peak shear stress. It appears from these results that the work-hardened state produced by any stress system is biased against the steady mean stress in the sense that the amount of slip in both directions is approximately equal, regardless of the stress applied in each direction. The fact that the time for inception of a crack is independent of the size of the stress peaks is incidentally evidence that local tensile stresses normally play no part in forming the initial fatigue crack.

A steady tensile stress applied to a specimen tested in alternating tension-compression always reduces the permissible fatigue range and a steady compressive stress increases it.[14] Judging from the results just mentioned, this is due to a more rapid spread of a crack. A typical set of results illustrating the reduction in fatigue range when a static tensile stress is superimposed is shown in Fig. 10.4. Empirical laws (Goodman's law, Gerber's law) have been devised to express the reduction in safe alternating range when a static stress is applied. Experiment shows that the effect of a superimposed stress is not the same for all metals, although the differences generally lie within the band enclosed by the empirical

[19] H. J. Gough, *Proc. A.S.T.M.*, 1933, **33**, 3.

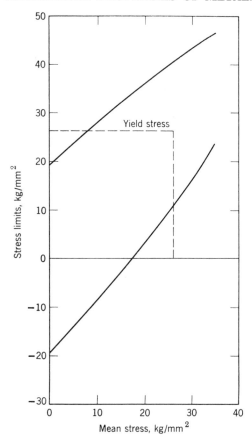

Fig. 10.4.   Effect of a superimposed static stress (mean stress) on fatigue stress range. 0.17% C steel (Ref. 20).

laws.   Attempts have also been made to devise formulae for more complex stress systems.[21]

Fatigue failure at stress raisers such as holes and keyways is a serious problem in engineering practice.   This problem has provoked experiments in which the precise location of the cracks that form at different points around holes drilled in fatigued specimens is compared with the stress distributions around the hole computed from elastic theory.[22]   Computations from elastic theory of the stresses around a hole of substantial size

[20] H. J. Tapsell, *J.I.S.I.*, 1928, **117**, p. 275.

[21] J. Marin, International Conference on Fatigue of Metals, *Inst. Mech. Engrs. London*, 1956, p. 184.

[22] H. L. Cox, International Conference on Fatigue of Metals, *Inst. of Mech. Engrs. London*, 1956, p. 212.

can be reliable because such a hole will not change shape appreciably during fatigue and the metal around it may work harden until relatively little cyclic plastic strain takes place (section 10.4). By employing various stress systems to produce different stress distributions, it transpires that a stress of about twice the average value restricted to a region a fraction of a millimetre in size is less effective in starting a crack than one not so high but spreading over a wider area.[23] This result recalls the situation at the end of a nonpropagating crack (section 10.5).

(c) *Temperature and Cycle Speed.* The fatigue strength shows the expected effect of temperature, being generally reduced by raising the temperature. At high temperature there is a correlation between the fatigue strength of several metals and their creep rupture strength.[24] Lowering the temperature toward absolute zero has been found to raise the fatigue strength in approximately the same proportion as the UTS.[25] It appears that the ratio of the stress for a long endurance to that for a short endurance increases as the temperature is decreased from above room temperature to near absolute zero.[24]

Superimposed on this general effect of temperature, with steel the special blue brittle effect is observed, since there is a peak in the curve of fatigue strength against temperature at 300–400°C resembling the peaks for yield and ultimate tensile strength. The temperature at which the peak was found to occur for a 0.17% carbon steel[26] decreased for a decrease in cycle speed but was unaffected by varying the number of cycles to fracture, which was, of course, controlled by varying the fatigue stress applied. Hence it was deduced that the peak is caused by a process that does not accumulate with successive cycles but operates afresh each cycle. A possible cause which has this feature is the Snoek effect (Chapter 6). Apart from this influence on blue brittleness, cycle speed over the usual range of, say, 10–10^4 cycles/min has not usually much effect on fatigue strength, but as the temperature is increased the total time of the test begins to affect the fatigue strength, so that for a given number of cycles to fracture the fatigue strength decreases with decrease in the frequency.

10.4 Plastic Strain, Hysteresis, and Hardening

During fatigue, plastic strain occurs in every half cycle. Part of that occurring on the first reversal seems to be simply a recoiling of the original strain since some of the diffuseness of the X-ray lines produced by the

[23] H. L. Cox, private communication.
[24] N. P. Allen and P. G. Forrest, International Conference on Fatigue of Metals, *Inst. Mech. Engrs. London*, 1956, p. 327.
[25] R. D. McCammon and H. M. Rosenberg, *P.R.S.*, 1957, **A.242**, 203.
[26] P. G. Forrest, *P.R.S.*, 1957, **A.242**, p. 223.

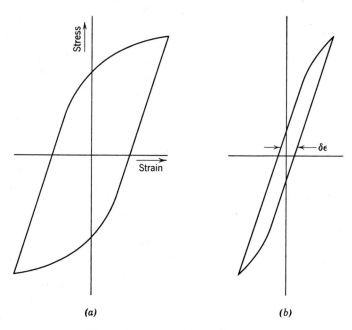

(a)   (b)

Fig. 10.5.   Hysteresis loops in fatigue.

original strain is eliminated by the first reversal,[27] but part is fresh plastic strain since the hardness increases as Fig. 10.6 shows.   With successive reversals the plastic strain per half cycle decreases, but eventually tends toward a fairly constant value that usually lasts for many cycles.   The plastic strain per half cycle in this stage ranges from less than 0.002% to about 0.3%, depending on the conditions, for example, metal and stress.[28] During this long stage no bulk changes in properties take place, but the very fact that fatigue failure eventually occurs shows that damage must be accumulating in tiny patches.   It is the smallness of the scale of fatigue damage and the unpredictability of its location that has made research into its mechanism so difficult.   Near failure, the plastic strain per half cycle increases again, probably because of the stress concentrations at cracks.

Somewhat distinct from the plastic strain is the hysteresis loss arising from the fact that the stress-strain curve is not exactly retraced on each reversal.   Figure 10.5a shows the wide hysteresis loop at the beginning of a fatigue test and Fig. 10.5b the narrow loop in the fairly constant stage,

[27] W. A. Wood and A. K. Head, *J.I.M.*, 1951, **79**, 89.
[28] P. G. Forrest, International Conference on Fatigue of Metals, *Inst. Mech. Engrs. London*, 1956, p. 171.

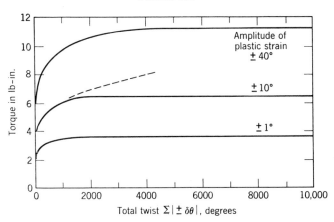

Fig. 10.6. Effect in Cu of plastic cycling on the torque needed to produce a given twist (Ref. 29).

both curves resembling Fig. 3.5*c*. Since the straight loading lines represent elastic deformation, the width of the hysteresis loop ($\delta\epsilon$ in Fig. 10.5*b*) is equal to the plastic strain.

Strain hardening occurs in fatigue and is of course responsible for the gradual closing up of the hysteresis loop. The rise in flow stress during fatigue stressing was followed in some tests on copper and alpha brass in which alternating cycles of constant plastic twist $\delta\theta$ were applied, and the steadily increasing peak torque needed is shown in Fig. 10.6 as a function of the total plastic strain $2\Sigma\delta\theta$, that is, the cyclic strains summed regardless of sign. For a wide range of amplitudes of cyclic plastic strain the peak torque, which is a measure of the flow stress, eventually reached a fairly constant value. Here, plastic strain occurs without causing any hardening. This nonhardening region was attained after a larger total strain, but a smaller number of reversals, the larger the amplitude. Similar results have been found with aluminium alloys, steels, nickel and titanium[30] and again with copper[31] and aluminium.[15] In the more conventional type of test, in which the peak alternating stress is kept constant, the proof stress has been found to rise to a value roughly equal to the peak fatigue stress.[32, 33, 34, 35] As an example, Fig. 10.7 shows the influence on the

[29] W. A. Wood and R. A. Segall, *P.R.S.*, 1957, **A.242**, 180.
[30] L. F. Coffin and J. F. Tavernelli, *T.A.I.M.E.*, 1959, **215**, 794.
[31] M. L. Ebner and W. A. Backofen, *T.A.I.M.E.*, 1959, **215**, 510.
[32] N. Polakowski and A. Polchoudhuri, *A.S.T.M.*, 1954, **54**, 701.
[33] E. P. Bullen, A. K. Head, and W. A. Wood, *P.R.S.*, 1953, **A.216**, 332.
[34] T. Broom and R. K. Ham, *P.R.S.*, 1957, **A.242**, 166.
[35] H. Conrad, *T.A.I.M.E.*, 1959, **215**, 58.

stress-strain curve of nickel of cyclic stressing. Evidently, after many cycles of cyclic stressing the new proof stress is somewhere in the region of the peak cyclic stress which was applied. The same tendency for the flow stress to approach the cyclic stress has also been observed with single crystals.[35] In creep tests on magnesium single crystals at room temperature in which the direction of the stress was periodically reversed, the creep rate increased transiently on each reversal. However, after a number of reversals the increase was smaller than on the first reversal. It might be remarked here that since the stresses applied in fatigue are always well below the UTS, the degree of cold work produced in fatigue as measured by increase in flow stress or hardness will generally be considerably less than that which can be produced in static straining.

The hysteresis in Fig. 10.5, the nonhardening region in Fig. 10.6, and

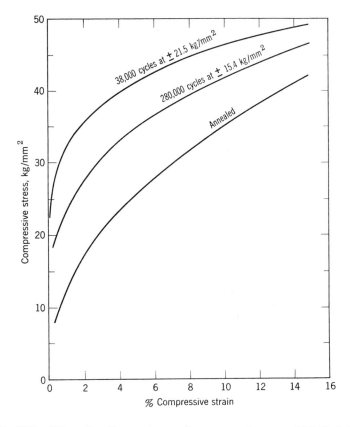

Fig. 10.7. Effect of cyclic stressing on the stress-strain curve of Ni (Ref. 32).

the rough equivalence of proof stress and cyclic stress in Fig. 10.7 are all different aspects of the same thing, namely, the small cyclic plastic strain occurring during fatigue. It is worth dwelling on the fact that this normally decreases from a relatively large amount at the beginning to a relatively small amount later on in order to draw attention to a feature of the strain-hardened state produced by alternating stress. This feature is that the state so produced therefore exhibits a smaller Bauschinger effect and is consequently more symmetrical than the strain-hardened state produced by a unidirectional stress, which implies that dislocations are anchored in such a way that they resist movement in opposite directions with nearly equal strength. This point is referred to again in section 10.7.

In mild steel, this typical behaviour of the cyclic plastic strain is complicated by the presence of the sharp yield point. The fatigue limit of mild steel is normally less than the lower yield stress[20, 26, 36]; for example, 14 kg/mm^2 in a steel with a lys of 22 kg/mm^2 [37] and 18 kg/mm^2 in a steel with a lys of 25 kg/mm^2.[38] Mild steel behaves under cyclic stress as though the dislocations are gradually unlocked. In fact, in iron and steel a simple tensile stress less than the yield stress (down to half the yield stress) and which therefore produces no measurable permanent set when applied once may produce measurable elongation when applied many times.[36] The ratio of fatigue limit to yield stress is in fact similar to the ratio at which dislocations have been observed first to move in silicon iron (section 4.1). Presumably a few dislocations are set in motion and gradually liberate others, so that quite large total slip movements take place. In iron and steel the plastic strain increases from a small value at first to the value characterising the constant region; a typical value near the fatigue limit is 0.1% per half cycle. A result is that the sharp yield behaviour tends to be removed by fatigue stressing. Even though the fatigue limit of mild steel is less than the lys, the ratio of fatigue limit/UTS is greater for mild steel (about $\frac{1}{2}$) than for most other metals because the ratio of lys/UTS is so high.

If material which has been strain hardened by unidirectional strain is subjected to fatigue by applying a cyclic stress whose peak value is less than the flow stress of the hardened state, the flow stress and hardness fall somewhat and the ductility increases.[32, 39] Cyclic stressing can thus induce some mechanical recovery. Figure 10.8, showing some stress-strain

[36] L. Bairstow, *Phil. Trans. Roy. Soc. London*, 1910, **A.210**.

[37] J. A. Ewing and J. W. C. Humfrey, *Phil. Trans. Roy. Soc. London*, 1903, **A.200**, 241.

[38] H. R. Tipler and P. G. Forrest, International Conference on Fatigue of Metals, 1956, *Inst. Mech. Engrs. London*, p. 510.

[39] N. H. Polakowski, *A.S.T.M.*, 1952, **52**, 1086.

tests on nickel before and after fatiguing, illustrates this. Here the flow stress does not fall as low as the peak fatigue stress. This seems to be typical and demonstrates that after many cycles the recovery effect of fatigue becomes very slow. Nevertheless this recovery effect helps to explain why in fatigue plastic strain can take place without any hardening. The amounts of plastic strain that do occur in fatigue, for example, 0.1% per cycle, are large enough to make it fairly certain that hardening would occur unless there were simultaneous recovery. In this respect fatigue is like steady-state creep.

There are other differences between the fatigue and statically hardened states besides the smaller Bauschinger effect and more symmetrical hardening. One is that fatigue hardening is more temperature sensitive than static work hardening. That is to say, if specimens of copper or aluminium are strained at one temperature and the flow stress is then determined over a range of temperatures, it will vary more if the specimen was strained by cyclic stress than if it was strained by unidirectional

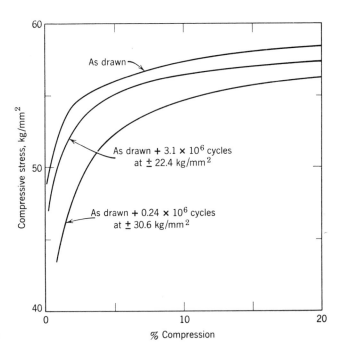

Fig. 10.8. Softening of cold-drawn Ni during fatigue as shown by stress-strain curves (Ref. 32).

stress.[34, 40]   The differences are small, but much larger than experimental error, and suggest that some of the hardening is due to point defects as these could enhance the temperature sensitivity of the flow stress by creating numerous obstacles of atomic size such as platelets of point defects, or perhaps by collecting on dislocations and creating numerous jogs.   There is other evidence that many point defects are produced during fatiguing (section 10.6).   Another feature of fatigue hardening is that a higher temperature is needed to anneal it out as compared with static work hardening.   In some experiments part of this difference seems simply due to the fact that the amount of strain hardening possible in fatigue is considerably less than that possible in static deformation since the fatigue strength is much less than the UTS.   However, there also seems to be a real difference[41]; for example, copper cold worked by a single tensile strain to a Vickers hardness of 67 recrystallised at 400°C, but when the copper was cold worked in fatigue ($\pm 10^5$ cycles at $10\frac{1}{2}$ kg/ mm² in push-pull) to a hardness of 66 it did not recrystallise until heated to 650°C.[42]   A curious behaviour was found in the creep tests on mag-nesium single crystals referred to earlier.[35]   Although some recovery creep occurred when the stress was first applied, as is normal for mag-nesium single crystals at room temperature, the creep curve on each subsequent reversal was of the logarithmic form (section 9.2), indicating that no thermal recovery was then taking place.

Despite these differences between the fatigue and statically strained states, there is no reason for disbelieving that the essential nature of strain hardening in the two states is the same.   One piece of evidence that this is so is that the electron microscope reveals similar structures in the two states (in aluminium), except that many small loops are seen after fatigue, suggesting that many point defects are generated during fatigue deforma-tion[43, 44]; Fig. 10.9 shows an example.   Another piece of evidence for similar hardening mechanisms is that multiple slip plays the same im-portant role in causing rapid hardening during cyclic straining as it does during unidirectional straining, for in push-pull tests on copper single crystals a similar dependence of rate of strain hardening on orientation has been observed as is found in unidirectional tests.[45]   For example, when a crystal was oriented for slip on a single plane the flow stress rose only a quarter to half as much after a number of cycles of a given strain as when oriented for slip on more than one plane.

[40] R. K. Ham, Symposium on Point Defects in Metals and Alloys, *Inst. Metals*, 1957.
[41] A. Siede and A. G. Metcalfe, *T.A.I.M.E.*, 1959, **215**, 947.
[42] W. A. Wood, *Phil. Mag.*, 1955, **46**, 1028.
[43] R. L. Segall and P. G. Patridge, *Phil Mag.*, 1959, **4**, 912.
[44] R. N. Wilson and P. J. E. Forsyth, *J.I.M.*, 1958–9, **87**, 336.
[45] M. S. Paterson, *Acta Met.*, 1955, **3**, 491.

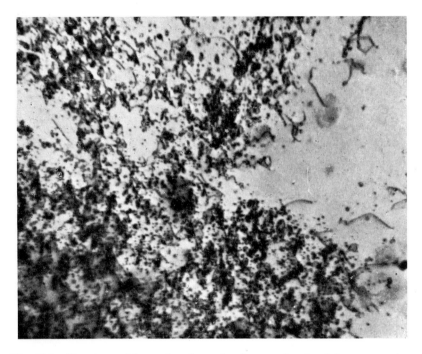

Fig. 10.9. Numerous defects, thought to be clusters of point defects, seen after fatigue. Transmission electron micrograph of aluminium after 3×10^5 cycles. $\times 18,000$. (P. J. E. Forsyth)

10.5 Development of Slip Bands and Grain Boundaries into Cracks

(*a*) *Slip.* Fatigue failure nearly always starts at the surface at cracks closely associated with slip bands (section 10.5*c*). This connection has given a special interest to studies of slip.

Although clear slip bands are not seen for many cycles in fatigue tests at low stress, there must be general fine slip to account for the general hardening. As one example of this situation, in annealed OFHC copper[18] slip bands were first seen after 10^3 cycles under conditions such that fracture occurred after 2×10^6 cycles; the fatigue stress was ± 8 kg/mm^2 and the UTS would have been about 20 kg/mm^2. After 10^3 cycles the flow stress had risen to about 8 kg/mm^2—it rose no more throughout the test—denoting fine slip that caused general hardening. Fine general slip has in fact been detected in fatigued copper.[34, 46] Eventually, easily visible slip bands begin to appear. They appear sooner the higher the

[46] D. Hull, *J.I.M.*, 1957–8, **86**, 425.

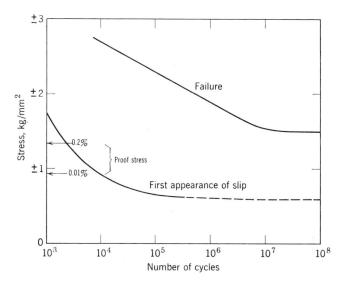

Fig. 10.10. *S–N* curves for fatigue failure and for the first appearance of slip. Al fatigued in bending. Static properties were UTS 5.1 kg/mm², *E*% 63.7% (Ref. 47).

stress as is illustrated in Fig. 10.10 in which, besides the usual *S/N* curve, a curve is drawn showing the *S/N* relation for the first appearance of slip. Slip bands eventually appear in iron even though the cyclic stress is less than the lys, as is to be expected from the plastic strain that occurs; for example, slip bands have been seen after 3×10^3 cycles at a cyclic stress of ± 10.6 kg/mm² in iron whose fatigue limit was 14 kg/mm² and whose lys was 22 kg/mm².[37] In general, with continuing alternations the slip bands become much more prominent than the slip bands seen after uni-directional strain. They also broaden and, especially at high stresses, new ones appear, until some parts of the surface are nearly covered with slip bands. All or part of this behaviour has been seen in iron,[37] mild steel,[48] aluminium,[47] copper, and nickel.[49]

The prominence of the typical fatigue slip band is due to its being a steep and high ridge or deep valley, and is connected with the test condi-tions in a significant way[15] as follows. These typical bands develop during the nonhardening stage in Fig. 10.6, which associates them with

[47] M. Hempel and A. Schrader, *Arch. Eisenhüttenw.*, 1957, **28**, 547.
[48] M. Hempel, International Conference on Fatigue of Metals, *Inst. Mech. Engrs. London*, 1956, p. 543.
[49] N. Thompson, International Conference on Fatigue of Metals, *Inst. Mech. Engrs. London*, 1956, p. 526.

the near instability of this stage, that is to say, in this stage the influence that strain hardening has of inhibiting continued slip in the same place is lacking. Moreover, when a specimen is annealed in this stage a new strain-hardening stage follows the anneal. By giving sufficiently frequent anneals the type of continuously rising hardening curve shown schematically by the dashed line in Fig. 10.6 is therefore produced, and the typical fatigue slip bands no longer develop. As might be expected, these bands develop much faster in single crystals oriented so that slip is perpendicular to the surface than when slip is parallel to the surface.

Evidently, therefore, slip occurs generally during fatigue to harden the metal against both forward and backward stress, and after this condition is reached significant slip that does not exactly reverse on each half cycle can still occur in some places, gradually building up more and wider visible markings.

(b) *Intrusions, Extrusions, and Persistent Slip Bands.* Slip bands produced by static stress generally look in cross section like a staircase, but slip bands produced by fatigue sometimes at least are trough or ridge-shaped.[37] Eventually "intrusions" (a small surface slit) and "extrusions" (a tongue of extruded metal) may appear.[47, 50, 51] The taper sections through the surface of fatigued copper specimens in Fig. 10.11 and 10.12 show intrusions and extrusions. The suspicion has naturally arisen that intrusions represent the beginnings of cracks. The extrusions are the easier to detect and were observed first.[37, 52] Since intrusions and extrusions have been observed in copper fatigued at 4.2°K[46] they are presumably produced by a purely mechanical slip action, and several suggestions have been made to explain how they are produced (section 10.7). Extrusions (and presumably also intrusions) seem to be particularly prominent in alloys liable to overage in the slip bands during fatigue (section 10.6). This suggests that slip concentrates more and more in the softened regions so produced and eventually produces extrusions there.[53]

There are several other distinctive features of the prominent fatigue slip bands. One is that, to remove all sign of them by electrolytic polishing, a thickness of several tens of microns must be polished off, which is many times greater than would be necessary to remove slip bands produced by unidirectional stress. Such slip bands have been called "persistent slip bands." After being removed by polishing, persistent slip bands have

[50] P. J. E. Forsyth, *P.R.S.*, 1957, **A.242**, 198.
[51] A. H. Cottrell and D. Hull, *P.R.S.*, 1957, **A.242**, 211.
[52] P. J. E. Forsyth and C. A. Stubbington, *J.I.M.*, 1955, **83**, 395.
[53] P. J. E. Forsyth and C. A. Stubbington, *J.I.M.*, 1956–7, **85**, 339.

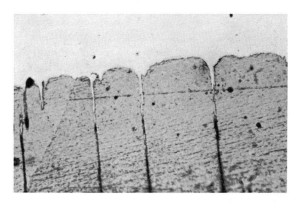

Fig. 10.11. Taper section through the surface of copper, which had been fatigued to one-tenth of its fatigue life, showing slip bands developing into notches (intrusions). × 20 × 1000. (W. A. Wood)

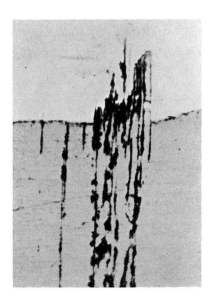

Fig. 10.12. As Fig. 10.11, but showing a slip band developing into a ridge (extrusion). × 20 × 1000. (W. A. Wood)

been found to re-etch as "striations,"[54, 55] indicating some derangement of the structure in the slip band. The dark markings below the notches in Fig. 10.11 and below the ridge in Fig. 10.12 are presumably such

[54] D. S. Kemsley, *Phil. Mag.*, 1957, **2**, 131.
[55] D. S. Kemsley, *Nature*, 1956, **178**, 653.

striations. Three experimental results show that persistent slip bands denote significant fatigue damage. (*a*) If an originally polished specimen is repeatedly polished, say after every 20% of the normal fatigue life, to remove any persistent slip bands that have developed, the fatigue life can be extended considerably,[56, 57] for example, it can be doubled.[58] (*b*) A tensile strain of the order of 5% opens up the larger persistent slip bands, perhaps only those larger than one grain, into cracks.[50, 56] (*c*) Annealing a copper specimen for 1 hour at 600°C after every 20% of the normal fatigue life neither removed the persistent slip bands nor increased the fatigue life,[56] although the anneal completely resoftened the material without, however, producing any grain growth or recrystallisation.

Other metallographic features have also been observed. Thus, at an early stage of fatigue electrolytic polishing has sometimes revealed, not persistent slip bands, but only rows of dots (in 67/33 brass, aluminium, copper, and mild steel)[59, 58] which appear to extend and join up on further fatiguing.[57] A detailed investigation[47] of these dots led to the conclusion that they were holes some microns deep, and that they were particularly prominent at points where one slip band intersected another. It is tempting to associate these etching effects and the striations underlying persistent slip bands with the dense patches of loops revealed by electron microscopy and illustrated in Fig. 10.9.

The suspicion inevitably arises that these various effects, namely intrusions, extrusions, persistent slip bands, striations, dots, and dense patches have something to do with the cracks which eventually form in the slip bands. Probably the intrusions and persistent slip bands are the same thing and both are incipient cracks. However, it is not known whether strong etching effects along slip bands only occur near the surface as might be expected if they are connected with fatigue damage.

(*c*) *Cracks.* Transcrystalline fatigue failure begins at the surface even when the stress is rather uniform as in well-aligned push-pull tests. Exceptions occur only if there is some obvious point of weakness away from the surface such as an inclusion in very hard steels.[60] As already pointed out in section 10.3 the interior must in fact have a much higher resistance to transcrystalline fatigue than the surface. It has further been known for a long time that transcrystalline fatigue failure starts with

[56] N. Thompson, N. Wadsworth and N. Lowat, *Phil. Mag.*, 1956, **1**, 113.

[57] G. C. Smith, *P.R.S.*, 1957, **A.242**, 189.

[58] N. J. Wadsworth, Conference on Dislocations and Mechanical Properties of Crystals, John Wiley and Sons, 1956, p. 490.

[59] P. A. Jacquet, International Conference on Fatigue of Metals, *Inst. Mech. Engrs. London*, 1956, p. 506.

[60] P. H. Frith, Special Report No. 50, *Iron and Steel Inst. London*, 1954.

cracks in the surface slip bands. This connection was first found in iron [37] and has since been discovered in other metals, for example mild steel,[48] aluminium,[47] copper,[49] and nickel[49, 61] and copper–nickel alloys.[61] When a crack has grown large it may be stepped, but most parts of it will still be parallel to slip bands.[56, 49, 59, 62] With the electron microscope fine black lines have been seen in slip bands in fatigued iron and are thought to be cracks.[48] Furthermore, there seems to be no recorded case in which transcrystalline fatigue failure has been proved to start with cracks elsewhere than in slip bands. It was mentioned earlier that applying a tensile strain usually of about 5% to a partially fatigued specimen produces definite cracks where there were slip bands (copper),[33] persistent slip bands (copper),[49, 56] and the same is true of extrusions (aluminium copper alloy).[63] All these facts, combined with micrographs such as Fig. 10.11, consistently stimulate the thought that the first stage of a fatigue crack is the formation of a notched slip band. It is supposed that the valleys mentioned in section 10.5a grow deeper and steeper and can be regarded successively as notches and then cracks.[15, 64]

The second stage is clearly the slow spread of the crack until it is of the order of a millimeter or so in size. The spreading cracks sometimes sidestep from one slip band to another nearby[48, 49] (copper, nickel, and mild steel) and may be bordered by short slip lines presumably provoked by the stress concentration at the tip of the spreading crack. Cracks may be held up for a considerable time at grain boundaries,[47] evidently encountering the same difficulty in crossing a grain boundary that slip does. With the aid of the change in direction at grain boundaries and the possibility of moving from one slip band to another a crack can adjust its average direction to become, for instance, normal to the tensile stress component as it is observed to be in push-pull tests. On a fractured surface the first and second stages occupy so little space that both together are seen as the origin of fracture.

A fatigue crack of engineering dimensions reduces the fatigue strength by a factor which depends on the cube root of the length of the crack[65] and is far smaller than the stress concentration at the crack tip as calculated by elastic theory, which proves that stress concentrations have limited effectiveness in spreading a fatigue crack when they are very localised. This explains the "nonpropagating" cracks which may start at

[61] C. A. Stubbington and P. J. E. Forsyth, *J.I.M.*, 1957–8, **86**, 90.
[62] H. A. Lipsitt and G. T. Horne, International Conference on Fatigue of Metals, *Inst. Mech. Engrs. London*, 1956, p. 513.
[63] P. J. E. Forsyth, *J.I.M.*, 1951–2, **80**, 181.
[64] W. A. Wood, *Phil. Mag.*, 1958, **3**, 692.
[65] N. E. Frost, *Proc. Inst. Mech. Engrs. London*, 1959, **173**, 811.

notches[16, 66, 67] under the influence of the stress concentration in the vicinity of the notch but fail to extend outside the region of influence of the notch.

Finally stage 3 is reached. The crack is now large enough for the stress at its tip on each tensile cycle to spread it by a much faster and presumably different mechanism. The size the crack has to be before spreading very rapidly varies considerably from metal to metal. This is an important factor in practice since the larger the critical size the more chance there is of detecting the crack by routine inspection before failure. From section 7.14 it might be expected that the critical size is larger the lower the ratio of proof stress to UTS. This seems to be borne out by experience with aluminium alloys.

Experiments have been made to determine how soon the first crack forms; this point is significant since at an earlier stage the original properties can be restored by heat treatment. Early experiments on steel showed that cracks large enough to be counted as well in the second stage may be present at about half the fatigue life.[68] In more recent work,[69] 70/30 brass annealed at 344°C was tested in a cantilever machine at 23.5 kg/mm². The mean life of 1.1×10^6 cycles was not significantly different from that of specimens again annealed at 344°C every 25 or 50% of this lifetime, indicating that cracks formed in the first 25% of the fatigue life. In work on copper,[48, 33] a 5% tensile strain given to specimens that had been fatigued to 50% of the life caused some slip bands to open up into cracks, proving therefore that the cohesion across these had at least been greatly reduced by the preceding fatigue. An aluminium alloy[70] in the solution treated and aged condition was subjected to 70% of its fatigue life, re-solution treated and aged, and subjected to a further 70%. As there were then no easily visible cracks, it was concluded that after the first 70% of the fatigue life the specimen had contained no cracks at all. As far as these experiments go, it appears that, depending on the conditions, cracks, or at least some kind of damage, may form at varying points in the fatigue life; in particular, they may be present for a large part of the life.

(d) *Grain-Boundary Effects.* Intergranular fractures occur in fatigue under the sort of conditions where they might be expected, for example, at relatively high temperature, and they have also been observed in an

[66] F. Bacon, *Engineering*, 1931, **131**, 280 and 341.

[67] N. F. Frost and C. E. Phillips, International Conference on Fatigue of Metals, *Inst. Mech. Engrs. London*, 1956, p. 520.

[68] F. Rogers, 1905, quoted in ref. 66.

[69] G. M. Sinclair and T. J. Dolan, *Proc. U.S. 1st Nat. Congress of Applied Mech.*, 1953, p. 647.

[70] R. F. Hanstock, *J.I.M.*, 1954–5, **83**, 11.

alloy (of phosphorus in iron) which showed marked grain-boundary brittleness under static stress.[38] Intergranular fracture in fatigue at high temperature takes place by the development of grain-boundary cavities like those which characterise intergranular creep fracture[24] and presumably the mechanism is very similar. However, the following observations suggest that there may also be special features about intergranular fracture in fatigue distinguishing it from intergranular fracture under static stress.

1. The temperature at which intergranular fracture predominates in fatigue may be much higher than that at which it predominates under unidirectional stress, as with Nimonic 90 alloy, in which it occurs at about 700°C in creep but at about 900°C in fatigue; this is typical of many metals and is probably the normal difference between creep and fatigue occasioned by the faster strain rates customary in fatigue. It may, however, be the same, as with lead in which it occurs at room temperature in fatigue[71] as well as in creep, or much lower, as with an Al–Zn–Mg alloy suitably heat treated[72] in which it occurs at room temperature in fatigue but would not be expected at so low a temperature in creep. The last result was probably due to overageing near grain boundaries during fatigue leading to a concentration of deformation there.

2. Whereas transcrystalline fatigue failure always starts with cracks on the surface, in Nimonic 90 and copper at least, intercrystalline fatigue cracks start throughout the volume.

Intergranular fatigue failure may be heralded by persistent grain boundaries, which have been seen in aluminium after electropolishing and, like persistent slip bands, open up into cracks under a tensile stress.[57]

10.6 Apparent Annealing Effects of Fatigue

Besides producing mechanical recovery (section 10.4), there are several other ways in which alternating stress acts like a partial anneal. One effect is that precipitation and diffusion processes are accelerated. Thus, in a copper–silicon alloy unusually fast precipitation has been observed during fatigue,[73] and cyclic stress applied to cold worked steel has also been found to provoke precipitation of cementite, although there was no precipitation when the cyclic stress was applied in the annealed state and was followed by static cold work.[74, 75] Ageing of an Al–4% Cu alloy is

[71] R. Cazaud, *Metaux corrosion*, 1952, **27**, 475.
[72] C. A. Stubbington and P. J. E. Forsyth, R.A.E. Tech. Note No. Met. 258.
[73] J. Holden, N.P.L. Report H.T. 75/54, 1954.
[74] H. R. Sander and M. Hempel, *Arch. Eisenhüttenw.*, 1952, **23**, 383.
[75] M. Hempel and E. Houdremont, *Stahl. u Eisen*, 1953, **73**, 1503.

particularly rapid along the heavy slip bands which develop during fatigue at 250°C.[53] A layer of aluminium clad to an aluminium alloy has been found to diffuse into the specimen along grain boundaries and also into the grains, apparently along heavy slip bands, during room temperature fatigue.[50] Structural changes in the matrix similar to those which would take place on heating also occur during cyclic stressing. X-ray reflections which have been broadened by cold work become sharper (iron and steel)[74, 75, 76] and even spotty (nickel)[29]; polygonisation[77, 63] and migration of grain boundaries[78, 53] take place in aluminium at room temperature to an extent that would occur during static deformation only at elevated temperature; the damping behaviour of age-hardening aluminium alloys has been found to be altered by fatigue in just the way that a tempering treatment altered it[70]; and the energy stored in the tensile part of a cycle is partly relieved during the compression cycle.[79, 80]

The steady temperature rise that occurs during fatigue is certainly insufficient to produce these effects, and calculation[81] suggests that the heat flashes along slip planes when they are active last too short a time to have much influence. A more likely explanation is that many vacancies are generated during fatigue and assist recovery and diffusion processes. In static straining the percentage concentration of vacancies produced seems to be about $10^{-4}E$, where E is the percentage elongation (section 2.3). If the same mechanism takes place during fatigue very large numbers will be produced; for instance, if the plastic strain per half cycle is 0.01%, in 10^7 cycles the total strain is 2×10^5%, corresponding to a total vacancy concentration produced during the test of 20%. Most of these will disappear in various ways during fatigue, causing diffusion and annealing effects in doing so.

There are several indications that numerous vacancies are produced in fatigue. Of these, the relatively high temperature sensitivity of the yield stress of fatigue-hardened metals and the large number of dislocation loops have already been mentioned as evidence for an unusually large vacancy concentration. Further evidence is that in experiments on copper at liquid helium temperature fatigue at a given stress introduced ten times as much increase in electrical resistance as the same stress applied unidirectionally.[82] A test for the vacancy theory is to carry out the fatigue

[76] H. Möller and M. Hempel, Arch. Eisenhüttenw., 1954, 25, 39.

[77] P. J. E. Forsyth and C. A. Stubbington, J.I.M., 1954–5, 83, 173.

[78] P. J. E. Forsyth, J.I.M., 1953–4, 82, 449.

[79] M. M. Destyarev, Teknicheskoi Fiziki, 1950, 20, 440.

[80] I. S. Iyer and P. Gordon, T.A.I.M.E., 1959, 215, 729.

[81] J. D. Eshelby and P. L. Pratt, Acta Met., 1956, 4, 560.

[82] H. M. Rosenberg, Symposium on Point Defects in Metals, Inst. Metals, 1958, p. 206.

experiment at a temperature where vacancies are immobile. In fatigue experiments at $-183°C$, which should meet this condition, overageing of aluminium alloys[83, 84] and softening of cold worked copper[34] are absent. Moreover, the flow stress of fatigue-hardened copper has been found to be reduced by annealing at $100°C$,[25] which is probably a high enough temperature for vacancies to migrate to sinks, but too low for dislocations to anneal out. On the other hand, however, measurements of the energy released on heating fatigue-hardened copper and nickel do not show clear evidence of vacancy elimination.[85]

10.7 Theory of Fatigue

The starting point for a discussion of the mechanism of fatigue is that fatigue cracks are started by slip. To summarise, the strongest evidence for this view is the observation that transcrystalline fatigue failure starts with cracks that form in or parallel to slip bands. Confirmatory evidence is that when at high temperature the grain boundaries slide easily fatigue failure starts there. Moreover, it has been found[86] that copper whiskers do not fail in fatigue even at very high stresses (e.g., equivalent to an elastic strain of $\pm 3\%$) as long as the whisker has not yielded plastically, that is, as long as it has not been taken past point A in Fig. 4.12. But after yielding plastically it fails easily in the yielded zone, where most of the imposed strain is then being accommodated by plastic deformation. That fatigue failure is not primarily due to developing a large internal stress is shown by the fact that fatigue failure occurs at stresses well below the static breaking stress and by the observation that cracks start on those slip bands on which there is the biggest range of stress, not those on which there is the highest peak stress.

One simple explanation of crack formation that suggests itself is that slip shifts from plane to plane and gradually builds up a notch. There is enough slip during fatigue to produce a deep crack in this way.[87] For instance, in a test on copper lasting 10^6 cycles 0.05% strain may take place in each cycle. With a grain size of 0.01 mm this means a slip of 5×10^{-7} cm per grain. If confined to one band, a notch $\frac{1}{2}$ cm deep could theoretically be produced. The incipient cracks shown in Fig. 10.11 could have been formed in this way.

[83] T. Broom, J. A. Mazza, and V. N. Whittaker, *J.I.M.*, 1957–8, **86**, 17.

[84] T. Broom, J. H. Molineux, and V. N. Whittaker, *J.I.M.*, 1955–6, **84**, 357.

[85] L. M. Clarebrough, M. E. Hargreaves, and G. W. West, *P.R.S.*, 1957, **A.242**, 160.

[86] E. Eisner, *Nature*, 1960, **188**, 1183.

[87] W. A. Wood, International Conference on Fatigue of Metals, *Inst. Mech. Engrs. London*, 1956, p. 531.

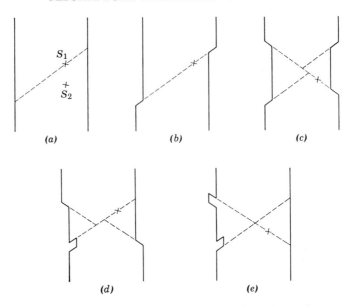

Fig. 10.13.   Sequence of slip movements producing an intrusion and an extrusion.

Dislocation theory gives three ways in which slip could shift from plane to plane to produce a notch (or an extrusion). One of these[51] is provided by the sequence of intersecting slip movements depicted in Fig. 10.13. The source S_1 operates before S_2 on each cycle because the resolved shear stress on its slip plane is supposed to be greater. If successive cycles exactly repeated the movements depicted, the notch and ridge would get deeper but not wider. Another mechanism[88] is that edge dislocations come opposite each other on nearby planes and combine to make the cavity $ABCDA'B'C'D'$ in Fig. 10.14, the edge dislocations having Burgers vectors parallel to AD. A screw dislocation PQ with the same Burgers vector moving round the cavity at its lower end P will then extrude the slab $CDD'C'EFF'E'$. This is the initial fatigue crack. The function of the initial cavity $ABCDA'B'C'D'$ is to keep the screw dislocation moving in a fixed path under an alternating stress suitably inclined to DF. The third mechanism is one suggested originally in connection with fracture under static stress.[89] A screw dislocation traverses the slip plane WXZ (Fig. 10.15) in the direction XW and produces a step in it at Y. Slip on the plane in the direction ZX then produces a cavity opening on the front face shown at $ABCD$. Such a cavity would only close up on reversing the stress if the slip movements exactly reversed.

[88] N. F. Mott, *Acta Met.*, 1958, **6**, 195.
[89] J. Fisher, *Acta Met.*, 1955, **3**, 109.

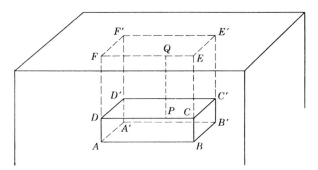

Fig. 10.14. Scheme for producing an extrusion.

The first two mechanisms clearly prefer a free surface and therefore fit the observation that transcrystalline fatigue failure has a very strong preference for starting at a free surface. The third mechanism would only prefer the surface if atmospheric contamination helped to keep the crack open. As this does not seem to be a necessary condition for fatigue failure to occur it is likely that the third mechanism is not generally important for transcrystalline fatigue failure. But at high temperature when fracture is intercrystalline cracks start at grain boundaries throughout the volume. Probably the third mechanism is then the main one, the "slip plane" XX' being a grain boundary and the step at Y being already

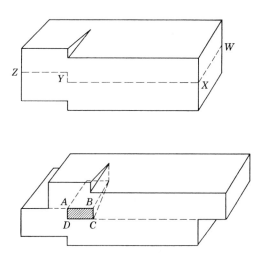

Fig. 10.15. Scheme for producing an intrusion.

present or produced by slip.   It is then the same mechanism as the one proposed for grain-boundary cavitation in creep (section 9.10).

It is worth noting that the mechanisms described require some slip to occur on other planes besides the main one.   We would then expect a marked difference between the fatigue behaviour of single crystals oriented for single slip and others oriented for multiple slip.   If cracks are produced efficiently only when multiple slip occurs, a single crystal oriented for multiple slip should fracture in fatigue with less total plastic strain (i.e., summed regardless of sign) than one oriented for single slip.   The former may stand a higher *stress*, because multiple slip will produce strain hardening, but what matters here is the amount of plastic *strain*—how much to-and-fro slip is needed to produce a crack.   Conclusive experiments of this kind have not yet been done, although a possible connection between fatigue failure and multiple slip has been observed[62] in experiments on iron single crystals, for in a range of alternating stress in which fatigue failure occurred the amount of observable cross slip increased rapidly with stress.

The theory of fatigue damage has not yet advanced beyond suggesting these mechanisms of starting cracks.   Thus the place of persistent slip bands, striations, holes and dense patches in the theory is not certain. Persistent slip bands for example might be caused by entraining environmental contamination along the rubbing slip planes or might be due to high defect concentrations, but beyond this it does not seem useful to speculate.   Likewise it is not clear how notches or intrusions spread in what in section 10.5c was called stage 2.   The simplest idea is that they spread by the same mechanism by which they form, but cracks should also be able to spread simply by dislocations running into positions just beneath them under the influence of the stress at the tip of the crack as indicated in Fig. 7.12.   Since the new surface energy is less than the energy of the disappearing dislocations, this process is energetically favourable.   Although atmospheric contamination is not essential to fatigue failure it might well play a part, for example, by preventing a crack that has once been opened from closing.   The questions which some of these uncertainties give rise to might be answered by studies of the inward growth of cracks.

Another problem is the nature of the fatigue-hardened state, which is important in connection with fatigue damage since it determines how much plastic deformation occurs.   Two respects in which fatigue hardening differs from static hardening are that the density of point defects produced is probably higher and that the Bauschinger effect is smaller, that is, the hardening is more symmetrical.   The simplest explanation of this symmetry is that dislocations get anchored, not on the slopes of the internal stress field, but in the valleys, for the reason that they can move preferentially in one direction or the other until they do so. Although to judge by the inactivity for long periods of much of a polished surface most of the specimen perhaps settles down to a fairly quiescent state, several observations imply that there is local slip activity: namely, the production of fatigue damage itself, the generation of new slip bands, and the cyclic plastic deformation, which is considerable in terms of dislocation movement. If the heterogeneities in the fatigue-hardened state which lead to this occasional slip could be removed, fatigue failure would be avoided. That is to say, if strain hardening in fatigue could be made more uniformly efficient so that all slip were stopped everywhere, failure by fatigue would cease to be a problem of practical importance. According to the explanation of coaxing in section 10.2 an action having this effect takes place in mild steel, for according to this explanation the reason why mild steel has such a high fatigue strength in relation to its UTS is because the weak spots are sealed by strain ageing.

10.8 Structure Required for Fatigue Resistance

The most important requirement for resistance to fatigue is a structure that stops slip and is resistant to overageing and particle growth. This is essentially the structure required for resistance to creep and explains the correlation[24] between the fatigue strength at elevated temperature and the creep strength of a number of alloys. Some differences may be expected, however, in the function asked of solute elements, because climb seems unimportant in fatigue (at room temperature). It might be useful, for example, if solutes could capture vacancies and effectively remove them from circulation. That strain ageing is valuable where dispersion hardening is weak is suggested by the high ratio of fatigue limit to UTS of steel and also of Al–Mg alloys.[84] Since fatigue is overwhelmingly a surface phenomenon the condition of the surface is particularly important. Clearly, soft surface layers should be avoided. What is wanted is a hard surface layer that resists slip. Besides dispersion hardening and strain ageing, a lower elastic modulus in the layer might be useful since, as the strain in the surface and core will be equal, the stress in the layer would be thereby reduced. Elastic anisotropy might be turned to advantage here, by forming a surface layer of randomly oriented grains on a core of grains oriented to have the direction of maximum modulus in the direction of the main stress. A pre-straining technique that leaves compressive stresses in the surface should undoubtedly be advantageous. It is often thought that some of the beneficial effect of shot peening arises from residual compressive stress, although the accompanying hardening makes the size of the contribution from compressive stress difficult to estimate.

Another requirement of a different sort is that there should be no paths of weak cohesion along which cracks can spread easily.   It has been suggested[84] that SAP is not particularly strong in fatigue, although otherwise apparently having a desirable structure, because the alumina-aluminium interfaces are weak.

11

Radiation Damage

11.1 Nature of Radiation Damage

Only a brief outline of this subject is necessary here. Several reviews have been published.[1, 2, 3, 4, 5, 6]

In a reactor the neutrons have energies spreading over a very wide range, since the fission neutrons with initial energies of about 1 to 15 Mev may be slowed down by the moderator until their energies are in the thermal range, say 0.05 ev. Neutrons with energies between the fission and thermal ranges are called epithermal neutrons. To measure the neutron energy spectrum in a reactor is difficult. It is usually accepted that in most reactors at any one moment a fraction of the order of half of all the neutrons have energies in the Mev range. The figure for flux density in a reactor usually given is that of the "slow," or thermal, neutrons, which is easier to measure than the fast neutron flux, and it is often accepted that the total flux density is very approximately twice the slow flux density.

[1] G. H. Kinchin and R. S. Pease, Reports on Progress in Physics, *Phys. Soc. London*, 1955, **18**, 1.

[2] F. Seitz and J. S. Koehler, *Solid State Physics*, Academic Press, New York, 1956, **2**, p. 307.

[3] A. H. Cottrell, Metallurgical Reviews, *Inst. Metals*, 1956, **1**, 479.

[4] G. J. Dienes and G. H. Vineyard, *Radiation Effects in Solids*, Interscience Publishers, New York, 1957.

[5] F. Seitz, *T.A.I.M.E.*, 1959, **215**, 354.

[6] H. Brooks, *J.A.P.*, 1959, **30**, 1118.

About 20 ev of energy is needed to displace a lattice atom in a metal such as copper, producing an interstitial atom and a vacancy. Consequently, when neutrons with energies in the Mev range enter a metal, most collisions they make displace a lattice atom with great vigour, even though the transference of energy is inefficient. The energy transferred may be estimated by simple mechanics, as for collisions between billiard balls, and the amount transferred depends on the atomic mass; for example, for copper about 3% and for aluminium about 7% of the neutron energy is transferred on average. The typical primary "knock-on," as it is called, produced by a 2 Mev neutron therefore has enough energy to displace about 1000 further atoms—the secondary knock-ons, as they are called. Each primary or secondary knock-on must leave a vacancy behind it. Whereas the primary knock-ons hit by a single neutron are widely spaced (some centimeters apart) because the neutrons, being uncharged, only make a collision when they hit an atom's nucleus, the primary knock-ons themselves make very frequent collisions since they move slowly enough for each other's electron shells to be effective barriers, and the secondaries are densely clustered. Thus, fast neutrons produce clusters of "damage," probably of the order of 100–1000 A in size, which at first are well separated from each other. However, in a power reactor with a fast neutron flux of 10^{13} neutrons/cm^2/sec* the damage clusters begin to overlap after about 1 month.

There are several uncertainties about the clusters of damage. In the first place experiment shows that the number of point defects produced is of the order of one-fifth of the number expected from theoretical calculation even when the irradiation is carried out at liquid helium temperature to avoid any annealing. At least part of this discrepancy is ascribed to the density of point defects being so high in some parts of a cluster that some secondary knock-ons finish next to vacant lattice sites, and fall into them. In the second place it has not been possible to fully explain the effects of neutron irradiation simply in terms of interstitials and vacancies. This has given rise to the proposal[7] that toward the centre of a damage cluster there must be a zone of lower density than average because atoms are knocked outward from the centre, and that this zone survives at temperatures greater than room temperature. Furthermore, some calculations indicate that toward the end of its path the primary knock-on makes collisions that knock out another lattice atom every atomic spacing of travel. It would be wrong to treat defects so closely spaced as separate;

* For comparison, background radiation from cosmic rays is about 1 quantum/ cm^2/sec, conventional X-ray sets give about 10^{10} quanta/sec, a 1 curie source gives about 10^9 particles/sec, and 6.3×10^{18} electrons/sec is a current of 1 amp.

[7] A. Seeger, 2nd Conference on Peaceful Uses of Atomic Energy, 1958, **6**, 250.

the disorder envisaged is more like local melting and has been called a "displacement spike." On the other hand, more recent calculations indicate that the damage is spread over a larger volume in certain close packed lattice directions which are effectively energy valleys than the earlier calculations suggested. Collisions of this nature are called "focussed collisions." Because of these uncertainties about the disorganisation in the damage clusters it is better to speak of radiation damage than simply of point defects, although it is fairly certain that much of the damage in metals does consist of vacancies and interstitials. Electron microscope studies are beginning to provide information, but so far only about the nature of the damage remaining at room or higher temperatures, which represents a substantial annealing treatment. With the electron microscope, dislocation loops and helical dislocations have been seen[8, 9, 10] similar to those in quenched specimens, where they have likewise been attributed to precipitation of point defects. There are also seen small dark spots of uncertain nature but which could simply be small loops. Since vacancies are much less mobile than interstitials near room temperature, the idea has arisen that the small spots are vacancy clusters and the larger loops represent interstitial platelets.

In a metal in a power reactor about 5% of the atoms are displaced each year, that is, after a neutron dose of about 10^{20} neutrons/cm². In a uranium fuel element, about 5% are displaced each day. It helps to put these large figures into perspective to compare them with movements due to ordinary thermal diffusion. In copper, for example, 5% of the atoms make one jump in a year at 180°C and in a day at 240°C. As this comparison suggests, much of the radiation damage anneals out quickly.

Annealing of radiation damage has been studied by observing the changes during annealing of various properties that are affected by irradiation—electric resistance, density, stored energy, and mechanical properties. The annealing process is more complicated than it would be if it consisted of simple recombination or precipitation of interstitials and vacancies, for it is more or less continuous from about 30°K (when the specimen is irradiated at less than 30°K) to room temperature and above. This is one of the reasons why neutron irradiation is believed to produce other defects besides simple interstitials and vacancies.

Besides the displacement collisions in which a primary knock-on displaces another atom and itself remains off a lattice site, replacement collisions are possible in which the moving atom takes the place of a lattice

[8] R. E. Smallman, K. H. Westmacott, and J. H. Coiley, *J.I.M.*, 1959–60, **88**, 127.
[9] D. Hull, Conference on Transmission Electron Microscopy, *Inst. Metals*, 1959, in discussion.
[10] J. Silcox and P. B. Hirsch, *Phil. Mag.*, 1959, **4**, 1356.

atom.   Less energy is required for a replacement than for a displacement collision since there is no increase in the number of displaced atoms, and there should therefore be more of them.   We might expect replacement collisions to be sometimes important in alloys, especially in alloys containing fine particles.   However, experiments have so far only been made with alloys which show ordering.   With these it is found that neutron irradiation partly disorders them if ordered and partly orders them if disordered.   The latter effect is simply an approach to equilibrium made possible by the increased atomic movement.

In a nuclear reactor the damage due to the fast (fission and epithermal) neutrons has attracted much attention, but another effect is potentially important where a long life is envisaged.   The slow neutrons, of thermal energies, are captured by all substances and gamma rays are emitted or transmutation may occur.   The capture cross section for thermal neutrons varies very widely from one atom to another, and for some atoms is many times larger than that for collision of a fast neutron, in which case the number of transmuted atoms will approach the number of displaced atoms even though each fast neutron displaces a hundred or more. Bearing in mind the critical behaviour of complex alloys with regard to conventional constitutional changes, the cumulative effect of transmutation over a 20-year service life will probably be sometimes important. U^{235} itself is of course the outstanding example of the consequence of capturing a slow neutron.   In some cases, as with U^{235}, the recoil energy accompanying gamma ray emission or transmutation is large enough to displace one or more atoms.

There is also in a reactor a flux of gamma radiation with energies up to about 15 Mev.   The number of atoms this displaces is orders of magnitude less than the number of atoms displaced by neutrons, but its heating effect, as a result of excitation of atoms, is substantial.

Pile irradiation thus produces complicated effects which are not easy to unravel.   It helps with the understanding of pile irradiation to study the simpler processes that take place during irradiation by, for example, a monochromatic beam of electrons, in which case only single knock-ons are produced.   Moreover, damage occurs faster than in a pile as a consequence of the fact that a beam of charged particles can interact with the electrons of the irradiated material.   They can thus interact with the atomic electron shells, which has the effect that the atomic cross section for collision with a charged particle is much larger than for collision with a neutron, and collisions are 10^6–10^7 times more frequent with charged particles.   Particle accelerators give beams of about the same flux density as the neutron density in a pile, and create damage about ten times faster than a pile.   However, interstitials and vacancies may not be the only kind of damage caused by irradiation with charged particles. Moving charged particles also give up energy to the valence electrons. In a metal this energy degenerates into heat, but in nonconducting materials the electrons are left in excited states, with sometimes big changes in properties.

11.2   Effect of Irradiation on Stress-Strain Behaviour*

Many studies have shown that neutron irradiation tends to introduce a ferrous type yield point, raises the yield stress markedly, and the UTS somewhat less markedly. Since the ratio of yield stress/UTS is thereby raised, the uniform $E\%$ is usually, and sometimes drastically, reduced, and early necking is more probable. The effects of 5×10^{19} neutrons/cm^2 on some metals is shown in the following Table 11.1.

Table 11.1

Effect of Irradiation with 5×10^{19} Neutrons/Cm^2 on Mechanical Properties[12]

		ys, kg/mm²		UTS, kg/mm²		$E\%$	
Metal	$T°C$	U	I	U	I	U	I
Mo	⎰ 20	66	70	70	73	24	22
annealed	⎱ 200	49.5	60	52	60	2.8	5.8
Ti cold	⎰ 20	56	62	59	65	10.4	8.3
worked	⎱ 200	26	32.5	37.5	39	9.4	8.4
Zr cold	⎰ 20	75	74.5	87	87	3.5	4.2
worked	⎱ 200	61	57.5	64	65	2.1	2.7
Cu	⎰ −195	7.5	30	32.5	37	41	22
annealed	⎨ 20	5.9	21.5	19	24	42	27
	⎩ 200	5.5	16.2	15.8	16.8	31	16

U = unirradiated   I = irradiated

Some examples of the effect of irradiation on stress-strain curves are shown in Figs. 11.1, 11.2 and 11.3. Saturation eventually occurs according to the results in Fig. 11.4 at fast neutron doses of about 10^{21} neutrons/cm^2. In neutron irradiation experiments it appears that any one set of results

---

* A detailed review of the effect of irradiation on mechanical properties is given in ref. 11.

[11] M. J. Makin, *Metallurgy and Fuels*, Pergamon Press, New York, 1959, **2**, 500.

[12] H. M. Finniston, *J.I.M.*, 1958–9, **87**, 360.

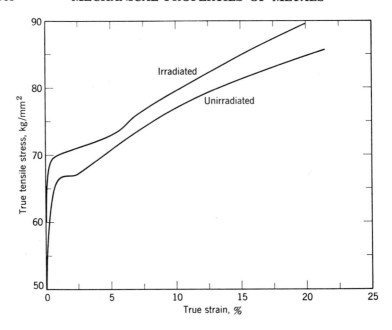

Fig. 11.1. Effect of neutron irradiation (5×10^{19} slow n/cm² at 100°C) on the stress-strain curve of Mo. Tensile tests at 20°C (Ref. 13).

can only be taken as an approximate guide for several reasons: the temperature of irradiation is difficult to control, the fast neutron dose is difficult to determine with good absolute accuracy, and there are indications that differences in impurity content may be important (see below). However, in spite of the uncertainty about the exact nature of radiation damage, the magnitude of the effects in Table 11.1 is of the order to be expected from a few per cent of point defects (section 2.3), which is the size of defect concentration to be expected from an irradiation dose of 5×10^{19} neutrons/cm².

Irradiation thus hardens a metal. This hardening behaves as though it can be divided into a friction force and a locking force on the dislocations. The existence of the friction force has been shown particularly clearly by making hardness impressions and observing the distance that slip lines (revealed with high sensitivity by etch pits) spread from them. After irradiation the slip lines are much shorter than before irradiation, evidently because some frictional resistance is introduced into the lattice by the irradiation. In an effort to obtain more detailed information,

[13] M. J. Makin and E. Gilles, *J.I.M.*, 1957–8, **86**, 108.

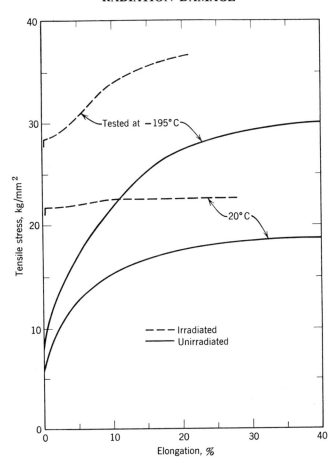

Fig. 11.2. Effect of neutron irradiation (5×10^{19} slow n/cm² at 100°C) on the stress-strain curve of Cu (Ref. 14).

grain size analyses of the yield stress have been made. Figure 11.5 shows the result of such an analysis for copper, which possessed a sharp yield after irradiation similar to that in mild steel (see Fig. 11.2). In Fig. 11.5 the slope of the lines, which is a measure of dislocation locking, and the intercept with the ordinate, which is the magnitude of the friction stress, are both increased by prolonging the irradiation. The curves also show that the irradiated yield stress was sensitive to temperature; when measured at a lower temperature a higher yield stress was found, and the increase

[14] M. J. Makin, *J.I.M.*, 1957–8, **86**, 449.

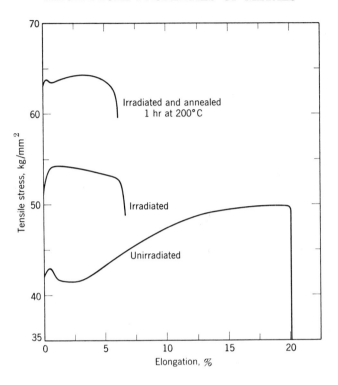

Fig. 11.3.   Effect of neutron irradiation (10^{20} fast n/cm^2 at 16°C) on the stress-strain curve of Cb.   Tensile tests at 20°C (Ref. 15).

was partly due to a greater frictional force and partly to an increased locking force.   A grain size analysis of irradiation hardening in a carbon steel shows differences from this behaviour.   Some results are shown in Fig. 11.6 and demonstrates that although the friction force is again increased the locking force in this case is not perceptibly affected, a result which might well be due to radiation locking being masked by the strong locking already present in this steel.   Figure 11.7 shows the effect on the friction force of this steel of varying the temperature (of test, not of irradiation) and neutron dose.   The friction force increases as (neutron dose)$^{1/3}$, but is nearly independent of temperature, being superimposed on an already present friction force that rises as the temperature falls.   The irradiation component of the friction force does vary slightly with temperature, however, although in absolute terms the variation is probably less than

[15] M. J. Makin and E. J. Minter, *Acta Met.*, 1959, **7**, 361.

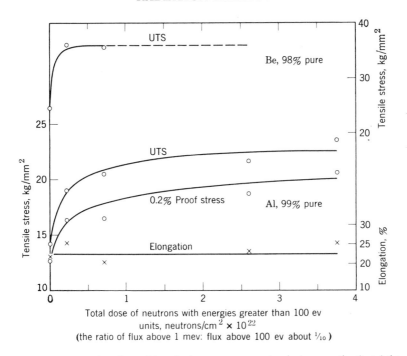

Fig. 11.4. Effect of prolonged irradiation on some mechanical properties (total time of irradiation 6 years) (Ref. 16).

in copper. The stress-strain curves of iron single crystals before and after irradiation in Fig. 11.8 also show that the yield stress is bigger after even a short irradiation than before, and also somewhat more temperature sensitive in the temperature region 0 to −100°C. Generalising from these results, the increased temperature sensitivity of the yield stress after irradiation, which has been shown up in several experiments besides those mentioned, can be due both to a temperature-sensitive friction component and to a temperature-sensitive locking component of irradiation hardening.

As might be expected, however, not all grain size analyses lead to such a neat interpretation. Figure 11.9 illustrates such an analysis on molybdenum before and after irradiation. The breakdown here of the interpretation recalls the qualifications mentioned in Chapter 6 about this method of analysis.

In Fig. 11.7 the friction stress is accurately proportional to (neutron dose)$^{1/3}$. In Fig. 11.10 the yield stress of copper again increases fairly closely as (neutron dose)$^{1/3}$, but the individual components do not. The

[16] M. H. Bartz, *2nd Conference on Peaceful Uses of Atomic Energy*, 1958, **5**, 466.

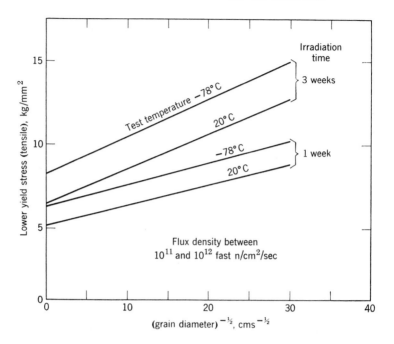

Fig. 11.5. Variation with grain size of the lower yield stress of irradiated Cu (spectrographic purity, 99.999%). Irradiation temperature 50°C (Ref. 17).

friction and locking forces were determined in this case not by a grain size analysis but by extrapolating the stress-strain curve back to zero strain as described in section 6.7h and illustrated in Fig. 11.11. In Fig. 11.10 the locking force decreases at high doses, possibly because some annealing effect is involved.

There are three other features of irradiation hardening.

1. It is less marked in cold worked than in annealed metals. For example, Fig. 11.12 shows that the irradiation hardening of nickel is diminished by prior cold work. In this respect, irradiation hardening differs from the usual course of alloy hardening.

2. It is affected by annealing. Figure 11.3, for example, shows that annealing at intermediate temperatures may increase the hardening—the temperature scale here, of course, depends on the metal. It is completely annealed out, however, at moderate temperatures, for example, 300–400°C for copper,[11] for which reason the direct effect of irradiation on

[17] M. A. Adams and P. R. B. Higgins, *Phil. Mag.*, 1959, **4**, 777.

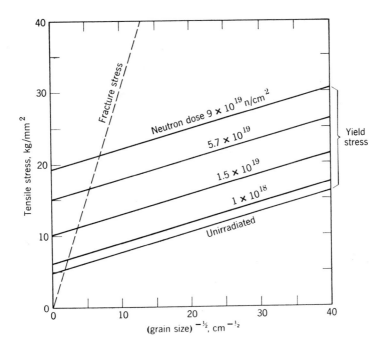

Fig. 11.6. Effect of neutron irradiation on yield stress and fracture stress of a 0.15% C steel. Tensile tests made at 20°C (Ref. 18).

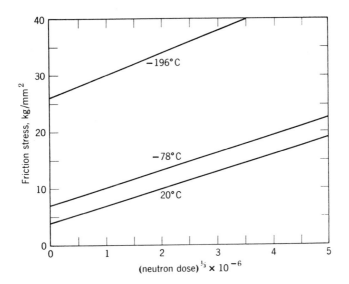

Fig. 11.7. Effect of neutron irradiation on the friction stress of a 0.15% C steel. Tensile tests at −196°C, −78°C, 20°C (Ref. 18).

[18] D. Hull and I. L. Mogford, *Phil. Mag.*, 1958, 3, 1213.

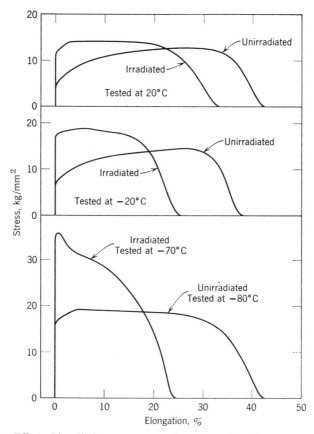

Fig. 11.8. Effect of irradiation on stress-strain curves of Fe single crystals tested at different temperatures.   Irradiation dose 8×10^{17} thermal n/cm^2 (Ref. 19).

mechanical properties is not likely to be important at high temperature. According to some experiments on copper[20] the locking force anneals out faster than the friction force.

3. In alloys there may be additional effects due, for example, to accelerated phase changes, particularly ageing.   Thus copper–beryllium alloys have been found to be hardened more than copper by irradiation, apparently because ageing was induced by the irradiation.[21]

A simple structural explanation of many of the features of irradiation hardening is suggested by the dislocation loops seen in irradiated metal

[19] B. Edmondson, *P.R.S..* 1961, **A264**, 176.

[20] M. J. Makin, A. T. Churchman, D. R. Harries, and R. E. Smallman, *2nd Conference on Peaceful Uses of Atomic Energy*, 1958, **5**, 446.

[21] G. T. Murray and W. E. Taylor, *Acta Met.*, 1954, **2**, 52.

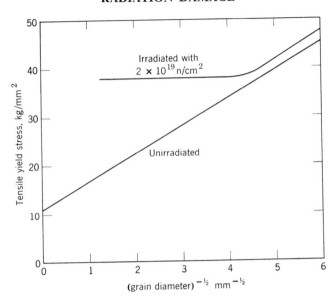

Fig. 11.9. Effect of neutron irradiation and grain size on yield stress of Mo (Ref. 22).

with the electron microscope. They give rise to a friction force because moving dislocations intersect them. Since the loops are small, the temperature-insensitive component of the force at each junction is smaller than usual, which enhances the relative importance of any temperature-sensitive components. Annealing at intermediate temperatures presumably enables more defects to collect into clusters, accounting for results such as those in Fig. 11.3. Perhaps in addition point defects collect on existing dislocations and make them joggy. However, whereas irradiation hardening in copper (temperature of irradiation $-196°C$) anneals out at $320°C$ with the activation energy of self diffusion, in aluminium (temperature of irradiation again $-196°C$) it anneals out at $-60°C$ with an activation energy about equal to that for vacancy migration.[23] Such differences suggest that this simple model is incomplete as it provides no reason for any such difference between copper and aluminium.

11.3 Effect of Irradiation on Fracture

As far as fracture is concerned a most important practical effect of irradiation is the rise in the transition temperature of metals susceptible to

[22] A. A. Johnson, *Phil. Mag.*, 1960, **5**, 413.
[23] A. W. M. Reynolds, W. Augustyniak, M. McKeown, and D. B. Rosenblatt, *Phys. Rev.*, 1955, **98**, 418.

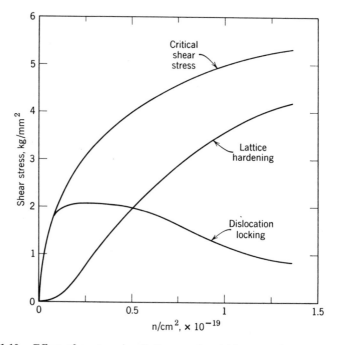

Fig. 11.10. Effect of neutron irradiation on the yield stress of Cu single crystals (Ref. 20).

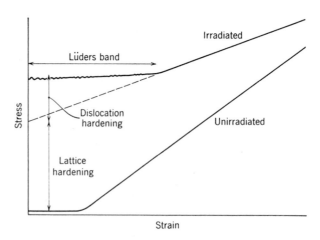

Fig. 11.11. Effect of irradiation on the stress-strain curve of a Cu single crystal (diagrammatic) (Ref. 20).

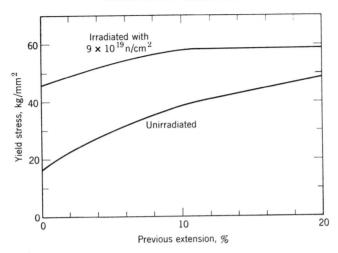

Fig. 11.12. Effect of irradiation on the yield stress of cold-worked Ni. Yield stress measured at 20°C (Ref. 11).

cold brittleness. Besides iron and steel, this effect has been observed in molybdenum and tungsten.[13] As an example of the magnitude of the effect, in some experiments[24] on mild steel having initially a transition temperature of $-60°C$ (using smaller than standard Charpy specimens), 4.4×10^{19} fast neutrons/cm^2 raised the transition temperature to 25°C and 1.2×10^{20} fast neutrons/cm^2 raised it to 60°C. This important effect has really already been discussed in section 11.2 since it appears to be due to the rise in yield stress produced by irradiation.[18] In Fig. 11.6 the fracture stress line is shown dashed and does not appear to be affected by irradiation. It cannot, of course, be determined over the whole grain size range directly from experiment. However, the effect of irradiation on the transition temperature could be here fully accounted for by the observed change in yield stress, supposing that the fracture stress line itself was unaffected by irradiation. With carbon steel the rise in transition temperature has been found to be larger for a given irradiation dose when the irradiation is made at 130°C than when made at 50°C,[12] from which it seems that some annealing, that is, migration or agglomeration etc., of the radiation damage occurs at temperatures in the neighbourhood of room temperature.

Another embrittling effect,[25] particularly important in uranium but

[24] L. P. Trudeau, *2nd Conference on Peaceful Uses of Atomic Energy*, 1958, **5**, 481.
[25] R. S. Barnes and nine others, *2nd Conference on Peaceful Uses of Atomic Energy*, 1958, **5**, 543.

which also occurs in some other materials, is the development of internal cracks as a result of the stresses set up by "growth" (section 11.4) and the accumulation of fission products, particularly the gaseous ones. If a crack is produced by the growth stresses, at high enough temperature the gas atoms can diffuse into it and set up large pressures which extend the crack. Boron, in which helium is produced by capture of slow neutrons, also behaves in this way and was found in one experiment to break into pieces during irradiation.[26]

Apart from these two embrittling actions no other special effect of irradiation on fracture process has yet been reported. As already mentioned, elongation is usually reduced by irradiation, but this seems only to be the expected result of the effect on the yield stress and strain hardening.

11.4   Transmutation and Other Effects of Irradiation

(a) Swelling. The "swelling" of uranium is a phenomenon in which transmutation plays an important part.[25] The gases xenon and krypton are produced during fission and the uranium becomes heavily supersaturated with them. As is usual with supersaturated solid solutions, at low temperatures where diffusion is restricted fine, closely spaced precipitates form, which in this case are tiny bubbles of gas. From the point of view of avoiding swelling this is a fortunate situation since the surface tension force of small bubbles can withstand a large gas pressure; the pressure needed to make a bubble of radius r expand is $2\gamma/r$ (γ is the surface energy of the metal) which is about 400 atm when r is 10^{-5} cm. However, on heating, coalescence of the "precipitate" occurs in the way customary for precipitates. The new feature with a gaseous precipitate is that at a certain bubble size the surface tension force is no longer able to restrain the gas pressure, which then enlarges the bubble against the creep strength of the metal and causes some swelling. When irradiation is itself carried out at high enough temperature the krypton and xenon apparently migrate to sites of easy nucleation; this again is the normal behaviour of a supersaturated solution. For gases, particularly good sites are existing cracks, and possibly inclusion interfaces. Cracks may have already been produced by the stress caused by radiation growth (section 11.4c), in which case the two effects augment each other as mentioned in section 11.3. In uranium, irradiation also produces, besides the gas atoms, solid fission products which have about twice the volume of the original uranium. This causes an expansion which however is relatively unimportant.

[26] R. S. Barnes and G. W. Greenwood, 2nd Conference on Peaceful Uses of Atomic Energy, 1958, 5, 481.

Transmutation resulting in gas being produced is caused also in lithium, boron, and magnesium by slow neutrons and in beryllium by fast neutrons. Qualitatively similar effects to those just outlined have been observed in these metals.[26]

(b) *Phase Changes, etc.* A phase change provoked by irradiation has been discovered in a U–9 wt % Mo alloy. At high temperature this alloy is single phase, but at lower temperature decomposes into lamellae of uranium and U_2Mo. During irradiation at the lower temperature it reverts to the single phase that was stable at the high temperature. Irradiation thus appears to extend the range of stability of this structure. An explanation put forward[27, 28] is that fission near an interface causes mixing up of the atoms. Each fission process then produces a small region of homogeneous composition which is quenched in by the rapid subsequent cooling. Successive fissions homogenise more and more of the specimen. In support of this explanation it has been found that the amount transformed depends on the total neutron dose and on the amount of U^{235} enrichment (the U^{238} being inert as far as fission is concerned). From the rate of transformation, an effective diffusion coefficient can be calculated. For example with 13.7% U^{235} and 2×10^{12} neutrons/cm²/sec the effective diffusion coefficient is 1.4×10^{-18} cm²/sec. This would be the rate of self diffusion in alpha uranium at about 550°C.

Other evidence of atomic rearrangement produced by irradiation is that for clustering of nickel in iron–nickel alloys,[29] of copper in aluminium–copper alloys,[30] and for an effect on the degree of order in Cu_3Au.[31, 32]

(c) *Radiation Growth.* Under irradiation an unstressed alpha uranium single crystal extends in one crystallographic direction (the b direction), shrinks in another (the a direction), and the third dimension (the c direction) does not change. One explanation of this phenomenon ascribes it to the combined effect of the local heating in a fission spike and the strong anisotropy of the expansion in alpha uranium.[33] The expansion coefficients along the a, b, and c axes are respectively $+36.7$, -9.3 and $+34.2$, all times 10^{-6}. Local heating therefore produces a strong compression in the a direction and a strong tension in the b direction. Edge dislocations in the vicinity will climb under these stresses. Those consisting of

[27] S. T. Konobeevsky and four others, *2nd Conference on Peaceful Uses of Atomic Energy*, 1958, **5**, 574.
[28] M. L. Bleiberg, *J. Nuclear Mat.*, 1959, **1**, 182.
[29] L. F. Porter and G. J. Dienes, *T.A.I.M.E.*, 1959, **215**, 854.
[30] C. W. Tucker and M. B. Webb, *Acta Met.*, 1959, **7**, 187.
[31] L. R. Aranin, *J.A.P.*, 1954, **25**, 344.
[32] J. A. Brinkman, C. E. Dixon and C. J. Meechan, *Acta Met.*, 1954, **2**, 38.
[33] A. H. Cottrell, *Inst. Mech. Engrs. London*, 1960, **174**, 16.

extra planes perpendicular to an a direction will climb in the direction that shrinks the area of extra plane; those consisting of extra planes perpendicular to the b direction will climb in the direction that extends the area of extra plane. The new positions are supposed to be quenched in by the rapid cooling, and the net result is a gradual reduction in the number of atomic planes perpendicular to the a direction and an increase in the number perpendicular to the b direction, which is the observed result. To explain the absence of any length change in the c direction it is suggested that there are no dislocations with half planes perpendicular to the c direction on the grounds that there is no slip in this direction. Growth decreases with rise in temperature and vanishes above 450°C, presumably because ordinary thermal diffusion becomes able to maintain the status quo.

A rather distinct variant of this explanation has also been proposed and is claimed to bring it into better quantitative agreement with experiment.[34] According to the new explanation, numerous point defects created by the fission process condense into platelets under the influence of the thermal stresses, the vacancies therefore condensing on planes perpendicular to the a direction and the interstitials on planes perpendicular to the b direction.

(d) *Creep.** One effect of irradiating uranium at low temperatures is to cause creep at stresses below the yield stress. Most of this creep at low temperature is ascribed to growth in the following way.[35] The grains in a polycrystal grow under irradiation in different directions and eventually impose stresses on each other equal to the yield stress. Any small applied stress can then cause plastic flow. An argument which gives the right creep rate is the following. Suppose the rate of extension in the b direction and of shrinkage in the a direction is $\dot{\epsilon}_g$. Elastic stresses are built up gradually which after a certain time reach the yield stress σ_y. Thereafter plastic deformation occurs in each grain without, however, any overall dimensional change in a randomly oriented polycrystalline sample. Zero applied stress therefore produces zero creep rate. However, if a stress σ_y is applied in one direction every element of growth operates in this direction. An applied stress σ_y hence causes a creep rate $\dot{\epsilon}_g$. If linearity is assumed, an applied stress σ therefore causes a creep rate

$$\dot{\epsilon} = \frac{\sigma}{\sigma_y} \dot{\epsilon}g$$

which is also the relation obtained in another way.[35]   This relation gives

* See footnote, p. 382.

[34] S. N. Buckley, *Properties of Reactor Materials*, Central Electricity Generating Board (London), 1962, p. 413.

[35] A. C. Roberts and A. H. Cottrell, *Phil. Mag.*, 1956, **1**, 711.

the correct rate of creep to within about 20%. The basic idea is also confirmed by the fact that the creep rate is accurately proportional to neutron flux over a 4:1 range.[36]

The same basic argument should apply however the internal stresses are built up. For example, it should apply when the stresses are set up by swelling. The fission spikes and atomic defects produced during irradiation may also assist ordinary creep by causing extra diffusion. Such considerations may explain why some low temperature, low stress creep occurs at low temperature and low stress during irradiation in a uranium–molybdenum alloy having a cubic lattice, the thermal isotropy of which should ensure absence of the kind of creep described in the previous paragraph. The amount was less than in alpha uranium,[27] as would be expected.

Since radiation growth in alpha uranium dies out at 450°C, the "growth" creep should die out also. The present evidence does in fact indicate that ordinary thermal creep begins to dominate at temperatures above 400°C, radiation having little effect. For example, in experiments at 450°C no strong effect of irradiation on the secondary creep rate was found when in-pile and out-of-pile creep rates were compared.[37] Some extra primary creep was observed in the in-pile specimens, but as it occurred after each pile start-up, it may have been due to thermal cycling (section 11.5).

In other metals no important effects of irradiation on creep yet seem to have been reported.

11.5 Thermal Cycling

Plastic deformation as a consequence of a temperature change was first observed in the anisotropic metals zinc, cadmium, and tin,[38] and has since been found to be of practical importance in alpha uranium as a result of the large thermal anisotropy of this metal (section 11.4c).

It appears[39] that plastic deformation can be produced by suitable thermal cycling in any metal, and that the effect can be large even in isotropic metals; for example, a 75% increase in length in pure aluminium thermally cycled five hundred times. In general, for thermal cycling to have a cumulative effect an upper temperature must be exceeded, presumably in order that a stress large enough to produce plastic deformation is generated. Four causes of dimensional changes have been isolated.

[36] A. S. Zaimovsky and four others, *2nd Conference on Peaceful Uses of Atomic Energy*, 1958, **5**, 566.

[37] H. C. Rose, *J.I.M.*, 1957, **86**, 122.

[38] W. Boas and R. W. K. Honeycombe, *P.R.S.*, 1946, **186**, 57.

[39] A. A. Bochvar, A. A. Gulkova, L. T. Kolobneva, G. I. Sergeev and G. I. Tomson, *2nd Conference on Peaceful Uses of Atomic Energy*, 1958, **5**, 288.

1. In single-phase cubic metals (which of course are isotropic as regards thermal expansion) when the cooling rate is fast enough to produce sufficient thermal stress.

2. In single-phase anisotropic metals the anisotropy of expansion generates a stress from which plastic deformation may result; in such metals the texture of a polycrystalline sample is important in this connection.

3. In multiphase alloys the stresses due to different thermal expansion coefficients of the different phases may give rise to important stresses.

4. Phase changes may generate stresses, as in iron.

Note added in proof: The theory of radiation creep (section 11.4 *d*) has been worked out in considerable detail by R. W. Anderson and J. F. W. Bishop, *Symposium on Uranium and Graphite*, Inst. Metals, London, 1962, and by S. N. Buckley, *ibid.*

12

Stress Corrosion

A metal may be ductile in one environment, such as air, but quite brittle in another, such as some corrosive solutions or liquid metals. This kind of behaviour is called, not altogether accurately from the point of view of this chapter, stress corrosion. Perhaps the best-known example of this behaviour is provided by annealed alpha brass, which in air is ductile and breaks at a stress of about 30 kg/mm², but in liquid mercury breaks at about one-tenth this stress with hardly any elongation. Sometimes in stress corrosion the fracture path is transgranular, but more often it is intergranular.

This chapter differs from others in this book, for the others review the experimental material of their subject as well as discussing the relevant theoretical ideas. Stress corrosion would be very complicated to review in this sort of way because the environment is as important as the alloy in determining susceptibility to stress corrosion and there are a great many separate cases to think about as a result. Instead, this chapter simply puts forward a way of looking at stress corrosion that is consistent with the ideas about brittle fracture described in chapter 7.

According to these ideas, a governing factor in brittle fracture is the energy of the new surfaces created during fracture, and for fracture to occur at a low stress this energy must be small. This immediately leads to the idea[1, 2] that stress corrosion occurs when the energy of the new

[1] B. E. Hopkins, Symposium on Precipitation Processes in Steels, *Iron and Steel Inst. London*, 1960, *Spec. Rep. No. 64*, p. 137.

[2] D. McLean, Conference on Grain Boundaries, 1961, Commissariat a l'Énergie Atomique, Saclay (Paris), p. 85.

solid-environment surfaces created by fracture is effectively small. Whatever other view is held about stress corrosion, according to the ideas of Chapter 7 it seems that this must always be true. For a detailed discussion it is best to consider stress corrosion in a liquid metal because some quantitative data are available and because the situation is not complicated by solid reaction products. It might be remarked that stress corrosion in liquid metals is growing in importance because liquid metals are envisaged as heat carriers in some reactors.

12.1 Stress Corrosion in a Liquid Metal Environment

The interfacial energies of several solid metal-liquid metal pairs have been measured, being expressed in terms of the dihedral angle.[3] The interfacial energy is directly obtained from the dihedral angle and for about half of the pairs is only a few dozens of ergs/cm^2. Thus, instead of a new surface energy of about 3000 ergs/cm^2 being required for fracture, as in air, in such a case only about 1/100 as much is needed in the liquid metal environment. According to chapter 7, fracture will then occur at low stress once a crack has been started, with little plastic deformation.

The real problem seems therefore to be how the crack starts rather than how it spreads. Now, stress corrosion cracking in liquid metal environments seems generally, if not always, to follow grain boundaries. The explanation of the start of cracking proposed here makes use of the known variability of grain boundaries. Given such variability, if the average dihedral angle is low, at certain grain boundaries it will be zero, that is, the liquid metal penetrates certain grain boundaries spontaneously, possibly even with a saving of energy. That this is feasible is shown by the system solid Al-liquid Ga, since when aluminium is dipped into liquid gallium at room temperature it spontaneously separates along grain boundaries.[4] Evidently liquid gallium can penetrate many grain boundaries of aluminium, and probably the average dihedral angle in this system is zero. In the more usual case where general spontaneous penetration does not occur because the average dihedral angle is not zero, the suggestion is that isolated penetration a full grain boundary deep will take place as depicted in Fig. 12.1, at the occasional boundaries where the dihedral angle is zero.

Each penetration is a crack that can spread as fast as the liquid can creep into it. With such a relatively long crack and on average a small new surface energy, fracture will spread at low stress, therefore with little

[3] C. S. Smith, *Imperfections in Nearly Perfect Crystals*, John Wiley and Sons, New York, 1952, p. 377.
[4] C. Elbaum, *T.A.I.M.E.*, 1959, **215**, 476.

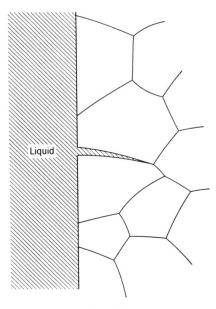

Liquid

Fig. 12.1.

plastic deformation, and the effective surface energy γ' in eqn. 7.1 will be small. Moreover, the crack length can be taken as proportional to the grain diameter, whence from eq. 7.1. the fracture stress will be proportional to (grain diameter)$^{-\frac{1}{2}}$. Both these expectations have been realised in experiments on brass immersed in liquid mercury,[5] the effective surface energy being only a few hundreds ergs/cm^2. It is thus not surprising that a metal which is highly ductile in air may become brittle without limit on immersion in an unsuitable environment.

12.2 Stress Corrosion in Chemically Active Environments

In chemically active environments the simple situation just described is complicated by at least three factors. In the first place, the energy of chemical reaction is available in principle to offset the new surface energy. Thus, the energy of reaction of aluminium in many media is many times greater than the surface energy of aluminium. This leads to the second factor. The reason why aluminium, for example, nevertheless does not usually spontaneously dissolve is that the product of reaction between the metal and the environment forms an impermeable film that separates the metal from the environment. It is well known that this is a frequent

[5] H. Nicholls and W. Rostoker, *Acta Met.*, 1960, **8**, 848.

situation, and aluminium and stainless steel exposed to air exemplify it. In turn, it leads to the third factor—the influence of impurities on the reaction product. An instance of this is that those parts of a protective film opposite grain boundaries may incorporate any impurities adsorbed or precipitated along the grain boundaries, affecting the protective quality of the film. For example, a reason for the susceptibility of some aluminium alloys to stress corrosion along grain boundaries in certain media may be that alloying elements adsorbed or precipitated at grain boundaries, when incorporated into the otherwise protective film, render it soluble or permeable and thus destroy its protective capacity.

Appendix

The Activation Energy
for Plastic Flow

One reason why activation energies for plastic flow vary with temperature is that elastic moduli vary. An analysis of the dependence arising in this way, and one which is closely connected with the experimental procedure involved, is the following:

The flow rate $\dot{\epsilon}$ is given by the relation

$$\dot{\epsilon} = Ae^{-U/kT} \tag{A.1}$$

where U is the thermal energy needed to overcome the barriers to flow and A is a frequency factor similar to those referred to in chapter 4 except for an entropy factor (see below). As has also been discussed in Chapter 4, the barriers to flow arise partly from processes (e.g., production of jogs or defects) involving sufficiently low energies that thermal agitation can help to overcome them, and partly from processes (overcoming internal stress fields and attractive junctions) requiring such large energies that only the applied stress can play a significant part in overcoming them, and which can therefore be regarded as equivalent to a back stress τ_0 opposing the applied stress τ. A net stress of $\tau - \tau_0$ is therefore available to assist in overcoming the thermal-sensitive barriers. If we suppose that the latter involve an energy W then

$$U = W - v(\tau - \tau_0) \tag{A.2}$$

where v is the activation volume ($= xbd$) discussed in Chapter 4. There are two points to note which determine the final result. In the theory of reaction rate processes, with which we are here concerned, W is a Gibbs free energy and can therefore be replaced by $W' - TS$, where W' is the enthalpy and S is the entropy of the process in question. And for a given strained state τ_0 is proportional to the shear modulus G and can be written βG, where β is a proportionality constant.

The kind of experiment with which we are concerned consists of altering the temperature while keeping the applied stress constant and of measuring the change in $\dot\epsilon$. Such an experiment can be represented by rewriting eq. A.1, after substituting for U from eq. A.2, as

$$\ln \frac{\dot\epsilon}{A} = \frac{S}{k} - \frac{W'}{kT} + \frac{v\tau}{kT} - \frac{v\beta G}{kT}$$

and then differentiating with respect to temperature at constant applied stress, giving

$$\left[\frac{\partial(\ln \dot\epsilon/A)}{\partial T}\right]_\tau = \frac{1}{k}\left(\frac{\partial S}{\partial T}\right)_\tau - \frac{1}{kT}\left(\frac{\partial W'}{\partial T}\right)_\tau + \frac{W'}{kT^2} - \frac{v\tau}{kT^2} - \frac{v\beta}{kT}\frac{dG}{dT} + \frac{v\beta G}{kT^2}$$

According to a standard thermodynamical argument the first two terms are together equal to zero, that is, the effect on the entropy of the change in temperature is counterbalanced by the effect on the enthalpy. The remaining terms yield

$$\left[\frac{\partial(\ln \dot\epsilon/A)}{\partial T}\right]_\tau = \frac{1}{kT^2}\left[W' - v\tau_0 + v\tau - vT\frac{\tau_0}{G}\frac{dG}{dT}\right]$$

and the material behaves as though it has an apparent activation energy

$$W_{\text{app}} = W'' - vT\frac{d(\ln G)}{dT}$$

where W'' is the true activation energy and is equal to $W' - v(\tau - \tau_0)$.

The error in the activation energy is $vT\, d(\ln G)/dT$. To get an idea of the range of magnitudes involved, we consider two cases:

(a) $v\tau_0 \sim W'$. Since $d(\ln G)/dT \sim 1/3000$ for most metals, at room temperature the error is $v\tau_0/10 \sim W'/10$, or 10%. At lower temperatures the error will be smaller.

(b) On raising the temperature the error will at first increase. However, recovery and steady-state creep eventually supervene, and in the steady-state creep range $v\tau_0$ may lie between practically zero and say $\frac{1}{2}v\tau$, which itself is very much smaller than W'. Consequently the error is then small.

Author Index

389

Subject Index